PSYCHOBIOLOGY OF CONVULSIVE THERAPY

EDITED BY MAX FINK
STATE UNIVERSITY OF NEW YORK AT STONY BROOK

SEYMOUR KETY
HARVARD MEDICAL SCHOOL

JAMES McGAUGH
UNIVERSITY OF CALIFORNIA AT IRVINE

and THOMAS A. WILLIAMS
UNIVERSITY OF UTAH COLLEGE OF MEDICINE

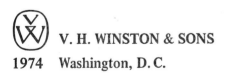 V. H. WINSTON & SONS

1974   Washington, D. C.

A HALSTED PRESS BOOK

JOHN WILEY & SONS
New York   Toronto   London   Sydney

V. H. Winston & Sons, Inc., Publishers
1511 K St. N.W., Washington, D.C. 20005

Distributed solely by Halsted Press Division, John Wiley & Sons, Inc., New York.

Library of Congress Cataloging in Publication Data:

Main entry under title:
    Psychobiology of convulsive therapy.

    Papers of a conference sponsored by the Depression Section, Clinical Research Branch, National Institute of Mental Health and the Dept. of Psychiatry of the New York Medical College, held at the Dorado Beach Hotel, Puerto Rico, Apr. 20–22, 1972.
    Includes bibliographical references.
    1. Shock therapy—Congresses.   I. Fink, Max, ed.   II. United States. National Institute of Mental Health. Depression Section.
    III. New York Medical College, Flower and Fifth Avenue Hospitals. Dept. of Psychiatry. [DNLM: 1. Shock therapy, Electric—Congresses. WM412 C748p 1972]
    RC484.9.P79   616.8'912   73–21990
    ISBN 0-470-25901-9

Printed in the United States of America

CONTENTS

Introduction   xi

1   INDUCED SEIZURES AND HUMAN BEHAVIOR, *Max Fink* **1**
   Axioms of Induced Seizures   **3**
   Theoretic Models   **7**
   Neurophysiologic-adaptive Hypothesis   **9**
   Conclusion   **13**
   References   **14**

1A DISCUSSION, *Jan-Otto Ottosson* **19**

2   UNILATERAL ELECTROCONVULSIVE THERAPY,
   Giacomo d'Elia **21**
   A Review of Current Clinical Issues   **21**
   Comparison of Unilateral and Bilateral Electrode Placement   **26**
   Summary   **31**
   References   **32**

3   IS EEG SLOWING RELATED TO THE THERAPEUTIC EFFECT
   OF CONVULSIVE THERAPY?, *Jan Volavka* **35**
   References   **39**

4   ELECTROCONVULSIVE THERAPY AND SLEEP, *Joseph Mendels,*
   Robert L. Van de Castle, and David R. Hawkins **41**
   Summary   **45**
   References   **46**

5   **EEG AND NEUROPHYSIOLOGICAL STUDIES OF CONVULSIVE THERAPIES,** *Joyce G. Small* 47
        Method and Material   **47**
        Results   **48**
        Discussion   **60**
        Summary   **62**
        References   **62**

6   **INHALANT CONVULSIVE THERAPY,** *Iver F. Small* 65
        Method and Materials   **66**
        Results   **67**
        Discussion   **74**
        Summary   **76**
        References   **76**

7   **MULTIPLE ECT: WHAT HAVE WE LEARNED?,** *Richard Abrams* . 79
        Discussion   **81**
        Summary   **82**
        References   **83**

8   **ELECTROCONVULSIVE SHOCK: EFFECTS ON LEARNING AND MEMORY IN ANIMALS,** *James L. McGaugh* 85
        Effects of a Series of ECS Treatments   **86**
        Effects of a Single ECS Treatment   **87**
        The Nature of the RA Gradient   **87**
        The Permanence of RA   **90**
        Brain Stimulation and RA   **91**
        Concluding Comments   **93**
        References   **94**

9   **RETROGRADE AMNESIA AND BRAIN SEIZURES IN RODENTS: ELECTROPHYSIOLOGICAL AND NEUROANATOMICAL ANALYSES,** *Steven Zornetzer* 99
        Methods   **102**
        Conclusions   **125**
        References   **126**

10   **EFFECTS OF FLUROTHYL (INDOKLON) UPON MEMORY IN THE CHICK,** *Arthur Cherkin* 129
        Methods and Materials   **131**
        Results   **132**
        Discussion   **137**
        Summary   **139**
        References   **140**

11   EFFECTS OF ELECTROCONVULSIVE SHOCK ON
NOREPINEPHRINE TURNOVER AND METABOLISM: BASIC
AND CLINICAL STUDIES, *Joseph J. Schildkraut and
Paul R. Draskoczy*   143
    Methods   **144**
    Results and Discussion   **144**
    Conclusion   **167**
    References   **168**

12   EFFECT OF REPEATED ECS ON BRAIN WEIGHT AND
BRAIN ENZYMES, *Gordon T. Pryor*   171
    Summary   **183**
    References   **183**

13   THE EFFECT OF ELECTROSHOCK ON BRAIN RNA AND
PROTEIN SYNTHESIS AND ITS POSSIBLE RELATIONSHIP
TO BEHAVIORAL EFFECTS, *Adrian Dunn, Antonio Giuditta,
John E. Wilson, and Edward Glassman*   185
    Postscript   **195**
    References   **195**

14   MEMORY AND ECT, *Rhea L. Dornbush and Moyra Williams*   199
    References   **205**

15   SYSTEMIC BIOCHEMICAL EFFECTS OF ECT, *Jan-Otto Ottosson* .   209
    Adrenal Medullary Activity   **210**
    Adrenal Cortical Activity   **211**
    Cause, Effect, or Coincidence   **211**
    Cerebrovascular Permeability   **211**
    Cerebral Hypoxia   **212**
    Mineral Metabolism   **213**
    Diencephalic Influences   **214**
    Summary   **217**
    References   **218**

16   EFFECT OF ELECTROSHOCK ON INDOLEAMINE
METABOLISM AND AGGRESSIVE BEHAVIOR, *Luigi Valzelli
and Silvio Garattini*   221
    Materials and Methods   **222**
    Results and Discussion   **222**
    Summary   **227**
    References   **227**

17   EFFECTS OF REPEATED ELECTROCONVULSIVE SHOCK ON
     BRAIN CATECHOLAMINES, *Seymour S. Kety*   231
        Discussion   233
        References   234

18   EFFECTS OF ELECTROCONVULSIVE SHOCK ON CEREBRAL
     PROTEIN SYNTHESIS, *Walter B. Essman*   237
        References   249

19   BRAIN ACETYLCHOLINE AND SEIZURES,
     Alexander G. Karczmar   251
        Current Status of the Role of ACh in the Central
           Nervous System   251
        Seizures Induced by Cholinergic Drugs   253
        Cholinomimetic Action on Reflexes, Particularly on the
           Spinal Cord Level   253
           Brain   254
        Cholinergic Effects on Brain Rhythmicity   258
        Endogenous Levels of ACh and Convulsive Susceptibility   259
        Seizures and ACh   261
        Cholinergic Drugs and Seizures   261
        Summary and Comment   264
        References   265

SUMMARIES AND DISCUSSION

20   CLINICAL PROGRESS IN CONVULSIVE THERAPY, *Max Fink* . .   271
        References   276

21   NEUROPHYSIOLOGICAL AND BEHAVIORAL EFFECTS OF
     CONVULSIVE PHENOMENA, *James L. McGaugh and*
     Thomas A. Williams   279
        References   283

22   BIOCHEMICAL AND NEUROCHEMICAL EFFECTS OF
     ELECTROCONVULSIVE SHOCK, *Seymour S. Kety*   285
        Biochemical Changes   287
        References   292

Author Index   295
Subject Index   306

ACKNOWLEDGMENT

Conference Committee

Max Fink, M.D., *Chairman*
Seymour Kety, M.D.
James McGaugh, Ph.D.
Thomas A. Williams, M.D.

This conference was sponsored by the Depression Section, Clinical Research Branch, National Institute of Mental Health, and the Department of Psychiatry of the New York Medical College; and supported, in part, by MH 20762 to the International Association for Psychiatric Research, Inc., Great Neck, New York. The conference was held at the Dorado Beach Hotel, Puerto Rico, April 20-22, 1972.

PSYCHOBIOLOGY OF CONVULSIVE THERAPY

Conference Participants

Dorado Beach, Puerto Rico

Numbers in parentheses indicate the pages on which the authors' contributions begin.

Richard Abrams, New York Medical College, New York, New York. (79)

Arthur Cherkin, Veteran Administration Hospital, Sepulveda, California. (129)

Rhea Dornbush, New York Medical College, New York, New York. (199)

Adrian Dunn, University of Florida College of Medicine, Gainesville, Florida. (185)

Giacomo d'Elia, University of Göteborg, Sweden. (21)

Walter Essman, Queens College, City University of New York, New York, New York. (237)

Max Fink, State University of New York at Stony Brook, Stony Brook, New York. (1, 271)

Alfred Freedman, New York Medical College, New York, New York.

Anne Geller, Albert Eistein College of Medicine, New York, New York.

Martin A. Green, Cornell University Medical College, and International Association for Psychiatric Research, Great Neck, New York.

Alex G. Karczmar, Loyola University Medical Center, Maywood, Illinois. (251)

Martin M. Katz, National Institute Of Mental Health, Rockville, Maryland. (vi)

Seymour Kety, Harvard Medical School, Boston, Massachusetts. (231, 285)

Irwin Kopin, National Institute of Mental Health, Bethesda, Maryland.

James McGaugh, University of California at Irvine, Irvine, California. (85, 279)

Joseph Mendels, University of Pennsylvania, Philadelphia, Pennsylvania. (41)

Jan-Otto Ottosson, University of Göteborg, Sweden. (19, 209)

Gordon Pryor, Stanford Research Institute, Menlo Park, California. (171)

Joseph Schildkraut, Harvard Medical School, Boston, Massachusetts. (143)

Steven Secunda, National Institute of Mental Health, Rockville, Maryland.

Iver F. Small, University of Indiana School of Medicine, Indianapolis, Indiana. (65)

Joyce G. Small, University of Indiana School of Medicine, Indianapolis, Indiana. (47)

Luigi Valzelli, Instituto di Ricerche Farmacologiche, Milan, Italy. (221)

Jan Volavka, New York Medical College, New York, New York. (35)

Moyra Williams, United Cambridge Hospitals, Cambridge, England. (199)

Thomas A. Williams, University of Utah College of Medicine, Salt Lake City, Utah, and National Institute of Mental Health, Rockville, Maryland. (279)

Steven Zornetzer, University of Florida, Gainesville, Florida. (99)

INTRODUCTION

Of the many treatments of the severe mentally ill, none is so effective for specific clinical disorders, and so misunderstood as induced convulsions or electroshock. The very term, "shock treatment" arouses fear and a negative attitude. Yet, for the ruminative and the suicidal, the fearful and the frightened, and the apathetic and withdrawn psychotic patient, convulsive therapy is frequently life saving and almost magical in its rapid and effective resolution of these hyperemotional states.

Many modifications of the treatment process have been introduced over the years so that the treatments are safe, without the historical complications of fractures and memory loss, and frequently effective within 4 to 10 days of treatment. Many studies of treatment modifications, as in changing the electrode location, frequency of seizures, and the seizure-inducing agent have contributed to an understanding of the elements of the process essential for a favorable therapeutic outcome.

Concurrent studies of the changes in cerebral neurohumors in psychotic states and with seizures, and the interest in memory mechanisms altered by electroconvulsive shock (ECS) provide data for speculations as to the mode of action of electroconvulsive therapy.

Improved therapeutic methods, widespread clinical use, and the contributions from the laboratory sciences stimulated the Clinical Research Branch (CRB) of the National Institute of Mental Health through the International Association for Psychiatric Research, Inc., to convene experienced clinicians and laboratory investigators to review the clinical, biochemical, psychological, and neurophysiological aspects of induced seizures. The conference was organized by Thomas Williams, formerly head of CRB's Depression Program, Professors Max Fink, now of SUNY at Stony Brook, Seymour Kety of Harvard Medical School, and James McGaugh of the University of California at Irvine. It was designed to provide the first hard scientific look at some 20 years of accumulated evidence on the basic mechanisms of actions, the broad psychological and biological effects, and the specific clinical efficacy of ECT. This volume presents the reports at the Conference, "Psychobiology of Convulsive Therapy," held at Dorado Beach, Puerto Rico, April 22-24, 1972.

In becoming the first systematic attempt to sort out the evidence, to turn a sharp scientific focus on the biological and psychological impact of ECT, the Conference and its distinguished editors accomplished the mission set by the Institute. This collection of papers represents the first attempt to bring the evidence together, and should serve as a primary sourcebook in this field for years to come.

Although it is too early to provide conclusive answers as to specificity and basic mechanisms of action, this effort is a real contribution to an understanding of the convulsive therapy process—as a treatment and as a clue to our understanding of the psychobiological roots of depression.

Martin M. Katz, Ph.D.

February, 1974

1
INDUCED SEIZURES AND HUMAN BEHAVIOR[1]

Max Fink, M.D.[2]

> The eighth remoter cause of Consequential Madness, viz Muscular Constriction, gradual, gentler and uniform, but more obstinate, may sometimes be relieved or as it were diverted by convulsion, that is by an alternate motion of muscular fibres artificially excited in some other part of the body. On which account vesicatories, vomits, rough cathartics, errhines, and the most poinant amongst the medicines called nervous, may in this particular case of spasm become even antispasmodic. For, ignorant as we are and perhaps shall always be of the reason, experience has shewn that, although many parts of the body may be convulsed together, one species of spasm however occasioned seldom fails to put an end to that other which before subsisted.

> William Battie, *Treatise on Madness,* Whiston & White, London, 1758, pp. 84–85.

The variety of interventions described as treatments of the mentally ill in past centuries reflects the diversity in concepts of the causes of mental illnesses, and man's innovativeness in affecting the welfare of others. Treatments have been often drastic: isolation and imprisonment, physical restraint, starvation and dieting, heat and burning, cupping, leeches, and bleeding, abdominal surgery, trephination and craniotomy, water immersion, and administration of innumerable drugs including laxatives, purgatives, antispasmodics, sedatives, opiates, and stimulants, to name but a part of the catalog. On occasion, perhaps in reaction to these measures or in response to other theories, some men have proposed

[1] Partial support for this research was provided by United States Public Health Service Grants Nos. MH-13358, 15561, and 20762.

[2] I am indebted to Drs. Richard Abrams, Rhea Dornbush, and Jan Volavka for the data of our recent studies; and to Drs. Robert L. Kahn, Max Pollack, Joseph Jaffe, Ira Belmont, and Edwin A. Weinstein for their participation in earlier studies.

1

"moral treatments"—retreats, pleasant discourse, travel, recreation, clean air, exercise, and balanced diets.

Our recent decades are no more enlightened, and while scholars discourse on the biochemical, psychological, genetic, or societal roots of disordered, non-conformist, socially unacceptable, and dysphoric behaviors, our treatments are not based on documented concepts of etiology, or disordered physiology, but on belief, practice, experience, and observation. For example, at the beginning of the century, syphilis was a prominent cause of mental disorder, classified as general paralysis of the insane. Before the advent of antibiotics, treatment was empiric, consisting of applications of various heavy metals. An observation that the psychosis of some patients improved after an acute illness in which fever was high led to the experimental induction of fevers as treatment. Fevers were first induced by injections of blood from malarious individuals allowing the patients to develop malaria (1917). A reputation of "success" of these heroic measures (Wagner-Jaureg received the 1927 Nobel prize for medicine) led to a therapeutic optimism which engendered many new interventions in central European clinics: continuous sleep in 1922, convulsions from the injection of camphor in oil and Metrazol in 1934, convulsions induced by electricity in 1937, insulin coma in 1934, and leucotomy (lobotomy) in 1935 (Kalinowsky, 1970).

Rationales for these interventions were often obscure. Convulsions were introduced in the belief that epilepsy was a rare diagnosis among schizophrenic patients, as if seizures "protected" the epileptic from psychosis. The first treatments were given to patients with dementia praecox, with limited success; the treatment of depressed patients was fortuitous, and its unanticipated success established induced seizures as a therapeutic modality.

With the development of psychotropic drugs in the early 1950s, comparisons of treatments showed these drugs to be more effective in modifying behavior, safer, and cheaper to administer than leucotomy, insulin coma, and continuous sleep, and these methods were rapidly abandoned. With the advent of thymoleptic drugs in 1958, many physicians claimed an end to convulsive therapies, and many clinical centers and practitioners, particularly those affiliated with university departments, abandoned these treatments. But, many depressed patients did not respond to thymoleptics, and even schizophrenics frequently exhibited an irrational recidivism after drug and psychotherapy. Clinicians, often in despair, turned to older methods, and found induced convulsions frequently helpful and occasionally lifesaving. They found that modifications in the ways seizures were induced were improved, so that the unpleasant aspects of impaired memory and fractures were reduced, relieving not only patient complaints, but the criticism of peers and the liability for lawsuits.

The published results of comparative clinical studies were also impressive, particularly in depressive illnesses where favorable results were reported in 70% to 95% of patients treated (Klein & Davis, 1969). In systematic comparisons of electrically induced convulsions (ECT) and antidepressant drugs, three studies found ECT superior to imipramine, and four found the two treatments equivalent. ECT was superior to phenelzine in two studies, and approximately equivalent to iproniazid 6 months after treatment. In an extensive British study, 50% of the patients who had not improved with imipramine improved with ECT. In a random assignment study, Greenblatt, Grosser, and Wechsler (1962) reported that ECT produced more improvement than imipramine, isocarboxazid, or phenelzine.

Favorable results were also reported in patients with acute schizophrenia, in whom improvement rates of 65% to 80% were recorded (Abrams, 1972). (For chronic schizophrenia, however, the outcome is as poor as with other interventions including psychotherapy and milieu therapy.) In a comparison of chlorpromazine and ECT in acute schizophrenia, improvement rates are similar with more frequent relapses for those treated with chlorpromazine in one study, and longer hospitalization periods for those treated with ECT in another. It is difficult to extend these data now, since the recent studies of ECT treatment of schizophrenia are confounded by the combined and successive use of psychotropic drugs, by the variety of treatments that each patient receives, and the frequent undertreatment of these patients.

Despite the irrational origins, despite an apparent similarity to many unsuccessful and historically discarded treatments, and despite the lack of a theoretical basis, repeated induced convulsions continue to have measured and salutary effects on human disordered behavior—effects which are daily put to therapeutic uses. For almost four decades, this persistent and widespread interest has led to the testing of many modifications: inductions of seizures by inhalants, intravenous chemicals, and electricity; varying dosages in single, multiple, focal, and "regressive" multiple seizures; changing electrical inductions by unidirectional, square-wave, aperiodic, pulsed, and alternating electrical currents; bitemporal, unilateral, and anterior electrode placements; combined insulin and electrical seizures, and combined petit mal-grand mal seizures; and nonconvulsive treatments. Treatments have been given with and without sedatives and anesthetics, muscle relaxants, atropine, and psychoactive drugs. To these imaginative modifications must be added a catholicism in the selection of subjects—ages that span all the decades of man, and a wide range in the numbers of treatments each session, and the numbers of treatments representing a "course."

From these diverse experiences and many methodical studies, it is possible to derive axioms which must be considered in any theoretic view of the therapeutic process.

AXIOMS OF INDUCED SEIZURES

1. The persistent behavioral or therapeutic effects lie in the changes in the central nervous system which accompany or result from repeated seizures, and not in changes in peripheral or visceral components.

Repeated grand mal seizures are essential to behavioral results. Comparisons of seizure and nonseizure treatments show seizures to elicit superior clinical effects (Fink, 1957; Fink & Kahn, 1957; Ottosson, 1960, 1968; Ulett, Smith, & Gleser, 1956). The peripheral (muscular) component of the seizure can be blocked by muscle paralyzing agents without reducing therapeutic effects. While seizures alter many aspects of brain function, two measures have received the most attention: persistent, interseizure electrical activity (EEG), and tests of memory and recall.

The resting EEG frequencies become slower, amplitudes (voltages) and seizure-type activity increase, and fast waves decrease following seizures. At first, these effects are seen for only a few hours after a seizure, but with repeated seizures the interseizure record becomes progressively filled with slower waves and higher voltages, for longer periods. When seizures are discontinued, voltages decrease and slow waves slowly disappear, leaving persistent, well-regulated alpha (8-12 Hz) activity as the dominant frequency in the recovered patient (Fink & Kahn, 1957; Hoagland, Malamud, Kaufman, & Pincus, 1946; Kurland, Hanlon, Esquibel, Krantz, & Sheets, 1959; Roth, 1951; Volavka, Feldstein, Abrams, & Fink, 1972).

Changes in tests of memory function and recall show a similar course. Initially, the subjects are confused and find tests of immediate recall difficult for a short period after each seizure. With increasing seizures, the deficits increase, recall of recently learned material worsens, and with minimal interpolation or delay, recall tasks show interference. The deficits are usually greater for verbal and auditory tasks, and less for visual tasks. The greatest effects are in recently learned material, and least in well-developed memories. After treatment, these functions "recover" so that deficits are rarely measurable 2 weeks after a course and performance may even exceed that recorded before treatment (Dornbush, 1972; Korin, Fink, & Kwalwasser, 1956; Millar, 1967; Ottosson, 1960).

Improvement in clinical symptoms and behavior is accompanied by alterations in these indices of brain function, and it is rare to observe improvement without such effects (Abrams, Fink, Feldstein, Volavka, & Roubicek, 1972; Dornbush, Abrams, & Fink, 1971; Fink & Kahn, 1957; Fink, Kahn, Karp, Pollack, Green, Alan, & Lefkowits, 1961; Green, 1957; Kahn & Fink, 1958; Kahn, Fink, & Weinstein, 1956; Korin et al., 1956; Ottosson, 1960; Roth, Kay, Shaw, & Green, 1957; Volavka, 1972). But the significance of the specific EEG and memory task changes to the therapeutic process is unclear. It is probable (but remains to be demonstrated) that the central nervous system changes which are the basis for heightened mood and improved thought processes (clinical improvement) are separate from the changes reflected in memory impairment and EEG slowing; but though separate, they are functionally (and probably anatomically) close, so that association of effects, while not causally related, must be considered in any theory. (As an analogy, the association of lessened psychosis with the muscular rigidity and other features of parkinsonism with phenothiazine drugs comes to mind.)

2. *The rate of change in behavior, and the evaluations of improvement, are directly dependent on the number and frequency of seizures. The time for*

measurable behavioral change can be reduced by more-frequent seizures. As there seems to be no inherent limitation in the number of seizures, the principal limitations are the deficits of the accompanying "untoward" effects of treatments.

Repeated seizures alter many brain functions, not only those which may be the basis for the psychotic state, but perception, recall, concentration, memory, and orientation as well. Deficits in these functions—in the perceptions of the subjects of themselves and their families—disturb patients and their families, and the anxiety occasioned by these effects limits the rate of treatment.

The range of treatments is broad, however, for as many as eight seizures can be given in one session, as in multiple ECT, or seizures may be elicited at rates from once a day to once a month, as in maintenance therapy (Abrams, 1972; Abrams & Fink, 1972; Blachly & Gowing, 1966; Green, 1957).

As a corollary, multiple seizures (MECT) may be given in one session, but in only rare instances does this enhanced treatment hasten a favorable clinical response. Our experience with multiple seizures suggests that clinical change evolves gradually—a change which is initiated by the seizure but sustained by repeated applications.

It was anticipated that when it was possible to reduce the secondary effects of seizures by unilateral applications of the electrodes, multiple seizures would reduce the duration of a treatment course (Abrams & Fink, 1972; Blachly & Gowing, 1966). In practice, in only a few patients have multiple treatments in 1 or 2 days allowed the development of a full clinical remission. In most subjects, while repeated treatments assure a rapid development of the clinical results, the time necessary for the maximum behavioral change remains 3-9 days, with a spacing no shorter than 24-48 hr between seizure sessions. We have concluded that the central processes set in motion by the seizure-inducing stimuli require this time to mature or ripen.

3. The method of inducing a seizure, whether electrical, chemical, photic, or inhalant, is less important than the number and frequency of the induced seizures. Thus, applications of electrical currents or chemical agents in amounts insufficient to elicit a seizure, or at rates that fail to provide persistent changes, are clinically ineffective.

As a corollary, the location of electrodes and the type and duration of the currents in ECT, and the type of chemical induction in flurothyl treatments, directly affect the degree and quality of changes in memory, orientation, and confusion, but not the clinical outcome.

Numerous studies contrast the effects of electrical inductions with flurothyl; each study concluded that the two methods are similar in their clinical effects, with the few measurable differences in the rate of behavioral change, the degree of memory deficit, or in the accompanying secondary effects (Fink et al., 1961; Kurland et al., 1959; Small & Small, 1972).

The type of current used for electrical induction (i.e., alternating, unidirectional, or square-wave currents) influences the rate and amount of EEG slowing, the decrements in task performance, and the peripheral components of the seizures, but affects the therapeutic process only minimally (Fink, Kahn, & Green, 1958; Green, 1957, 1960; Small & Small, 1968).

By changing the location of electrodes in ECT, the effects on memory tasks are modified. Unilateral electrode placement elicits less memory deficits than bitemporal placement, and anterior frontal placement elicits still less memory impairment. The location of the electrodes also defines the sensory modality affected: auditory tasks are more severely impaired than visual tasks with the usual paramotor unilateral electrode placement, suggesting that the path of the current, which is presumed to be maximal in the shortest path between the electrodes has measurable direct effects on brain function (Abrams, Volavka, Roubicek, Dornbush, & Fink, 1970; Abrams et al., 1972; Dornbush et al., 1971; Volavka et al., 1972).

With lessened effects on memory tasks, unilateral and bifrontal electrode placements elicit "almost equivalent" clinical results. "Almost" but not equivalent, for the rate of improvement with bitemporal electrodes is quicker than unilateral and bifrontal placements (Abrams et al., 1970, 1972). Thus, while some separation between the degree of memory impairment and the amount of improvement has been recorded, there still may be a more direct interaction between the mechanisms underlying improvement and those underlying deficits in task performance. One view of the data is that while the memory changes are probably not the basis for clinical effects, the memory changes are derived from the same biochemical mechanisms which underlie the physiologic changes necessary for improvement in depressed patients.

4. *Treatment outcome for induced convulsions varies from 70% to 90% in patients with endogenous depressive psychoses. When seizures are given in other populations, a greater number of seizures are needed for clinical effects, the response rate is less, and the clinical outcome is less favorable and less predictable.*

The target populations for convulsive therapy are the endogenous psychoses. These patients share many physiologic and behavioral characteristics—characteristics which reflect an organization of the brain that is particularly responsive to repeated seizures. When seizures are applied in other populations, as in schizophrenic patients, more seizures must be applied more frequently to achieve behavioral effects, and to achieve measurable changes in the EEG and in memory, motor, and sensory tasks (Fink, 1957, 1972a, 1972b; Rose, 1963). The sensitivity of depressed patients to seizures, such that many patients recover with 3 to 5 seizures, is in marked contrast to the insensitivity of severely ill schizophrenic patients, who may exhibit neither behavioral changes, nor EEG or memory task defects with 12 to 20 seizures. The diversity in response, and a lack of an objective "end-point" to treatment, leads to undertreatment and varied, often unsatisfactory, therapeutic results in mixed or poorly diagnosed populations.

5. *Improvement in behavior (clinical remission) is characterized by a gain in weight and increased appetite, increased duration and amount of Stage 4 sleep,*

increased libido, increased interest in the environment, and by facilitation of the mental mechanisms of denial and euphoria.

The characteristic behavioral syndrome after ECT includes decreased restlessness, reduced discrimination of sensory stimuli, impaired concentration and recall of multiple stimuli, increased distractibility, repetitiveness of simple tasks, heightened mood, increased lability of affect and decreased rate and diversity of speech, imagery, and phantasy (Fink & Kahn, 1961). Behavioral changes depend not only on the direct effects of seizures, but also on the subject's psychological (personality) organization. For example, fewer seizures are required to develop behavioral, memory, and EEG effects in the patients who conventionally use mechanisms of denial in speech and behavior. These patients also find difficulty in discriminating figures from backgrounds and in localizing multiple stimuli. They also score as more authoritarian on sociologic tasks. By contrast, patients who are not authoritarian, who do not habitually use denial mechanisms, and are capable—even with altered consciousness—to discriminate multiple stimuli and complex figures from their backgrounds, exhibit behavioral syndromes that are less favorably evaluated after ECT (Fink, Kahn, & Pollack, 1959; Jaffe, Esecover, Kahn, & Fink, 1961; Kahn & Fink, 1957; Kahn, Pollack, & Fink, 1960a, 1960b; Pollack & Fink, 1961; Pollack, Kahn, Karp, & Fink, 1962).

6. *The behavioral syndrome and the EEG changes of seizures are exaggerated by intravenous barbiturates, and reduced (reversed) by intravenous anticholinergic drugs (as benactyzine, Ditran, or diethazine), antihistaminics (diphenhydramine), and sympathomimetics (dextroamphetamine and lysergide [LSD]).*

In patients exhibiting the behavioral and EEG effects of repeated seizures, these biochemical interventions reversibly alter the behavioral state of the subjects (Fink, 1958, 1960; Lennox, Ruch, & Guterman, 1951; Roth, 1951; Roth et al., 1957; Shagass, 1956). The changes can be measured using quantitative indices as EEG and language measures (Fink, 1958, 1960; Jaffe et al., 1961; Roth et al., 1957; Shagass, 1956, 1957; Shagass & Jones, 1958). To the extent that the pharmacologic effects of these compounds in the central nervous system can be inferred from their peripheral effects, it is possible to interpret these observations as suggesting that repeated seizures result in an increase in central cholinergic activity and some increase in histaminic activity.

THEORETIC MODELS

From the clinical observations that are the basis for these "axioms," a viable theory of the mode of action of induced convulsions must not depend on a specific method of inducing seizures, nor on any single behavioral consequence (eg., memory loss), nor on the peripheral systemic effects. The theory must incorporate the biochemical phenomena subsequent to seizures, with a rate of development in the order of days after seizures, and additive for rates varying between 12 and 72 hr between seizures. The biochemical events must be enhanced by barbiturates, and reduced by anticholinergic, sympathomimetic, and antihistaminic agents. The theory must also make allowances for differences in the rate of response of different populations of the mentally ill and accommodate the differences in behaviors which are expressed, and which seem related not only to the type of symptoms manifested by patients, but their individual psychological organization (personality) as well.

In 1948, Gordon listed 50 theories of the mode of action of repeated seizures. He described biological models based on biochemical and neurological effects, and psychological hypotheses emphasizing repression, enhanced fears, and deficits in memory function. The psychological theories encompassed concepts of the fear of seizures, expiation of internalized guilts, and deficits in memories affecting highly cathected, emotional experiences. A more recent hypothesis based on memory changes was presented by Millar (1967, 1970) who viewed each seizure as disrupting the consolidation of previously learned material, with several seizures producing a focal "confusional" or attention deficit.

The early biological theories ascribed significance to structural changes in the central nervous system, to endocrine effects, and changes in autonomic functions and in cell permeability (Fleming, 1956). Much of the data was poorly controlled, however, or derived from peripheral measures bearing little relevance to the cerebral effects of seizures. Following an extensive review, Fleming concluded that:

> Manifestations of such a hypothetical cellular shake-up may be the shifts in ionic concentration, appearance of new substances outside the cell, change in the blood-brain barrier, restorative effects of pyrimidines, changes in cellular appearance, and so forth. Why a convulsion is necessary to produce this change and why it affects the course of the mental disease, are unanswerable questions at present. Indeed, at this level of study, the problem of the mechanism of action of electric shock treatment begins to merge with the problem of the causation of psychoses [p. 446].

Holmberg (1963) reduced the range of speculations, concluding it was

> possible to eliminate many factors formerly considered to be therapeutically active without reducing the therapeutic effect (including) . . . 'stress' factors such as anoxia, hypercapnia, muscular exertion, adrenal reaction, peripheral excretion of catechol amines, and other biochemical changes detectable in the blood [pp. 403, 404].

He found unsatisfactory the evidence for the relevance of central nervous system changes, such as slowing of the EEG and intellectual impairment, and suggested that, "It is only to be expected that some correlation would exist between therapeutic effect and side effects, since both result from the action of the therapeutic procedure on the brain [p. 404]."

Ottosson (1968) discussing Millar's review of the psychological theories of ECT, stressed that "the therapeutically active component is contained in the convulsion (or, more exactly, in the cerebral changes of which the convulsion is an expression) . . . ." He supports a biochemical view of the ECT process:

A feasible hypothesis of the ECT effect is that it increases the amount of catecholamines in the central synapses. Other neurochemical and psychopharmacological studies have provided evidence that changes in the natrium (sodium) metabolism are correlated with states of depression and with lithium treatment . . . the antidepressive effect of ECT is due to influence on the cell membrane with changed permeability of electrolytes and amines, which are thereby set free to a greater degree in the synapses. [Another point] is the increased cerebrovascular permeability [p. 173]. . . .

None of these theories is acceptable. The psychologic theories that emphasize fear and repression fail to include the efficacy of seizures modified by barbiturates and succinylcholine. Dependence on memory mechanisms is unsatisfactory since the modifications of seizures by unilateral nondominant placement of electrodes and by flurothyl provide dissociations between the therapeutic results and the degree of clinical confusion and memory deficit. The biochemical and physiologic theories lack relevance since the evidence on which their formulation was based was obtained principally from measurement of changes in peripheral systems. As with the many recent studies of catecholamines in depression, the changes in blood and urine from muscles and tissues outside the central nervous system are large, tending to overshadow and mask the smaller, more subtle, and perhaps more critical, central changes. The biochemical and physiologic theories also fail to account for differences in the individual response of patients, taking little cognizance of each individual's unique experience and personality organization, and the role psychologic factors play in both the short term and persistent behavioral effects.

NEUROPHYSIOLOGIC–ADAPTIVE HYPOTHESIS

In 1957, a "neurophysiologic-adaptive" view of convulsive therapy was described, based on extensive studies of the interaction of brain function, personality, and barbiturates in patients with cerebral damage due to tumors, trauma, and infections (Weinstein & Kahn, 1955). In our examination of these mechanisms in patients in whom cerebral "trauma" was experimentally (therapeutically) induced by electroshock, we noted that changes in brain function were accurately reflected in increased EEG slow-wave activity and that the EEG changes always accompanied changes in behavior (Fink & Kahn, 1957). We found that individual patterns of behavioral change, however, could not be related to the number or type of seizures, nor to any specific aspect of the treatment course, but were related to individual personality attributes (Fink & Kahn, 1961). Because some patients sustained their improvement and others did not, and because some behavioral worsening could frequently be related to environmental "traumatic" events, we pictured contributions of the environment (particularly the attitudes of relatives and staff) to the duration of behavioral improvement, and to our evaluations of change and "improvement." We were impressed that while all patients showed changes in behavior, only some behaviors were rated favorably by physicians, friends, and relatives, and thereby encouraged; while other behaviors were regarded unfavorably and discouraged.

A "biological-psychological" view still seems to best satisfy the experimental data. We envision the biological substrate to be the persistent postseizure biochemical changes in the central nervous system (Fink, 1966; Fink & Kahn, 1957; Ottosson, 1960, 1968). These changes have been studied most extensively by neurophysiologic, particularly EEG, measures, by pharmacologic methods, and by biochemical assays of brain tissues and spinal fluid changes.

While there is some controversy as to the relation between postseizure behavioral changes and changes in EEG measures, there is agreement that EEG slow-wave activity increases with each seizure, fading gradually, and after three to five seizures, slow waves persist throughout the interseizure period. After a course of treatment is completed, slow-wave activity slowly recedes, and is often followed by prolonged, synchronized alpha activity (Fink & Kahn, 1957; Volavka, 1972).

EEG slow-wave activity may be experimentally and transiently inhibited by anticholinergic drugs, such as diethazine, benactyzine, and Ditran. With the reduction in slow waves, the patient's behavior shows pretreatment patterns, only to have EEG and behavior return to preexperimental levels as the effect of the anticholinergic drug wanes (Fink, 1958, 1960, 1966). EEG slow-wave activity may be enhanced by thiopental and amobarbital, and this increase is accompanied by clinical mood elevation and denial. Indeed, barbiturates stimulate a temporary "improvement" in patients after a few seizures—when these behaviors would ordinarily not be manifest until additional seizures have been induced. This observation has been recommended to predict the outcome of ECT (Kahn, Fink, & Weinstein, 1956; Roth et al., 1957; Shagass & Jones, 1958).

LSD, dextroamphetamine, imipramine, and diphenhydramine also reduce slow-wave activity, although less efficiently and less rapidly than anticholinergic drugs, with an accompanying transient reduction in behavioral improvement (Fink, 1960; Lennox et al., 1951).

In reviewing these experiments and some corroborative evidence from spinal fluid studies, I concluded that the basis for postseizure behavioral changes and EEG hypersynchrony lay in increased cerebral acetylcholine levels (Fink, 1966). I suggested that:

> Induced convulsions, like craniocerebral trauma and spontaneous seizures, are associated with an increase in free acetylcholine in intercellular fluids, altering cerebral permeability and enhancing the appearance of cholinesterases. The level of free acetylcholine is maintained by repeated induced seizures. EEG hypersynchrony is one reflection of altered levels of acetylcholine and the altered permeability of electrolytes and other substances, including cholinesterases. The changes in intercellular electrolytes, including acetylcholine, provide the biochemical substrate for the persistent behavioral changes and EEG hypersynchrony following induced convulsions [p. 480].

Reviewing these data recently, this view seemed too circumscribed, for it did not account for the changes in central catecholamines in depressive states (Coppen, 1967) and the central anticholinergic activity of thymoleptic antidepressants (Fink, 1972a).

These data are inconsistent with the classical views of catecholamines and acetylcholine acting in opposite directions on central receptors, and a simplistic view of competing neurohumors is undoubtedly incorrect. If we postulate a massive nonspecific increase in various neurohumors in response to induced seizures, norepinephrine levels would increase, as has been observed for acetylcholine [p. 106].

For example, increased serotonin levels in the spinal fluid of patients after seizures have been reported (Fink, 1972b). The interaction of acetylcholine and other brain amines is more probable, these neurohumors not acting in isolation as is suggested in a report that acetylcholine levels increase in the spinal fluid of amphetamine addicts prior to detoxification (Jonssen, Schuberth, & Sundwall, 1969).

While there is much conjecture about the biochemical mechanisms that underlie these neurophysiologic changes, there is little disagreement either about their dependence on the rate and number of seizures or their prominence. The controversy is focused on the significance of these effects for therapeutic outcome and their usefulness as measures of relevant central nervous system biochemical events. From the experience described here, the correlations of therapeutic outcome with neurophysiologic (EEG) measures are on more secure footings than the biochemical mechanisms derived from extensive animal experiments or the limited human cerebrospinal fluid studies.

Perhaps more critical to our understanding of the ECT process is our inability to relate behavioral and psychologic changes to biochemical and neurophysiologic mechanisms alone—our understanding seems to require an augmentation from psychological constructs. Psychological aspects of the convulsive therapy process have been studied from many points of view, including the relevance of memory degradation and repression, psychopathological features related to treatment outcome, and personality factors (long term adaptive modes) in the adaptive response.

Memory changes play a small role in the therapeutic process (Dornbush, 1972; McGaugh, this volume). In part, this attitude is based on the successful dissociation of clinical efficacy and memory deficits by the judicious placement of electrodes in ECT, and is reinforced by the discussions in this volume.

Specific aspects of psychopathology, as conventionally defined and measured, are also not directly related to outcome. Individual or grouped psychopathologic items are poorly predictive of treatment outcome or of individual changes in psychopathology (Abrams, 1972; Abrams et al., 1972). Clinical diagnosis, emphasizing the distinction between depressive states and schizophrenia, and within depressive states, the distinction between endogenous and neurotic depressions, does bear predictable relations to outcome. Improvement is more rapid and more likely in patients classified as suffering from endogenous depression than in those classed as neurotic depression or acute schizophrenia.

Some personality factors, however, may bear more specific relationships to the type of adaptation and to our evaluation of treatment results. In studies of depressed and schizophrenic patients, we examined the behavioral adaptations of those patients who exhibited large amounts of EEG slow-wave activity after a set number of seizures (6-9 and 10-12). The types of posttreatment behaviors varied, but we were able to define four adaptive modes, that we descriptively entitled "euphoric-hypomanic," "somatization," "paranoid-withdrawal," and "panic." Patients exhibiting the euphoric-hypomanic mode were most often rated as much improved and recovered, while patients exhibiting the paranoid-withdrawal and panic modes were rated unimproved (Fink & Kahn, 1961; Jaffe et al., 1961).

In examining the psychological test scores, improved patients who developed the euphoric-hypomanic adaptation were older, less educated, and more frequently foreign born than the patients rated as unimproved (Kahn & Fink, 1959; Kahn, Pollack, & Fink, 1959; Pollack & Fink, 1961). Furthermore, on the California F scale (an index of compliance and discrimination) their pretreatment scores were higher (Kahn et al., 1960b). On the Gottschaldt hidden figures test, a measure of figure-ground discrimination, they made more errors (Kahn et al., 1960a). On the Rorschach test, their protocols exhibited an absence of human movement (M) and form color (FC) responses, and a greater number of color (C) and color-form (CF) responses (Kahn & Fink, 1960; Kahn & Pollack, 1959). On language tests they exhibited a higher number of denial language patterns following amobarbital; and in family interviews, their scores on a denial inventory were higher (Jaffe et al., 1961; Kahn & Fink, 1958). We interpreted these findings as indicating that the pretreatment psychologic organization was intimately related to the type of adaptation that accompanied the induced changes in brain function. We viewed increased verbal denial, displacement, minimization, and euphoria as defense mechanisms and adaptations that are exaggerated in the patients in whom they are already present in their pretreatment repertoire (Kahn et al., 1956). With altered brain function, and the accompanying decreased perceptual discrimination, recall, and modified thought processes, these adaptations become more prominent. Small doses of amobarbital, which enhance the neurophysiologic changes of the brain, increase the difficulties in discrimination, recall, and thought, encouraging the expression of these adaptations of denial and minimization (Fink, 1957; Roth, 1951; Shagass & Jones, 1958; Weinstein & Kahn, 1955).

We also found that the changes in the test scores were greater for patients who improved than for those who failed to improve. Thus, the increase in California F scale score, errors on the Gottschaldt hidden figures test, denial language scores after amobarbital, errors on tachistoscopy tests, and errors in tasks discriminating simultaneous tactile stimuli were greater for the patients who exhibited denial-euphoria adaptations than for those who were rated unimproved (Fink et al., 1959; Kahn & Pollack, 1959).

We believe that the present view of the convulsive therapy process should encompass these psychologic aspects as well as the neurophysiologic. The neurophysiologic-adaptive view (or, more appropriately, the biological-psychological) provides a structure for the many observations associated with improvement of depressive psychoses by a repeated induction of grand mal seizures. The view has some advantages over partial theories, in that it attempts to relate changes in brain function with preexisting history and personality structure of the subjects, and does not depend on a specific biochemical or psychologic mechanism alone. It views the convulsive therapy process as nonspecific, that is, the improvement in depressive symptoms is related to changes in pathophysiology and not in the etiological process, much like insulin may alter the pathophysiology of diabetes without modifying the genetic-structural defects. While it is possible that the physiological effects of seizures may reverse some pathological features underlying depressive illness, specificity seems unlikely for such a fortuitously derived therapy. It is more likely that the cumulative effects of seizures are related to changes in cerebral chemistry and physiology that occur in all subjects with repeated seizures; and that the changes are salutary in some patients because they reverse some pathologic biochemical states (as reduced cholinergic activity in thalamic nuclei?) and thereby stimulate behavioral adaptations that modify the psychological aspects of the illness. In part, this view is consistent with the temporary nature of many of the treatments—the patients "recovering" for the period of maximum physiological effect alone; and with the continuing effects in some individuals, those with a psychologic organization described in the experimental studies, which allows some subjects to persist in their use of exaggerated defense mechanisms. Indeed, the interrelation of physiologic and psychologic variables is useful not only as a theory of induced convulsions in depressive states, but also allows a kinship to a more general hypothesis of the association of EEG and behavior with psychoactive drugs, a hypothesis that finds applications in defining new drugs for modifying human behavior, particularly in defining new psychotropic substances (Fink, 1969). Thus, convulsive therapy may be viewed as a complex procedure to produce central nervous system biochemical changes, representing, thereby, a special case of clinical psychopharmacology.

CONCLUSION

For more than 35 years, induced convulsions have successfully alleviated symptoms of endogenous depressive psychoses and reduced the thought disorder, overactivity, and withdrawal of schizophrenia. Clinical experience indicates that persistent postseizure events in the brain are critical for the behavioral change. While detailed studies of the biochemical changes of the brain are few, interest has increased with descriptions of the significance of brain catecholamines in depressive illness.

Neither the psychologic nor the somatic theories of the mode of action of repeated seizures are tenable when treated alone. A more satisfactory view is derived from the interrelation of the neurophysiologic events of the seizure, and the psychologic organization of the target population, the depressive states. In the present formulation, repeated seizures are manifestations of biochemical changes which, if repeated at optimal rates, produce a persistent state of altered brain function. From the available data, this change is characterized by increased levels and turnover of neurohumors, specifically acetylcholine and norepinephrine (or serotonin), increased vascular permeability, and altered ionic equilibria.

The psychologic consequences of these biochemical events are decreased discrimination of sensory stimuli, altered perception, decreased short term memory and recall, mood elevation, and the physiologic changes of increased appetite, weight, salivation, libido, and Stage 4 sleep; and decreased restlessness, sweating, and heart rate.

While the outward expressions in interpersonal behavior of these biochemical and physiologic events vary, we believe the expressions depend on each subject's habitual modes of adaptation. Patients who habitually use denial and displacement as defense mechanisms, for example, will prominently increase their use of these mechanisms, and will be viewed as hypomanic and "improved." The type of adaptation may be predicted from pretreatment psychologic test performance and makes probable a more complete calculus of the relations of brain neurohumors and behavior which may yet provide biochemical constructs for these "psychologic" events.

The clinical efficacy of repeated seizures is well documented. Despite its empiric origins and the risks and inelegance of its administration, induced convulsions provide persistent changes in brain function which alleviate the symptoms of depression. These experiences are the basis for an appreciation of both the clinical utility and the theoretic significance of this unique mode of psychiatric treatment.

REFERENCES

Abrams, R. Recent clinical studies of ECT. *Seminars in Psychiatry,* 1972, 4, 3-12.

Abrams, R., & Fink, M. Clinical experiences with multiple electroconvulsive treatments. *Comprehensive Psychiatry,* 1972, 13, 115-121.

Abrams, R., Fink, M., Feldstein, S., Volavka, J., & Roubicek, J. Unilateral and bilateral ECT: Effects on depression, memory and electroencephalogram. *Archives of General Psychiatry,* 1972, 27, 88-94.

Abrams, R., Volavka, J., Roubicek, J., Dornbush, R., & Fink, M. Lateralized EEG changes after unilateral and bilateral electroconvulsive therapy. *Diseases of the Nervous System,* 1970, 31 (S), 28-33.

Blachly, P. H., & Gowing, D. Multiple monitored electroconvulsive treatment. *Comprehensive Psychiatry,* 1966, 7, 100-109.

Coppen, A. The biochemistry of affective disorders. *British Journal of Psychiatry,* 1967, 113, 1237-1264.

Dornbush, R. L. Memory and induced ECT. *Seminars in Psychiatry,* 1972, 4, 47-54.

Dornbush, R. L., Abrams, R., & Fink, M. Memory changes after unilateral and bilateral convulsive therapy. *British Journal of Psychiatry,* 1971, 119, 75-78.

Fink, M. A unified theory of the action of physiodynamic therapies. *Journal of Hillside Hospital,* 1957, 6, 197-206.

Fink, M. Effect of anticholinergic agent, diethazine, on EEG and behavior: Significance for theory of convulsive therapy. *Archives of Neurology and Psychiatry* 1958, 80, 380-387.

Fink, M. EEG and human psychopharmacology. *Annual Review of Pharmacology,* 1969, 9, 241-258.

Fink, M. Effect of anticholinergic compounds on post-convulsive EEG and behavior of psychiatric patients. *Electroencephalography and Clinical Neurophysiology,* 1960, 12, 359-369.

Fink, M. Cholinergic aspects of convulsive therapy. *Journal of Nervous and Mental Disease,* 1966, 142, 475-484.

Fink, M. CNS effects of convulsive therapy. In J. Zubin & F. Freyhan, (Eds.), *Disorders of mood.* Baltimore: Johns Hopkins Press, 1972. (a)

Fink, M. The therapeutic process in ECT. *Seminars in Psychiatry,* 1972, 4, 39-46. (b)

Fink, M., & Kahn, R. L., Relation of EEG delta activity to behavioral response in electroshock: Quantitative serial studies. *Archives of Neurology and Psychiatry* 1957, 78, 516-525.

Fink, M., & Kahn, R. L. Behavioral patterns in convulsive therapy. *Archives of General Psychiatry,* 1961, 5, 30-36.

Fink, M., Kahn, R. L. & Green, M. A. Experimental studies of the electroshock process. *Diseases of the Nervous System,* 1958, 19, 113-118.

Fink, M., Kahn, R. L., Karp, E., Pollack, M., Green, M., Alan, B., & Lefkowits, H. J. Inhalant induced convulsions: Significance for the theory of the convulsive therapy process. *Archives of General Psychiatry,* 1961, 4, 259-266.

Fink, M., Kahn, R. L., & Pollack, M. Psychological factors affecting individual differences in behavioral response to convulsive therapy. *Journal of Nervous and Mental Disease,* 1959, 128, 243-248.

Fleming, T. C. An inquiry into the mechanism of action of electric shock treatments. *Journal of Nervous and Mental Disease,* 1956, 124, 440-450.

Gordon, H. L. Fifty shock therapy theories. *Military Surgeon,* 1948, 103, 397-401.

Green, M. A. Significance of individual variability in EEG response to electroshock. *Journal of Hillside Hospital,* 1957, 6, 229-240.

Green, M. A. Relation between threshold and duration of seizures and electrographic change during convulsive therapy. *Journal of Nervous and Mental Disease,* 1960, 130, 117-120.

Greenblatt, M., Grosser, G. H., & Wechsler, H. A comparative study of selected antidepressant medications and EST. *American Journal of Psychiatry,* 1962, 119, 144-153.

Hoagland, H., Malamud, W., Kaufman, I. C. & Pincus, G. Changes in electroencephalogram and in the excretion of 17-ketosteroids accompanying electroshock therapy of agitated depression. *Psychosomatic Medicine,* 1946, 8, 246-251.

Holmberg, G. Biological aspects of electroconvulsive therapy. *International Review of Neurobiology,* 1963, 5, 389-412.

Jaffe, J., Esecover, H., Kahn, R. L., & Fink, M. Modification of psychotherapeutic transactions by altered brain function. *American Journal of Psychotherapy,* 1961, 15, 46-55.

Jonsson, L. E., Schuberth, J., & Sundwall, A. Amphetamine effect on the choline concentration of human cerebrospinal fluid. *Life Sciences,* 1969, 8, 977-981.

Kahn, R. L., & Fink, M. Perception of embedded figures after induced altered brain function. *American Psychologist,* 1957, 12, 361.

Kahn, R. L., & Fink, M. Changes in language during electroshock therapy. In P. Hoch & Zubin (Eds.), *Psychopathology of communication,* New York: Grune & Stratton, 1958.

Kahn, R. L., & Fink, M. Personality factors in behavioral response to electroshock therapy. *Journal of Neuropsychiatry,* 1959, 1, 45-49.

Kahn, R. L., & Fink, M. Prognostic value of Rorschach criteria in clinical response to convulsive therapy. *Journal of Neuropsychiatry,* 1960, 1, 242-245.

Kahn, R. L., Fink, M., & Weinstein, E. A. Relation of amobarbital test to clinical improvement in electroshock. *Archives of Neurology and Psychiatry,* 1956, 76, 23-29.

Kahn, R. L. & Pollack, M. Prognostic application of psychological techniques in convulsive therapy. *Diseases of the Nervous System*, 1959, **20**, 180-184.

Kahn, R. L., Pollack, M. & Fink, M. Sociopsychologic aspects of psychiatric treatment in a voluntary mental hospital: Duration of hospitalization, discharge ratings and diagnosis. *Archives of General Psychiatry*, 1959, **1**, 565-574.

Kahn, R. L., Pollack, M., & Fink, M. Figure-ground discrimination after induced altered brain function. *Archives of Neurology*, 1960, **2**, 547-551. (a)

Kahn, R. L., Pollack, M., & Fink, M. Social attitude (California F Scale) and convulsive therapy. *Journal of Nervous and Mental Disease*, 1960, **130**, 187-192. (b)

Kalinowsky, L. Biological psychiatric treatments preceding pharmacotherapy. In F. J. Ayd & B. Blackwell (Eds.), *Discoveries in biological psychiatry*. Philadelphia: J. B. Lipincott, 1970.

Klein, D. F., & Davis, J. M. *Diagnosis and drug treatment of psychiatric disorders.* Baltimore: William & Wilkins, 1969.

Korin, H., Fink, M., & Kwalwasser, S. Relation of changes in memory and learning to improvement in electroshock. *Confinia Neurologica*, 1956, **16**, 88-96.

Kurland, A. A., Hanlon, T. E., Esquibel, A. J., Krantz, J. C. Jr., & Sheets, C. S. A comparative study of hexaflurodiethyl ether (Indoklon) and electroconvulsive therapy. *Journal of Nervous and Mental Disease*, 1959, **129**, 95-98.

Lennox, M. A., Ruch, T. C. & Guterman, B. The effect of benzedrine on the post-electroshock EEG. *Electroencephalography and Clinical Neurophysiology*, 1951, **3**, 63-69.

Millar, E. Psychological theories of ECT: A review. *British Journal of Psychiatry*, 1967, **113**, 301-311.

Millar, E. The effect of ECT on memory and learning. *British Journal of Medical Psychology*, 1970, **43**, 57-62.

Ottosson, J. -O. Experimental studies of the mode of action of electroconvulsive therapy. *Acta Psychiatrica et Neurologica Scandinavica.* 1960, **35**, (Suppl. 145), 1-141.

Ottosson, J. -O. Psychological or physiological theories of ECT. *International Journal of Psychiatry*, 1968, **5**, 170-174.

Pollack, M., & Fink, M. Sociopsychological characteristics of patients who refuse convulsive therapy. *Journal of Nervous and Mental Disease*, 1961, **132**, 153-157.

Pollack, M., Kahn, R. L., Karp, E., & Fink, M. Tachistoscopic perception after induced altered brain function: Influence of mental set. *Journal of Nervous and Mental Disease* 1962, **134**, 422-430.

Rose, J. T. Reactive and Endogenous depressions—response to E.C.T. *British Journal of Psychiatry*, 1963, **109**, 213-217.

Roth, M. Changes in the EEG under barbiturate anesthesia produced by electro-convulsive treatment and their significance for the theory of ECT action. *Electroencephalography and Clinical Neurophysiology*, 1951, **3**, 261-280.

Roth, M., Kay, D. W. K., Shaw, J., & Green, J. Prognosis and pentothal induced electroencephalographic changes in electroconvulsive treatment. *Electroencephalography and Clinical Neurophysiology*, 1957, **9**, 225-237.

Shagass, C. Sedation threshold. A neurophysiological tool for psychosomatic research. *Psychosomatic Medicine*, 1956, **18**, 410-419.

Shagass, C. A measurable neurophysiological factor of psychiatric significance. *Electroencephalography and Clinical Neurophysiology*, 1957, **9**, 101-108.

Shagass, C., & Jones, A. L. A neurophysiological test for psychiatric diagnosis: Results in 750 patients. *American Journal of Psychiatry*, 1958, **114**, 1002-1010.

Small, I. F., & Small, J. G. Ictus and amnesia. *Recent Advances in Biological Psychiatry*, 1968, **10**, 144-159.

Small, J. G., & Small, I. F. Clinical results: Indoklon *vs.* ECT. *Seminars in Psychiatry*, 1972, **4**, 13-26.

Ulett, G. A., Smith, K., & Gleser, G. C. Evaluation of convulsive and subconvulsive shock therapies utilizing a control group. *American Journal of Psychiatry,* 1956, 112, 795-802.

Volavka, J. Neurophysiology of ECT. *Seminars in Psychiatry,* 1972, 4, 55-66.

Volavka, J., Feldstein, S., Abrams, R., & Fink, M. EEG and clinical change after bilateral and unilateral electroconvulsive therapy. *Electroencephalography and Clinical Neurophysiology,* 1972, 32, 631-639.

Weinstein, E. A., & Kahn, R. L. *Denial of illness.* Springfield, Ill.: Charles C Thomas, 1955.

1A
DISCUSSION

Jan-Otto Ottosson, M.D.

The evidence on which Fink is formulating his neurophysiologic-adaptive view of ECT seems partly to be obtained from patient groups and strategies of therapy which are different from most European clinics. Fink has mixed groups of psychotic patients; our studies are made on patients with endogenous depression, unipolar and bipolar. He has been more generous with treatments (10-12); we are more moderate, about 6 treatments are an average number in several European series of endogenous-depressive patients. We seldom see the consequences of ECT he describes: impaired concentration, increased distractibility, repetitiveness of simple tasks, decreased rate and diversity of speech, and increased lability of affect. We express more assuredness about which behavior change is favorable; in these patients there is full consensus that elevated mood, diminished retardation, and reduced anxiety are desirable effects of the therapy. We have no impression that barbiturates have a real antidepressive effect nor that anticholinergic drugs are depressiogenic. Conclusions drawn from a mixed group of psychoses having obtained a long series of treatments need not apply to a homogenous group of endogenous depression. Rather, his description seems to illustrate an organic shock syndrome which is seen only exceptionally in antidepressive therapy.

I am not antipsychodynamic in my orientation, but I find it farfetched to see denial and displacement as essential mechanisms in the recovery of endogenous depression. Nor is there among endogenous-depressive patients any convincing evidence that some types of personalities react better than others. There is accumulating evidence that endogenous depression is a somatogenic disease with little need for psychodynamic hypotheses in etiology and therapy.

19

The word specific in relation to ECT is *equivocal* and Fink uses it in the sense of *symptomatic*. Clinical experience indicates that there is a specific effect of ECT in the following senses: (*a*) ECT is better than any other treatment in endogenous depression. (*b*) The antidepressive effect of ECT is better than any other effect of ECT (antipsychotic, antimanic etc.). (*c*) The antidepressive effect is not bound to and not dependent upon the "organic" effect (memory disturbance, deterioration). These circumstances indicate that it may not be fruitful to formulate a unitary hypothesis which can explain all the effects of ECT. Instead, the antidepressive action of ECT should be associated with the action of antidepressive and depressiogenic drugs and we should elaborate an antidepressive hypothesis based in its turn on a hypothesis for endogenous depression. Recent research on humoral transmission in the central nervous system has produced several such hypotheses (cathecholamine, indolamine, electrolyte, and various permeability hypotheses).

Fink acknowledges the dissociation between antidepressive effect and memory disturbance but still believes in a common anatomical and functional (even biochemical) basis. In fact, there are several circumstances indicating no relationship: (*a*) Different mechanisms of origin, the antidepressive effect being seizure related, the memory disturbance seizure and current related. (*b*) There is no memory disturbance from antidepressive drugs. (*c*) There is no antidepressive effect from other memory-disturbing measures. The present evidence indicates that the neural substrate for depressive states is in the hypothalamic area and for the memory disturbance after ECT (diminished retention) in the hippocampal-mamillary system. The only reason why we still have to consider memory disturbance is that we cannot restrict seizure activity to the cerebral areas which are relevant for the antidepressive effect.

The bilaterally synchronous slow waves which are seen in the EEG after ECT indicate involvement of brain-stem structures. Since we do not see them in treatment with antidepressive drugs they are probably not a component of the antidepressive process and may be regarded—like the memory disturbance—as a coincidental phenomenon of ECT. Contrary to the memory disturbance, the EEG changes can be used—as suggested by Roth (1951)—as a signal that enough treatments have been given. However, close attention to the clinical course is mostly sufficient for deciding an appropriate series of treatment.

Clinical experience tells that ECT is not one but several treatments with different mechanisms of action. We need then several hypotheses for the action in specific psychopathologic states. When more is known about central neurochemical events a biologic theory will probably be sufficient for the antidepressive action. A combined psychobiologic-adaptive theory may be useful to explain other effects of ECT.

2
UNILATERAL ELECTROCONVULSIVE THERAPY

Giacomo d'Elia, M.D.

A REVIEW OF CURRENT CLINICAL ISSUES

The adverse effect on memory of electroconvulsive therapy (ECT) is regarded by most investigators as unnecessary for the treatment of depressive states. It has been shown that the memory disturbances and the antidepressant effect arise, at least partly, via different mechanisms: the memory impairment is mainly determined by the amount of electrical current, and partly by the seizure, while the antidepressant effect is bound to the cerebral seizure activity induced by the electrical stimulation (Ottosson, 1960). Continuous efforts have been made to improve techniques of treatment to reduce the undesirable effects on memory functions, and three main trends may be distinguished:

1. modification of the type of electrical current employed in the stimulation
2. replacement of the electrical current by a chemical agent
3. modification of the position of the stimulating electrodes

The transformation of electrical stimuli from diphasic sinusoidal waveform pulses to unidirectional fractionated ones made it possible to induce generalized convulsions with a reduced amount of energy, and consequently with reduced memory disturbances. The replacement of the electric current by a chemical convulsant agent, flurothyl, has not shown any advantages (Fink, Kahn, Karp, Pollack, Green, Alan, & Lefkowits, 1961; Laurell, 1970). With unilateral electrode placement, i.e., both electrodes applied to one side of the head in contrast to previous bilateral application, a considerable reduction of side-effects has been achieved.

Antidepressant efficiency. Therapeutic efficiency is obviously an aspect of essential importance when a new or modified treatment is introduced. At this point, while there is a concordance of views about the beneficial properties of unilateral ECT as compared with bilateral ECT in regard to memory effects, opinions about its antidepressant efficiency are divergent. A therapeutic advantage for bilateral ECT has been recently reported by Abrams (1972) and some impressions of not completely equal effectiveness have been previously reported. In Table 1, number of convulsions and conclusions about the effectiveness of unilateral ECT as compared with bilateral ECT in different studies are presented. These studies, however, are hardly comparable with each other in many respects, such as the criteria of patient selection, number of treatments and their frequency, method of symptom rating, parameters of electrical stimuli, and electrode position.

A possible explanation of the divergent judgments in the literature may be that with the unilateral technique it is more difficult to provoke maximal seizure activity (i.e., submaximal seizures may be induced). As reported by Ottosson (1960), maximal depression-relieving effect is coupled with a maximal grand mal seizure pattern. There are probably some minimal technical requirements that must be met if maximal generalized seizure activity is to be evoked. Too deep a barbiturate narcosis must be avoided; a certain distance between homolaterally applied electrodes must be ensured; and pads that are neither too dry nor too soaked in saline have to be used: in the first case there is an insufficient passage of current; in the second, excessive soaking may result in trickling of saline between the electrodes and consequent short-circuiting (Zinkin & Birtchnell, 1968; S. M. Cannicott, personal communication, 1971). In the region of the convulsive threshold, the convulsant stimulus probably does not produce an all-or-none response (d'Elia & Perris, 1970), and gradation of the seizure pattern may be the result of insufficiently liminal stimulations. In animal experiments, a progressive response to increasing stimulus intensity from threshold seizure, generalized clonic seizure, clonic-tonic-clonic seizure, and finally to the tonic-clonic seizure has been described (Tedeschi, Swinyard, & Goodman, 1956). Subtotal, dissociated seizure patterns have been observed in humans after ultrabrief stimulus treatment technique (Liberson, 1948, 1953; Cronholm & Ottosson, 1963). Unilateral or focal seizures have not infrequently been observed after unilateral stimulations. The quantity of energy delivered from an ECT machine that is sufficient to induce a generalized seizure may vary among individuals and, in the same individuals, in different treatment sessions. Standard electrical doses are, therefore, not to be recommended. Finally, difficulty in inducing a generalized seizure may also vary with different unilateral electrode placements.

Anterograde amnesia. Although the studies differ in methodology, they agree that unilateral electrode placement reduces the anterograde amnesic effects of ECT (i.e., difficulty in remembering information acquired after treatment) as compared with bilateral stimulations (Martin, Ford, McDonald, & Towler, 1965; Zamora & Kaelbling, 1965; Impastato & Karliner, 1966; Abrams 1967; Cannicott & Waggoner, 1967; Rinaldi, Manacorda, & Mastrosimone, 1967;

TABLE 1

Antidepressant Efficiency of Unilateral ECT and Bilateral ECT

Author(s)	Number of convulsions		Antidepressant efficiency		
	Bilateral ECT	Nondominant unilateral ECT	Lower	Not completely equal	Equal
Cannicott, 1962 (pilot study)	7.2	6.3			+
Cannicott, 1962	6.7	7.0		+	
Martin, Ford, McDonald, & Towler, 1965	10.0	10.0			+
McAndrew, Berkey, & Matthew, 1967	8.0	7.4			+
Halliday, Davison, Browne, & Kreeger 1968	4.0	4.0		+	
Levy, 1968	6.0	6.0		+	
Strain et al., 1968	7.5	8.4		+	
Valentine, Keddie, & Dunne, 1968	8.8	7.2			+
Zinkin & Birtchnell, 1968	8.3	8.0			++[a]
Abrams & de Vito, 1969	6.0	6.0			+
Di Perri, Meduri, Megna, Messina, & Puca	6.0	6.0			+
Giberti, 1969	8.0	8.0		+	
Sutherland, Oliver, & Knight, 1969	5.6	5.5			++
d'Elia, 1970	6.2	7.0			+
Cronin et al., 1970	6.0	6.0		+[b]	+[c]
Fleminger et al., 1970a, 1970b	6.8	7.2			+
Bidder, Strain, & Brunschwig, 1970	10.2	8.2		not reported	
Small, Small, Perez, & Sharpley	-	-		+	
Abrams, 1972	-	-	+		

[a]++ Slightly better effect of nondominant unilateral ECT.
[b]Endogenous depression.
[c]Neurotic depression.

Cohen, Noblin, & Silverman, 1968; Levy, 1968; Strain, Brunschwig, Duffy, Agle, Rosenbaum, & Bidder, 1968; Zinkin & Birtchnell, 1968; Man & Bolin, 1969; Dornbush, Abrams, & Fink, 1971). This is true even when dominant applications are used Halliday, Davison, Browne, & Kreeger, 1968; Pancheri, 1969; Sutherland, Oliver, & Knight, 1969; Cronin, Bodley, Potts, Mather, Gardner, & Tobin, 1970; and Fleminger, de L. Horne, Nair, & Nott, 1970; Fleminger, de L. Horne, & Nott, 1970).

Retrograde amnesia. In studies of the retrograde amnesic effects, i.e., difficulty in remembering information acquired before treatment, unilateral stimulations, on either the nondominant or dominant hemisphere, were also found to reduce the memory-disrupting effects of treatment (Lancaster, Steinert, & Frost, 1958; Impastato & Karliner, 1966; Cannicott & Waggoner, 1967; Valentine, Keddie, & Dunne, 1968; Zinkin & Birtchnell, 1968; Dello Russo, 1969; Sutherland et al., 1969; Costello, Belton, Abra, & Dunn, 1970). In two studies, however, verbal recall after one treatment (Gottlieb & Wilson, 1965) and after six treatments (Wilson & Gottlieb, 1967) was found significantly more impaired after unilateral dominant than after bilateral stimulations. These divergent results may probably be explained by different methodology in ECT (supraliminal stimuli with glissando technique) and in test procedure (digit span and proverb memory). The advantage of unilateral nondominant over dominant electrode position is reported by all observers (Gottlieb & Wilson, 1965; Wilson & Gottlieb, 1967; Dello Russo, 1969; Sutherland et al., 1969; Costello et al., 1970).

Posttreatment confusion. Posttreatment confusion, disorientation for time, confusional behavior such as agitation, restlessness, and automatism, have been found, with few exceptions, to be of shorter duration and less pronounced (or absent) after unilateral ECT than after bilateral ECT (Frost, 1957; Lancaster et al., 1958; Cannicott, 1962; Martin et al., 1965; Impastato & Karliner, 1966; Halliday et al., 1968; Valentine, et al., 1968; Man & Bolin, 1969; Sutherland et al., 1969; Cronin et al., 1970; Fleminger et al., 1970a, 1970b). Opposite observations, of longer reorientation time after dominant unilateral ECT than after bilateral ECT (Gottlieb & Wilson, 1965; Wilson & Gottlieb, 1967), may probably be explained by methodological differences. There is general agreement about the advantages of nondominant unilateral ECT as compared with dominant ECT with regard to confusion.

Dominant versus nondominant electrode placements. The results of antero-grade and retrograde studies may be discussed from the aspect of hemispheric dominance for verbal and nonverbal memory. The few investigations where dominant and nondominant electrode placements were used and where verbal and nonverbal tasks were considered (Cohen et al., 1968; Halliday et al., 1968) showed different deficits in verbal tests after dominant and in nonverbal tests after nondominant treatments.

The problem of memory impairment after ECT has not only a quantitative but also a qualitative aspect. The quantitatively lower degree of memory impairment after unilateral ECT may possibly be explained by a lower quantity of electrical energy reaching the brain tissues or by different or more limited spreading of the current. The higher degree of memory impairment after bilateral ECT suggests an analogy with some effects of bilateral neurological lesions or neurosurgical operations on the brain, mainly temporal lobes, which produce a more generalized memory impairment, cutting across the distinction between verbal and nonverbal material (Milner, 1958). Observations from unilateral lesions of the brain suggest, on the other hand, an interaction between the hemispheres and the probable existence of an interhemispheric compensatory mechanism for memory. Unilateral lesions show milder memory disturbances than bilateral ones. It is then possible that the reduced impairment of memory after unilateral ECT may be due, among other factors, to a possible compensatory mechanism of this sort. This quantitative explanation, of course, is not sufficient to explain the different effects of dominant and nondominant ECT. An additional hypothesis is necessary, that the two hemispheres have a different functional organization. Even here, the qualitatively different responses to unilateral dominant and nondominant ECT may suggest a speculative inference from the effects of neurosurgical operations. Left anterior temporal lobectomy in the dominant hemisphere for speech causes a persistent impairment of memory for verbal material (Meyer & Yates, 1955; Milner, 1958), regardless of whether auditory or visual presentation is used and regardless of the precise test technique (Milner & Kimura, 1964; Milner, 1967). Conversely, right temporal lobectomy impairs memory for both visual and auditory patterned stimuli to which a verbal label could not readily be assigned (Milner, 1958). Thus, there seems to be a hemispheric "dominance" for memory functions as well as for speech and motor skills.

Critical comments. As recently suggested by Dornbush (1972), not only the content (verbal or nonverbal) but also the modality of presentation of the task (auditory or visual) may be relevant in measuring performance efficiency and in the exploration of asymmetric functions. The same author's findings (Dornbush, 1970), and those of others (Meyer, 1959; Lindsay, Cuddy, & Tulving, 1965; Tulving & Lindsay, 1967; Inglis, 1969, 1970) suggest that auditory-verbal tasks are the most sensitive and appropriate in the measurement of memory deficits related to lesions of the dominant hemisphere, while visual nonverbal ones are to be preferred when functions of the nondominant hemisphere are explored. It is conceivable that such a distinction may be particularly useful in unilateral ECT studies where slight memory changes need sophisticated and sensitive methods to be detected and properly measured.

Reviewing the literature of unilateral ECT, one notices a lack of clarity in experimental design (anterograde and retrograde effects have often been considered jointly in the same study) and inadequate attention to the effect of electrode placement on memory retention (or delayed recall) which, in contrast to learning, is specifically impaired by ECT (Cronholm, 1969). In agreement with Dornbush (1972), an indiscriminate study of memory impairment after unilateral ECT is no longer sufficient to increase our insight into the intricate and varying problem of memory functions and their functional localization. Future research has to consider the methodological aspects, time of administration (anterograde and retrograde designs), modality of input (auditory and visual), content of the tasks (verbal and nonverbal), method of testing (recognition, relearning, recall) and type of memory variable (learning and retention).

While the anterior electrode has usually been applied in similar frontotemporal position in all studies, there have been many loci for the homolateral application of the posterior electrode, either on the dominant or on the nondominant hemisphere (Figure 1). It is probable that responses differ not only with the hemispheres stimulated, but also with different placements on the same hemisphere. It can truly be said that there are as many unilateral treatment methods as there are different electrode placements.

COMPARISON OF UNILATERAL
AND BILATERAL
ELECTRODE PLACEMENT

A systematic evaluation of the effects of different electrode placements in electroconvulsive therapy has been presented previously (d'Elia, 1970). The electrode positions were bifrontotemporal and unilateral, i.e., on the same side of the head, either to the nondominant or to the dominant hemisphere. Convulsive threshold stimuli with constant peak intensity (0.8 amp) and individually varying duration (2-6 sec) were used. The time of stimulation was similar for the different electrode placements and the duration of the generalized seizure, recorded either clinically or by EEG, did not show intraindividual or interindividual variations in relation to electrode placement. All treatments were given under narcosis, muscle relaxation, and oxygenation.

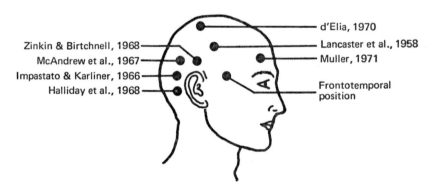

FIG. 1. Unilateral electrode placements.

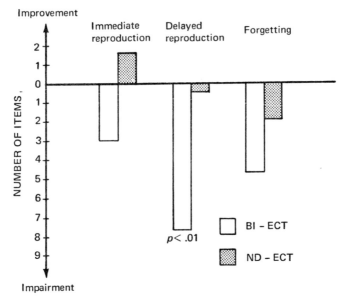

FIG. 2. Anterograde amnesia. Differences in immediate reproduction, delayed reproduction, and forgetting between, before, and after treatment series. (Mean number of treatments: BI-ECT 6.0, ND-ECT 6.6)

Antidepressant efficiency.   An interindividual double-blind comparison of bilateral and unilateral nondominant ECT in patients with endogenous depression, randomly assigned to the two treatment groups, showed agreement in several measures of antidepressant efficiency: rating of depressive symptoms, global rating of change, number of treatments, improvement ratio, time in hospital and time between first and last treatment.

Anterograde amnesia.   To evaluate memory changes after ECT, a memory test battery of Cronholm and Molander (1957) was used. Three to seven days after a series of generalized seizures, at a constant time of the day and with an interval of 3 hours, the anterograde effect on immediate and delayed reproduction was examined. In the unilateral electrode group, memory functions were practically uninfluenced, when compared with pretreatment values, while in the bilateral group, there was a significant impairment of delayed reproduction and a pronounced increase in forgetting (Figure 2). The changes could be ascribed mainly to a negative effect on verbal items (30 word-pair test). Further, there was a significant intergroup difference in delayed reproduction (Figure 2). The main effect seemed to be exerted on the variable delayed retention. The intergroup difference may be, at least partly, explained by a lack of direct involvement by the current of the centers of language and verbal memory in the unilateral group.

Retrograde amnesia.   In another study, the anterograde effect on delayed reproduction of the first in a series of treatments was examined in random groups of diagnostically miscellaneous patients treated with bilateral, nondominant and dominant ECT. The memory test was the same as that described above. The day before and on the day of treatment, immediate and delayed reproduction were measured with an interval of 6 hr at a constant time of the day. ECT was given 1 hr after presentation of the test. Impairment of delayed reproduction and increase in forgetting were most pronounced in the group with bilateral electrode placement and least after nondominant (Figures 3 & 4). Differences in forgetting in two subtests, the 30-figure test and the 30 word-pair test, are shown in Figure 5. Altogether, treatment with bilateral electrodes elicited a more pronounced degree of forgetting than the other two treatment methods. However, in the 30 word-pair subtest, which is a purely verbal test, there is no difference between the bilateral and dominant unilateral electrode placements, while difference in forgetting (between the day before and the day of treatment) is clearly lower after nondomiant unilateral placement. Hence, there seems to be a relation between a higher degree of verbal memory impairment and electrical stimulations directly involving the dominant hemisphere.

On the other hand, in the 30-figure subtest which is a combined figurative and verbal test, there is a significant difference between bilateral and dominant unilateral electrode positions which suggests lower impairment of "figurative" memory when stimulations involve the dominant hemisphere. However, the

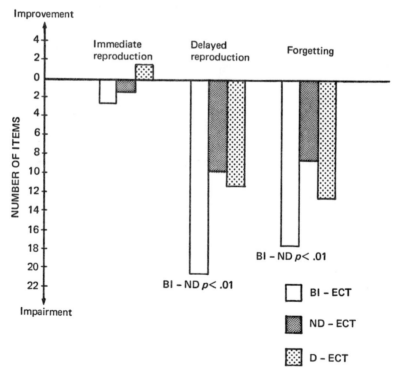

FIG. 3. Retrograde amnesia. Differences in immediate reproduction, delayed reproduction, and forgetting between the day before and the day of treatment.

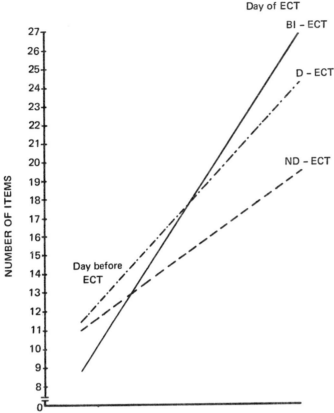

FIG. 4. Retrograde amnesia. "Forgetting" the day before and the day of treatment.

difference between nondominant and dominant electrode placements is not clear cut, for which reason the latter possible relation remains speculative. The lack of relationship may be due to the heterogeneous content of the test, and to the fact that it is recognition rather than recall (as in the case of the 30 word-pair test) that is measured.

Posttreatment confusion. The duration of posttreatment confusion was studied after the second, third, and fourth treatments in 15 patients randomly assigned to three treatment groups. Each patient was treated with bilateral, unilateral nondominant and unilateral dominant electrode positions, with different orders of succession of the treatments in the groups. The time of reorientation for different variables, chosen as an operational measure of the duration of confusion, was significantly shorter after unilateral treatments, particularly to the nondominant hemisphere (Figure 6). Swallowing and spontaneous breathing occurred significantly earlier and headache significantly less frequently after nondominant stimulations.

Comment. In the present study, unilateral nondominant and bilateral ECT

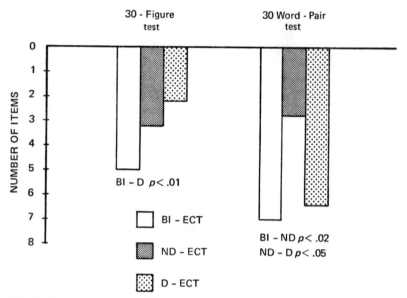

FIG. 5.   Retrograde amnesia. Differences in forgetting in two subtests between the day before and the day of treatment.

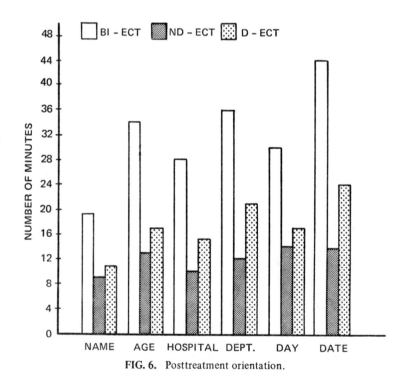

FIG. 6.   Posttreatment orientation.

were found to have equal antidepressant efficacy. Because of the variety of unilateral electrode positions and other methodological differences which make different studies not completely comparable, there is some disagreement in the literature about the similarity in antidepressant efficacy of bilateral and unilateral ECT.

Halliday et al. (1968) reported unilateral ECT to dominant left hemisphere to be particularly unfavorable, as compared with bilateral and nondominant unilateral, in that a significantly larger number of patients relapsed and dropped out of the trial while on this treatment. Cronin et al. (1970) found their unilateral dominant group to be more depressed than the bilateral and nondominant, both after final ECT and at follow-up. Sutherland et al. (1969) found nondominant ECT slightly more effective, while Fleminger et al. (1970a) could not confirm this superiority. From these sporadic observations it may be inferred that the hemispheric dominance may apply to emotional functions as well as to cognitive and motor skills. This interesting aspect, probably deserves further exploration. The memory tests employed in the studies presented here demonstrate differential effects of stimulations with differently placed electrodes, and confirm that ECT exerts a specific influence on delayed reproduction, which is an indicator of retention. Changes in verbal memory have been shown to be clearly related to electrode position. Finally, the reduction or absence of memory impairment with retained antidepressant efficacy confirms the lack of relation between these two factors in electroconvulsive therapy of depressive states.

SUMMARY

Electroconvulsive therapy using unilateral electrode placements has made possible a reduction in memory impairment and posttreatment confusion. There remain, however, divergent opinions about its antidepressant efficacy compared with traditional bilateral treatment. A comparison of the different studies is difficult, since different treatment methods have been used, and since unilateral treatments differ widely because of differing electrode placements. To increase our insight into the functional localization of memory functions, more sophisticated studies of electroconvulsive therapy are stressed.

With retained therapeutic efficacy in the treatment of endogenous depression, electroconvulsive therapy with unilateral electrode placement to the nondominant hemisphere, considerably reduces the anterograde effect of the electrical stimulation on memory retention. The retrograde effect of ECT with unilateral nondominant electrode placement is less pronounced than that of bilateral placement. Unilateral dominant placement has more adverse effects on verbal memory than the nondominant placement.

Unilateral treatment, nondominant and dominant, reduces the duration of posttreatment confusion. One explanation of these reduced effects is that less electrical current reaches the brain, or that there is a more limited spreading of the current in the cerebral tissues. These studies confirm the role of electrical stimulation for the impairment of memory, specifically for retention, and the dichotomy between the depression-relieving and the memory-disturbing effects of electroconvulsive therapy.

REFERENCES

Abrams, R. Daily administration of unilateral ECT. *American Journal of Psychiatry*, 1967, 124, 384–386.

Abrams, R. Recent clinical studies of ECT. *Seminars in Psychiatry*, 1972, 4, 3–12.

Abrams, R., & de Vito, R. A. Clinical efficacy of unilateral ECT. *Diseases of the Nervous System*, 1969, 30, 262–263.

Bidder, T. G., Strain, J. J., & Brunschwig, L. Bilateral and unilateral ECT: follow-up study and critique. *American Journal of Psychiatry*, 1970, 127, 737–745.

Cannicott, S. M. Unilateral electroconvulsive therapy. *Postgraduate Medical-Journal*, 1962, 38, 451–459.

Cannicott, S. M., & Waggoner, R. W. Unilateral and bilateral electroconvulsive therapy. A comparative study. *Archives of General Psychiatry*, 1967, 16, 229–232.

Cohen, B. D., Noblin, C. D., & Silverman, A. J. Functional asymmetry of the human brain. *Science*, 1968, 162, 475–477.

Costello, C. G., Belton, G. P., Abra, J. C., & Dunn, B. E. The amnesic and therapeutic effects of bilateral and unilateral ECT. *British Journal of Psychiatry*, 1970, 116, 69–78.

Cronholm, B. Post-ECT amnesias. In G. A. Talland & N. C. Waugh (Eds.), *The pathology of memory*. New York: Academic Press, 1969.

Cronholm, B., & Molander, L. Memory disturbances after electroconvulsive therapy. 1. Conditions 6 hours after electroshock treatment. *Acta Psychiatrica et Neurologica Scandinavica*, 1957, 32, 280–306.

Cronholm, B., & Ottosson, J. -O. Ultrabrief stimulus technique in electroconvulsive therapy. II: Comparative studies of therapeutic effects and memory disturbances in treatment of endogenous depression with the Elther ES electroshock apparatus and Siemens Konvulsator III. *Journal of Nervous and Mental Disease*, 1963, 137, 268–276.

Cronin, D., Bodley, P., Potts, L., Mather, M. D., Gardner, R. K., & Tobin, J. C. Unilateral and bilateral ECT: A study of memory disturbance and relief from depression. *Journal of Neurology and Psychiatry*, 1970, 33, 705–711.

d'Elia, G. (Ed.) Unilateral electroconvulsive therapy. *Acta Psychiatrica Scandinavica*, 1970, 46 (Suppl. 215), 1–98.

d'Elia, G., & Perris, C. Comparison of electroconvulsive therapy with unilateral and bilateral stimulation. I. Seizure and post-seizure electroencephalographic pattern. *Acta Psychiatrica Scandinavica*, 1970, 46 (Suppl. 215).

Dello Russo, G. Effetti clinici dell'E. S. monolaterale. *Sistema Nervoso* 1969, 5, 217–222.

Di Perri, R., Meduri, M., Megna, G., Messina, C., & Puca, F. M. Effetti dell'elettroshock transtemporale od unilaterale (sull'emisfero minore) in un gruppo di pazienti depressi. *Folia Neuropsychiatrica*, 1969, 12, 395–409.

Dornbush, R. L. Attention in bisensory simultaneous short-term memory. *Perception Psychophysics*, 1970, 4, 244.

Dornbush, R. L. Memory and induced ECT convulsions. *Seminars in Psychiatry*, 1972, 4, 47–54.

Dornbush, R. L., Abrams, R., & Fink, M. Memory changes after unilateral and bilateral convulsive therapy. *British Journal of Psychiatry*, 1971, 119, 75–78.

Fink, M., Kahn, R. L., Karp, E., Pollack, M., Green, M. A., Alan, B., & Lefkowits, H. J. Inhalant induced convulsions: Significance for the theory of the convulsive therapy process, *Archives of General Psychiatry*. 1961, 4, 259–266.

Fleminger, J. J., de L. Horne, D. J., Nair, N. P. V., & Nott, P. N. Differential effect of unilateral and bilateral ECT. *American Journal of Psychiatry*, 1970(a), 127, 430–436.

Fleminger, J. J., de L. Horne, D. J., & Nott, P. N. Unilateral electroconvulsive therapy and cerebral dominance: Effect of right- and left-sided electrode placement on verbal memory. *Journal of Neurology, Neurosurgery and Psychiatry*, 1970(b), 33 408–411.

Frost, I. Unilateral electroshock. *Lancet*, 1957, 19, 157–158.

Giberti, F. Aspetti comparativi degli effetti dell'elettroshock (bi-e monopolare), dell'elettronarcosi e del trattamento chemioconvulsivante (flurotil) in pazienti psichiatrici. *Sistema Nervoso*, 1969, 21, 210–216.

Gottlieb, G., & Wilson, I. C. Cerebral dominance: Temporary disruption of verbal memory by unilateral electroconvulsive shock treatment. *Journal of Comparative and Physiological Psychology*, 1965, 60, 368–372.

Halliday, A. M., Davison, K., Browne, M. W., & Kreeger, L. C. A comparison of the effects on depression and memory of bilateral ECT and unilateral ECT to the dominant and non-dominant hemispheres. *British Journal of Psychiatry*, 1968, 114, 997–1012.

Impastato, D. J., & Karliner, W. Control of memory impairment in EST by unilateral stimulation of the non-dominant hemisphere. *Diseases of the Nervous System*, 1966, 27, 182–188.

Inglis, J. Electrode placement and the effect of ECT on mood and memory in depression. *Canadian Psychiatric Association Journal* 1969, 14, 463–471.

Inglis, J. Shock, surgery and cerebral asymmetry. *British Journal of Psychiatry*, 1970, 117, 143–148.

Lancaster, N., Steinert, R., & Frost, I. Unilateral electroconvulsive therapy. *Journal of Mental Science*, 1958, 104, 221–227.

Laurell, B. (Ed.) Flurothyl convulsive therapy. *Acta Psychiatrica Scandanavica*, 1970, 46 (Suppl. 213).

Levy, R. The clinical evaluation of unilateral electroconvulsive therapy. *British Journal of Psychiatry*, 1968, 114, 459–463.

Liberson, W. T. Brief stimulus therapy. Physiological and clinical observations. *American Journal of Psychiatry*, 1948, 105, 28–39.

Liberson, W. T. Current evaluation of electric convulsive therapy. Correlation of the parameters of electrical current with physiologic and psychologic changes. *Research Publications of the Association for Research in Nervous and Mental Disease*, 1953, 31, 199–231.

Lindsay, P. H., Cuddy, L., & Tulving, E. Absolute judgements of simultaneously presented visual and auditory stimuli. *Psychonomic Science*, 1965, 2, 211.

Man, P. L. & Bolin, B. J. Further exploration of unilateral electroshock treatment. *Diseases of the Nervous System*, 1969, 30, 547–551.

Martin, W. L., Ford, H. D., McDonald, E. C., & Towler, M. L. Clinical evaluation of unilateral EST. *American Journal of Psychiatry*, 1965, 121, 1087–1090.

McAndrew, J., Berkey, B., & Matthew, C. The effect of dominant and non-dominant unilateral ECT as compared to bilateral ECT. *American Journal of Psychiatry*, 1967, 124, 483–490.

Meyer, V. Cognitive changes following temporal lobectomy for relief of temporal lobe epilepsy. *Archives of Neurology and Psychiatry*, 1959, 81, 200.

Meyer, V., & Yates, A. Intellectual changes following temporal lobectomy for psychomotor epilepsy. *Journal of Neurology, Neurosurgery and Psychiatry*, 1955, 18, 44–52.

Milner, B. Psychological defects produced by temporal-lobe excision. *Research Publications of the Association for Research in Nervous and Mental Disease*, 1958, 36, 244–257.

Milner, B. Brain mechanisms suggested by studies of temporal lobes. In F. L. Darley (Ed.), *Brain mechanisms underlying speech and language*. New York: Grune & Stratton, 1967.

Milner, B., & Kimura, D. Dissociable visual learning defects after unilateral temporal lobectomy in man. Cited by B. Milner & H. L. Teuber, 1964. (Paper read at Eastern Psychological Association, April, 1964)

Milner, B., & Teuber, H. L. Alteration of perception and memory in man: Reflections on methods. In L. Weiskrantz (Ed.), *Analysis of behavioral change*. New York: Harper & Row, 1968.

Muller, D. J. Unilateral ECT. *Disease of the Nervous System.* 1971, **32**, 422–424.

Ottosson, J. -O. (Ed.), Experimental studies on the mode of action of electroconvulsive therapy. *Acta Psychiatrica Scandinavica,* 1960, **35** (Suppl. 145).

Pancheri, P. Esperienze cliniche con l'elettroshock unilaterale. *Sistema Nervoso,* 1969, **21**, 223–233.

Rinaldi, F., Manacorda, A., & Mastrosimone, F. L'elettroshock unilaterale. Rilievi psicometrici sulle funzioni mnesiche in una serie di pazienti sottoposti a trattamento elettroconvulsivante sull'emisfero non-dominante. *Folia Neuropsychiatrica,* 1967, **10**, 557–566.

Small, J. G., Small, I. F., Perez, H. C., & Sharpley, P. Electroencephalographic and neurophysiological studies of electrically induced seizures. *Journal of Nervous and Mental Disease,* 1970, **150**, 479–489.

Strain, J. J., Brunschwig, L., Duffy, J. P., Agle, D. P., Rosenbaum, A. L., & Bidder, T. G. Comparison of therapeutic effects and memory changes with bilateral and unilateral ECT. *American Journal of Psychiatry,* 1968, **125**, 294–304.

Sutherland, E. M., Oliver, J. E., & Knight, D. R. EEG, memory and confusion in dominant, non-dominant and bitemporal ECT. *British Journal of Psychiatry,* 1969, **115**, 1059–1064.

Tedeschi, D. H., Swinyard, E. A., & Goodman, L. S. Effect of variations in stimulus intensity on maximal electroshock seizure pattern, recovery time and anticonvulsant potency of phenobarbitone in mice. *Journal of Pharmacology and Experimental Therapeutics,* 1956, **116**, 107–113.

Tulving, E., & Lindsay, P. H. Identification of simultaneously presented visual and auditory stimuli. *Acta Psychologica; European Journal of Psychology,* 1967, **27**, 101.

Valentine, M., Keddie, K. M. G., & Dunne, D. A comparison of techniques in electroconvulsive therapy. *British Journal of Psychiatry,* 1968, **114**, 989–996.

Wilson, I. C., & Gottlieb, G. Unilateral electroconvulsive shock therapy. *Diseases of the Nervous System,* 1967, **28**, 541–545.

Zamora, E. N., & Kaelbling, R. Memory and electroconvulsive therapy. *American Journal of Psychiatry,* 1965, **112**, 546–554.

Zinkin, S., & Birtchnell, J. Unilateral electroconvulsive therapy: Its effects on memory and its therapeutic efficacy. *British Journal of Psychiatry,* 1968, **114**, 973–988.

3
IS EGG SLOWING RELATED TO THE THERAPEUTIC EFFECT OF CONVULSIVE THERAPY?[1]

Jan Volavka, M.D.

The principal persistent physiological consequence of repeated convulsions is a slowing of the background electroencephalographic (EEG) activity (Fink & Kahn, 1957; Volavka, Feldstein, Abrams, Dornbush, & Fink, 1972). Equally, ample evidence of the therapeutic efficacy of convulsive therapy in depressive states exists (Kalinowsky & Hoch, 1961). Are the changes in the EEG related to the therapeutic effect of ECT? If they are, we have a clue to the mechanism of behavioral modification achieved by convulsive therapy. One could hypothesize that other agents eliciting a similar EEG pattern would also relieve depressive states. Conversely, agents that abolish EEG slowing should also interfere with the behavioral change elicited by ECT. This relationship was indeed observed by Fink (1960) who demonstrated concurrent blocking of EEG and behavioral effects of ECT by anticholinergic drugs. Also, if there is a strong relationship between the therapeutic and EEG effects of convulsive therapies, the EEG could be used as an objective and easily recordable physiological measure of treatment response.

This question has been repeatedly examined, with unconvincing results (Volavka, 1972). In a mixed patient sample, Hoagland, Malamud, Kaufman and Pincus (1946) reported that the amount of EEG activity greater than 13 Hz (beta activity) decreased as the mental state improved. Cremerius and Jung (1947) found the greatest EEG slowing to occur in patients who failed to improve, but their sample included psychopaths and epileptics. A similar conclusion was reached by Weil and Brinegar (1947) but the data they presented

[1] Partial support for this research was provided through United States Public Health Service Grants MH-15561 and MH-13358.

does not justify their statement. Moriarty and Siemens (1947) asserted that they did not find any differences between the EEG response to ECT in psychotics who recovered and those who did not, but they did not present the data. Mosovich and Katzenelbogen (1948) found slightly more abnormal EEGs in clinically unimproved psychotics after ECT, but their data are not significant (X^2 = 2.13, df = 1), nor is the relationship between EEG slowing and clinical improvement significant in data published by Blaurock, Lorimer, Segal, and Gibbs (1950).

Roth, Kay, Shaw, and Green (1957) studied a homogeneous group of 41 endogenous psychotic depressives. They measured the amount of EEG delta activity elicited by thiopentone in post-ECT patients and found a correlation with long term clinical outcome: the more delta activity, the smaller the probability of a relapse at 3 and 6 months after the treatment course. They did not find a relationship between the clinical scores assessed within 3 days of the end of treatment and the thiopentone-induced delta activity, but they did not separate the contribution of the short term memory effects to their behavioral evaluations.

Fink and Kahn (1957) also measured the amount of posttreatment EEG delta activity and found this to be directly related to measures of short term clinical improvement. They did separate the contribution of memory changes to the evaluation (although this is not explicitly described in the paper). This relationship was found in two samples of 24 and 54 consecutive patients. EEGs were taken 25-31 hr after a treatment, and the clinical response was evaluated during an observation period of at least 8 weeks following the termination of ECT.

In a later study, Fink (1958, 1960) reported that anticholinergic drugs, notably diethazine, benactyzine, and Ditran would elicit a relapse in symptoms which persisted for the duration of the drug's action. Johnson, Ulett, Johnson, Smith, and Sines (1960) attempted a blockade of the ECT effects by chronic administration of atropine in 30 patients: 14 with depressive reaction, 16 with schizophrenia. Fifteen patients received atropine and ECT, and 15 ECT only. EEGs were obtained before the first treatment and again 24-48 hr after the 6th and 12th treatments. Using a frequency analyzer measure of EEG changes a significant negative correlation between the amount of slow EEG activity after the 6th treatment and the immediate clinical improvement was found. No correlation after the 12th treatment was detected. Confounding this study, also, was a failure to separate short term memory changes from the mood and ideational effects of treatment, as well as the direct effects of high-dose atropine on the estimates of behavior of EEG.

In a study of the relation of seizures to the memory, EEG, and therapeutic effects of seizures, Ottosson (1960) reported the antidepressant effects to be related to the induced seizure activity, while the memory changes were more related to the direct effect of currents on the brain. With the availability of flurothyl-induced seizures, these relationships were reexamined. Comparisons of flurothyl and ECT generally found the clinical results to be therapeutically equivalent, but there were lesser degrees of memory impairment with flurothyl (Small and Small, 1972). The amount of interictal EEG slowing induced by ECT is not different from that following the flurothyl seizures, and the relationship to improvement was found similar to that for ECT (Fink, Kahn, Karp, Pollack, Green, Alan, & Lefkowits, 1961). A decrease in performance on a simple memory test was also found to be related to the degree of EEG slowing after both ECT and flurothyl seizures (Fink et al. 1961). These studies utilized bitemporal placement of electrodes.

Changing the site of electrodes from bitemporal to unilateral resulted in a lateralization of the EEG slowing to the side of electrode placement (d'Elia & Perris, 1970; Volavka et al., 1972). Comparisons of clinical efficacy generally suggest that seizures induced with unilateral electrodes are slightly less clinically effective than bitemporal placement (Abrams, Fink, Dornbush, Feldstein, Volavka, & Roubicek, 1972), but the relation of clinical effects to EEG changes were not well defined.

Despite many studies, the relation between cerebral and behavioral effects of seizures remains elusive. The studies are difficult to evaluate because of differences in patient samples, the mode of seizure induction, concurrent medication, techniques of EEG and clinical assessment, number of treatments, and timing of tests in relation to the last treatment.

Our studies concentrated on short term therapeutic effects and their relation to the EEG slowing (Abrams et al., 1972; Dornbush, Abrams, & Fink, 1971; Volavka et al., 1972). Thirty-one depressed patients were the subjects. EEG records were obtained from two frontocentral derivations 24 hr after a seizure; and clinical assessments (Hamilton rating scale) were obtained on the day following the last treatment. The number of treatment sessions varied between four and eight. Sinusoidal current was used. Electrodes were applied bitemporally in 22 patients, and unilaterally on the nondominant hemisphere in 9 patients. Changes in EEG frequencies and amplitude were measured by period analysis (Fink, Shapiro, Hickman, & Itil, 1968).

The usual product-moment correlation coefficient showed no significant relationship between the short term scores of clinical improvement and EEG slowing as measured by the amount of delta activity ($r = -.17$). Using multiple stepwise regression analyses (Cohen, 1968), we accounted for the effects of concurrent antidepressant medication, number of convulsions, and treatment mode before investigating the relation between clinical effects and EEG. We found the increase in the amount of EEG slow-wave activity to be related to the number of treatments and to the treatment mode, but not to changes in the Hamilton rating scale (Table 1). We thus failed to find a relation between short term mood changes and EEG slowing. (But, the question of association between postseizure EEG and long term clinical effects was not examined).

Additional studies are needed in which the time of evaluation is varied and the predictability of relapses from nonactivated posttreatment EEGs is assessed.

TABLE 1
ECT Clinical Outcome and Adjusted Right and Left EEG Parameters

Independent variable	df	Dependent variable	Left (F7-Cz)			Right (F8-Cz)		
			r_p	r^2 incr.	F	r_p	r^2 incr.	F
Number of ECT sessions	1/26	Average frequency	−0.70	0.43	25.24*	−0.52	0.23	9.78*
		Δ% time	0.66	0.42	19.58*	0.50	0.22	8.62*
		Θ% time	0.10	0.01	0.27	0.16	0.02	0.64
		First derivative average frequency	−0.30	0.09	2.51	−0.16	0.02	0.72
Treatment mode	1/24	Average frequency	0.41	0.02	4.91**	−0.48	0.04	7.11**
		Δ% time	−0.42	0.02	5.04**	0.34	0.02	3.07
		Θ% time	0.00	0.00	0.01	0.01	0.00	0.06
		First derivative average frequency	−0.25	0.01	1.59	0.13	0.00	0.07
Hamilton rating scale (adjusted)	1/23	Average frequency	−0.32	0.01	2.67	0.15	0.00	0.55
		Δ% time	0.30	0.01	2.22	−0.13	0.00	0.37
		Θ% time	0.0C	0.01	0.55	0.00	0.00	0.00
		First derivative average frequency	−0.17	0.01	0.73	0.09	0.00	0.18

*$p<0.01$.
**$p<0.05$.

The independent variables were entered into the regression analysis in the order in which they are listed. The first column contains the partial correlation coefficients (r_p) which assess the relation of the associated independent variable to the dependent variable after the effects of prior independent variables has been removed. The r^2 increments express the proportion of variance contributed by each independent variable. The significance of an r^2 increment is indicated by its associated F ratio. The treatment was coded "1" for bilateral ECT and "2" for unilateral ECT. Consequently, a positive r_p indicates that an increase of the dependent variable was associated with unilateral ECT or a decrease with bilateral ECT or both. A negative r_p indicates the converse. *(Derived from J. Volavka, S. Feldstein, R. Abrams, R. L. Dornbush, and M. Fink, "EEG and Clinical Change After Bilateral and Unilateral Electroconvulsive Therapy," Electroencephalography and Clinical Neurophysiology, 32 (1972), 631-639, Table III.)*

Since Roth et al. (1957) and Fink and Kahn (1957) published their studies, the technical capability to measure EEG variables has greatly increased, and it may now be possible to extract the information required for relapse prediction from the record without thiopentone activation. The time and scales used for the assessment of the clinical state are other important problems. The available scales reflect the transitory memory impairment caused by ECT. Since EEG changes may be related to memory impairment, the relationship between EEG and global clinical improvement can thereby be obscured. In future studies, memory data should be obtained separately from measures of clinical effects. The relation of memory and EEG changes should be taken into account before the correlation between EEG and clinical effect is investigated. It may well be that the commonly used total scores of clinical rating scales are too complex and that clusters of items should be separately related to the EEG.

Timing of the evaluation may be as critical as the content of the behavioral measurements. The EEG is a measure of ongoing cerebral activity summed over several minutes, while global ratings measuring clinical improvement are broad estimates of behavior in large time segments. In drug evaluation studies, the probability of defining relationships between EEG and behavioral measures decreases with the time intervening between the measurement of the different forms of data acquired and with differences in the time span included in each estimate.

Apart from the problem of a relationship between posttreatment EEG and clinical outcome, the pretreatment EEG has been examined as a predictor of therapeutic effect. Little systematic data has been reported, although in their quantitative measures, Fink and Kahn (1957) found better therapeutic results and higher degrees of EEG changes in patients with slower average alpha frequencies before treatment. In our studies, we calculated the product-moment correlation coefficient between pretreatment EEG average frequency and the $\Delta\%$ time from two scalp derivations with the post-ECT global clinical rating, and the coefficient was low (maximal $r = -0.13$, df = 30).

The evidence supporting the hypothesis that EEG slowing is related to the therapeutic effect of ECT is limited. Where quantitative methods were applied, EEG changes are found related to some aspects of behavior, and to rate and number of treatments. But the significance of these relationships remains obscure and a challenge to systemic study.

REFERENCES

Abrams, R., Fink, M., Dornbush, R. L., Feldstein, S., Volavka, J., & Roubicek, J. Unilateral and bilateral ECT: Effects on depression, memory and the electroencephalogram. *Archives of General Psychiatry,* 1972, **27**, 88-94.

Blaurock, M. F., Lorimer, F. M., Segal, M. M., & Gibbs, F. A. Focal electroencephalographic changes in unilateral electric convulsion therapy. *Archives of Neurology and Psychiatry,* 1950, **64**, 220-226.

Cohen, J. Multiple regression as a general data-analytic system. *Psychological Bulletin,* 1968, **70**, 426-443.

Cremerius, J., & Jung, R. Changes of the electroencephalogram after electro-shock treatment. *Nervenarzt,* 1947, 18, 193-205.

d'Elia, G., & Perris, C. Comparison of electroconvulsive therapy with unilateral and bilateral stimulation. I. Seizure and post-seizure electroencephalographic pattern. *Acta Psychiatrica Scandinavica,* 1970, 46 (Suppl. 215) 9-29.

Dornbush, R. L., Abrams, R., & Fink, M. Memory changes after unilateral and bilateral convulsive therapy. *British Journal of Psychiatry,* 1971, 119, 75-78.

Fink, M. Effect of anticholinergic agent, diethazine, on EEG and behavior: Significance for theory of convulsive therapy. *Archives of Neurology and Psychiatry,* 1958, 80, 380-387.

Fink, M. Effects of anticholinergic compounds on post convulsive electroencephalogram and behavior of psychiatric patients. *Electroencephalography and Clinical Neurophysiology,* 1960, 12, 359-369.

Fink, M. & Kahn, R. L. Relation of electroencephalographic delta activity to behavioral response in electroshock. *Archives of Neurology and Psychiatry,* 1957, 78, 516-525.

Fink, M., Kahn, R. L., Karp, E., Pollack, M., Green, M. A., Alan, B., & Lefkowits, H. J. Inhalant-induced convulsions. *Archives of General Psychiatry,* 1961, 4, 259-266.

Fink, M., Shapiro, G., Hickman, C., and Itil, T. Digital computer EEG analyses in psychopharmacology. In N. S. Kline & E. Laska (Eds.), *Computers and electronic devices in psychiatry.* New York: Grune & Stratton, 1968.

Hoagland, H., Malamud, W., Kaufman, I. C., & Pincus, G. Changes in the electroencephalogram and in the excretion of 17-ketosteroids accompanying electroshock therapy of agitated depression. *Psychomatic Medicine,* 1946, 8, 246-251.

Johnson, L. C., Ulett, G. A., Johnson, M., Smith, K., & Sines, J. O. Electroconvulsive therapy (with and without atropine). *Archives of General Psychiatry,* 1960, 2, 324-336.

Kalinowsky, L., & Hoch, P. *Somatic treatments in psychiatry.* New York: Grune & Stratton, 1961.

Moriarty, J. D., & Siemens, J. C. Electroencephalographic study of electric shock therapy. *Archives of Neurology and Psychiatry,* 1947, 57, 712-718.

Mosovich, A., and Katzenelbogen, S. Electroshock therapy, clinical and electroencephalographic studies. *Journal of Nervous and Mental Disease,* 1948, 107, 517-530.

Ottosson, J. -O. Experimental studies of the mode of action of electroconvulsive therapy. *Acta Psychiatrica Scandinavica,* 1960, 35 (Suppl. 145).

Roth, M., Kay, D. W. K., Shaw, J. & Green, J. Prognosis and pentothal induced electroencephalographic changes in electroconvulsive treatment. *Electroencephalography and Clinical Neurophysiology,* 1957, 9, 225-237.

Small, J. G. & Small, I. F. Clinical results: Indoklon versus ECT. *Seminars in Psychiatry,* 1972, 4, 13-26.

Volavka, J. Neurophysiology of ECT. *Seminars in Psychiatry,* 1972, 4, 55-65.

Volavka, J., Feldstein, S., Abrams, R., Dornbush, R., & Fink, M. EEG and clinical change after bilateral and unilateral electroconvulsive therapy. *Electroencephalography and Clinical Neurophysiology,* 1972, 32, 631-639.

Weil, A. A., & Brinegar, W. C. Electroencephalographic studies following electric shock therapy. *Archives of Neurology and Psychiatry,* 1947, 57, 719-729.

4
ELECTROCONVULSIVE THERAPY AND SLEEP[1]

Joseph Mendels, M.D., Robert L. Van de Castle, Ph.D., and David R. Hawkins, M.D.

Varying patterns of disturbance have been found in the sleep electroencephalographic recordings of psychiatric patients. As the clinical course of the illness may be reversed by the administration of electroconvulsive therapy (ECT), it is of interest to consider the associated changes in the sleep pattern and how these changes relate to the diagnosis and therapeutic outcome.

Two groups of investigators have studied the effect of a course of ECT on sleep in cats. Cohen, Duncan, and Dement (1967) found that cats who had been deprived of Stage 1 rapid eye movement (REM) sleep for 10-12 days and who were given a course of electrically induced convulsions on the last 3 days of deprivation and on the first recovery day, had significantly less compensatory rebound in REM sleep during the recovery period than did control animals who did not receive ECT. In a related experiment, Cohen and Dement (1966) found that the administration of ECT during the period of REM deprivation (for up to 7 days) also significantly reduced the usual rebound in REM sleep after discontinuation of the REM deprivation. They suggested that the electrically induced convulsion was substituting for a component of REM sleep, thus reducing the accumulated "need" for REM sleep. The significant reduction in REM rebound with the administration of ECT at the end of the deprivation period was achieved by only four convulsions. They suggested that this may reflect the mechanism whereby ECT exerts its therapeutic effect in the treatment of depression in that, "if the various manifestations of the REM

[1] This research was supported by National Institute of Mental Health grants MH-17551, MH-6633, and MH-14421 and research funds from the Veterans Administration.

deprivation effect contribute to the psychotic process, then it is not unreasonable that an alleviation of this effect by electroconvulsive shock therapy may be a critical factor in the successful course of treatment" (Cohen et al., 1967, p. 1648).

Kaelbling, Koski, and Hartwig (1968) studied the effect of daily ECT on the 5th through 9th days of a 12-day experiment in which sleep of four cats was continuously monitored. They found significant reduction in REM sleep during the period of ECT administration (a reduction in mean REM time from 134.5 min to 95.9 min, $p < .01$). Further, there was no compensatory rebound in REM sleep during the recovery period, suggesting to the authors that ECT was substituting for REM sleep. Indeed, they speculated that ECT and REM sleep are interchangeable.

Studies of the effects of ECT on the sleep EEG of man are sparse. Green and Stajduhar (1966) studied the effect of ECT on the sleep of a single patient who was severely ill with a psychotic depression. This study must be interpreted with some caution in that it involved only one patient, and monitoring in the sleep laboratory was restricted to only 2 baseline nights and thereafter for a single night each week for 9 weeks. Evidence from other studies (Mendels & Chernik, 1972) suggests that these periods of very brief and intermittent recording may produce misleading findings because there is considerable variation from night to night in the sleep of psychotically depressed patients, and also because of the need for the patients to readapt repeatedly to the sleep laboratory setting. It requires 3 to 5 continuous nights of recording to obtain a reasonably reliable picture of a depressed patient's sleep pattern. Green and Stajduhar found that ECT administration was associated with an increase in the percentage of the total sleep time occupied by Stage 1 REM sleep. During the baseline period, REM sleep occupied 20.5% of the total sleep period, while by the end of the second week of treatment it had increased to 35.9%. The latency to the first REM period of the night also decreased during this time, indicating an increased pressure to achieve REM sleep. This change was most marked after the patient had had three treatments. Thereafter the percentage of total sleep time occupied by REM decreased to approximately baseline levels (with one exception during the 9th week). The latency to first REM increased to normal values at a slower rate. It is difficult to evaluate changes in other parameters of sleep in this report. Further, care must be taken about interpreting the relationship between changes in REM sleep and the administration of ECT since ECT was given three times a week and only a single sleep recording was made each week. Further, it is impossible to separate the direct effects of ECT and the effects of clinical improvement. (This difficulty also applies to the other clinical studies to be discussed in this chapter.)

Zarcone, Gulevich, and Dement (1967) studied the effect of ECT in 10 psychiatric patients. They noted a number of significant problems, including the absence of information about the effect of ECT on control subjects; limited baseline periods prior to the onset of ECT administration; the varying mental status of their patients; and a variety of drugs used in associated treatment. Bearing these limitations in mind, they suggested that ECT decreased Stage 1 REM sleep (both the number of minutes and the percentage of the night's sleep spent in Stage 1 REM), and increased slow-wave sleep (Stages 3 and 4). They also noted an increased latency to the first REM period of the night.

The patients studied by Zarcone et al. (1967) appear to have been schizophrenic or suffering from a paranoid reaction. Depression was the associated rather than the primary clinical feature. Schizophrenic and paranoid patients do not show as satisfactory a response to ECT as do depressed patients, resulting in a greater number of treatments, an associated use of phenothiazines, and, perhaps a less complete clinical response than that seen by us in our study of depressives (infra vide). They excluded one patient (No. 10) because of the development of a severe acute brain syndrome after eight treatments. However, another patient (No. 6) also showed signs of a severe acute brain syndrome and was included in the data analysis. Further, the authors commented on the "relatively high incidence of acute brain syndrome" in their entire sample. If the data on patient No. 10 were included, then the average score for the number of minutes of REM per night and the latency to the first REM period of the night no longer show a significant alteration (t = 1.31 and 0.64 for REM latency and minutes of REM, respectively). Consideration must also be given to the fact that the decrease in REM sleep noted by these investigators may have been due to chlorpromazine and amitriptyline that these patients received. These drugs are known to reduce REM sleep (King, 1971). A further limitation in interpreting the findings of this study arises from the fact that only one patient was recorded on most nights of the study. The other patients were studied on an occasional basis, making it even more difficult to discriminate between fluctuations in sleep from night to night, drug effects, changes associated with clinical improvement (or remission), or with the acute brain syndrome that developed in several of the patients. For example, we have compared the sleep patterns of three depressed patients studied early in hospitalization with their sleep patterns 2 weeks later when they showed clinical improvement but had not received ECT. They showed a change in sleep patterns similar to that reported by Zarcone et al. (1967), with an increase in slow-wave sleep and a decrease in REM %. Thus, one must be careful in attributing the changes observed by Zarcone et al. to the convulsive therapy.

We have studied eight depressed patients before, during, and after a course of ECT. The patients were hospitalized and were studied frequently in the sleep laboratory during hospitalization. Each patient received an average of six treatments and the group was monitored in the sleep laboratory on 36 nights immediately after ECT administration. A comparison of the 36 sleep-monitored nights with 3 to 4 baseline nights obtained from each subject revealed several changes of significance. There was an increase in total sleep, more minutes of Stages 3, 4, and 1 REM, an increase in the number of REM periods, and a reduction in the number of spontaneous awakenings.

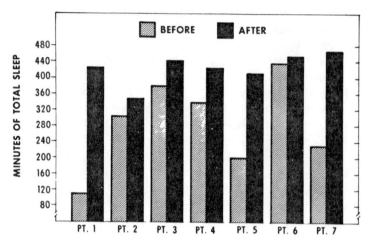

FIG. 1. Total sleep on night before and night after first ECT for seven patients.

A comparison between the baseline nights with the night after the first ECT in seven subjects revealed that a single treatment produced an increase in total sleep time, an increase in the number of minutes of Stage 1 REM and in the number of REM periods. Figures 1-3 reflect these changes.

Zarcone et al. (1967) reported an overall reduction in REM time in their patients, with an initial increase in the number of minutes spent in REM sleep from 87 to 93 in four patients who were studied after one to three treatments (REM % increased from 21% to 24%). In our studies, we compared REM sleep in five patients during the first ECT administrations (Treatments 1, 2, and 3) with those later in the course of treatment (4 or more treatments) (Figures 2 & 3). It

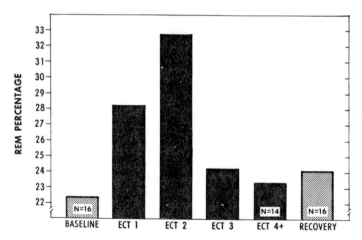

FIG. 2. REM % sleep during baseline, ECT, and recovery nights for five patients.

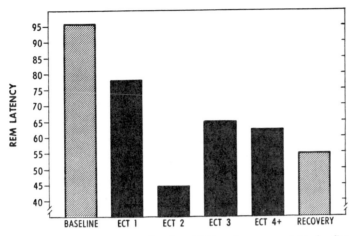

FIG. 3.   REM latency during baseline, ECT, and recovery nights for five patients.

can be seen that REM % increased after the first and second treatment and then decreased. The values after the first and second treatments of 28% and 33% are both above control values. REM % after the third and subsequent treatments was very similar to that during the recovery period (24-26%). REM latency decreased substantially after the first and second treatments (from 96 to 78 and 46 min) and then rose (Figure 3).

SUMMARY

Our study of the effect of ECT on the sleep of a group of psychotic depressives revealed an increase in total sleep time, in Stages 3 and 4 sleep, and in Stage 1 REM with a decrease in REM onset latency. The number of REM periods increased, and there was a reduction in the number of spontaneous awakenings. Overall, sleep was less disturbed, longer, and closer to control values. Changes in REM sleep anteceded the changes in Stages 3 and 4.

These observations must be interpreted with some caution. While the patients were moderately to severely ill and suffered from a depressive illness, there were significant differences among them. They differed in the type of depression (e.g., unipolar or bipolar), the duration of illness, the administration of drugs prior to electroconvulsive treatment, and the number of treatments. Despite these factors, a relatively consistent pattern did emerge.

The sleep patterns seen in our depressed patients differed considerably from that noted by Zarcone et al. (1967) in their patients, as well as that suggested by the animal studies. However, there is no reason to suppose that the response of depressed patients to ECT will be the same as that of cats (either REM deprived or not) or of schizophrenic or paranoid patients concomitantly treated with phenothiazines and amitriptyline and receiving more than twice as many treatments.

REFERENCES

Cohen, H. B., & Dement, W. C. Sleep: Suppression of rapid eye movement phase in the cat after electroconvulsive shock. *Science*, 1966, **154**, 396-398.

Cohen, H. B., Duncan, R. F., II, & Dement, W. C. Sleep: The effect of electroconvulsive shock in cats deprived of REM sleep. *Science*, 1967, **156**, 1646-1648.

Green, W. J., & Stajduhar, P. P. The effect of ECT on the sleep-dream cycle in a psychotic depression. *Journal of Nervous and Mental Disease*, 1966, **143**, 123-134.

Kaelbling, R., Koski, E. G., & Hartwig, C. D. Reduction of rapid eye movement sleep after electroconvulsions—an experiment in cats on the mode of action of electroconvulsive treatment. *Journal of Psychiatric Research*, 1968, **6**, 153-157.

King, C. D. The pharmacology of rapid eye movement sleep. In S. Garattini, A. Goldin, F. Hawkins, I. J. Kopin (Eds.), *Advances in pharmacology and chemotherapy*, Vol. 9. New York: Academic Press, 1971.

Mendels, J., & Chernik, D. A. REM sleep and depression. *Association for the Psychophysiological Study of Sleep*, July, 1972.

Zarcone, V., Gulevich, G., & Dement, W. C. Sleep and electroconvulsive therapy. *Archives of General Psychiatry*, 1967, **16**, 567-573.

5
EEG AND NEUROPHYSIOLOGICAL STUDIES OF CONVULSIVE THERAPIES[1]

Joyce G. Small, M.D.

Convulsive treatment is still a mainstay in the hospital treatment of severe mental disorders. It is known to be associated with therapeutic benefits and to produce alterations in memory and cognitive functions as well as changes in the scalp electroencephalogram. The clinical and psychological effects may vary somewhat depending upon the method of induction of seizures, some of which have been discussed in other chapters of this volume. In this chapter, the EEG and neurophysiological concomitants of different kinds of convulsive therapy will be reviewed. Four different methods of seizure induction will be considered namely, convulsive therapy by means of chemical inhalation of flurothyl (Indoklon), or bitemporal electrical stimulation, or by passage of electrical current through the dominant or the nondominant hemisphere of the brain. Findings already published and reports and results of some recent work are compiled in this survey.

METHOD AND MATERIAL

The EEG and neurophysiological data to be described here were derived from studies of convulsive treatment conducted at the Larue D. Carter Memorial Hospital from 1966 to the present. This institution is an acute intensive psychiatric treatment facility which serves all age groups. It has primary responsibilities for undergraduate and residency training in psychiatry and for clinical and neurophysiological research. The patients selected for studies of convulsive therapy were all hospitalized adults, referred for such treatment by their attending psychiatrists.

[1] This research was supported in part by National Institute of Mental Health grant MH-14638.

The particular kind of seizure induction was selected independently and governed by research protocols, but decisions both about institution and termination of convulsive treatment were the responsibility of the clinicians. All patients received treatment three times weekly and different kinds of EEG recordings and neurophysiological procedures, as well as clinical and other studies, were accomplished at specific intervals before, during and after the series of seizures. For further methodological details the reader is referred to other publications (Small & Small, 1968, 1971; Small, Small, Sharpley, & Moore, 1968; Small, Small, Perez, & Sharpley, 1970; Small, Small, Milstein, & Sharpley, 1973).

The identifying characteristics of the patients who received convulsive therapy (CT) are shown in Table 1. The figures indicate that the flurothyl and bilateral ECT groups were very similar in terms of these variables, as were the patients who received ECT on the right or the left side of the head. However, there were significant differences between the unilateral-treated patients and the others with variations in age and sex distribution, psychiatric diagnoses, and numbers of treatments administered. Thus, some of the variations between unilateral ECT and other forms of treatment must be interpreted in the light of initial group differences, but the bilateral ECT and flurothyl patients and those who received unilateral ECT on the nondominant and dominant sides were quite similar beforehand.

RESULTS

Ictal Studies

The first issue to be considered is the ictal phase of the seizures themselves. Since the literature is quite conclusive on the point that grand mal or generalized motor seizures must be induced for therapeutic benefits, only the characteristics of major seizures induced by these methods will be described. (Abortive, partial, or minor seizures can sometimes occur with each kind of induction.) Most investigations of seizure activity during convulsive treatment have been concerned with bilateral ECT in which seizures are produced by passing an electrical current through the bitemporal regions of the head. A typical example of the electrical activity accompanying a seizure so induced is shown in Figure 1.

EEG activity some 4 to 6 sec after the electrical stimulus is shown in the tracing on the left (the circuit must be broken during the stimulus itself to avoid overloading of the recording instrument). There is diffuse, bisynchronous, generalized spike and multiple spikewave activity in all monitored scalp regions. The EEG and the muscle activity monitors (despite succinylcholine) indicate ˙first the tonic and then the clonic phases of the seizure. This illustration from the first treatment in a series has some importance in determining the characteristic ending of the seizure which is shown on the right. There is gradual diminution in spiking and increased wavelength of paroxysmal slowing followed by abrupt cessation of seizure activity and a flat electroencephalogram (except for EKG and 60-cycle artifacts). In our series, such seizures lasted from 34 to 70

TABLE 1

Patient Characteristics – CT Studies

Convulsive treatment	n	Sex		Age $\bar{\text{x}}$ Years	Psychiatric diagnosis			$\bar{\text{x}}$ # CT
		m	f		Affective psychosis	Schizophrenia	Other	
Flurothyl (Indoklon)	50	27	23	32	16	26	8	21
Bilateral ECT	50	21	29	34	15	28	7	21
Unilateral ECT								
Right side	24	7	17	38	14	8	2	11
Left side	24	6	18	37	10	9	5	15

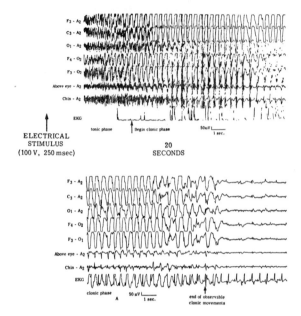

FIG. 1. Scalp EEG recording during bilateral ECT; first
seizure in the treatment series.

sec with a mean duration of 44 sec, timing from the onset of the electrical
stimulus until the end of apnea.

Somewhat more detailed illustrations of EEG activity during seizures induced
with flurothyl are shown in Figure 2 with recordings showing first the resting,
waking background activity prior to treatment, and then generalized high
amplitude paroxysmal slowing which follows the intravenous injection of
sodium methylhexital, a fast-acting barbiturate, and succinylcholine chloride, a
muscle relaxant. The EEG after the vapor was inhaled is shown in the next
tracing in which there is a gradual buildup of myoclonic jerking with the
development of high amplitude generalized repetitive spiking. Continued
recording illustrates the transition from myoclonus to tonic seizure which is then
followed by the clonic phase. The last frame shows the termination of the
seizure which is associated with progressively longer wavelengths and abrupt
cessation of paroxysmal activity followed by electrical silence.

Flurothyl-induced seizures were longer than seizures induced with bilateral
electrical stimulation, even when the preliminary myoclonic phase was omitted
from consideration. In our experience with flurothyl, the seizures lasted 60 to
134 sec with a mean time of 104 sec.

We have found that the mode of termination of the seizure alters with
increasing numbers of induced seizures (Figure 3). In most patients the abrupt
transition from paroxysmal EEG activity to an isolectric tracing early in the

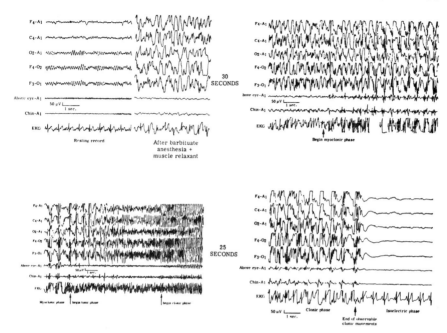

FIG. 2. Scalp EEG recording during flurothyl convulsive therapy; first seizure in the treatment series.

treatment series changes after several treatments are administered. The termination of the 9th electrically induced seizure in the series is shown on the left in Figure 3. The termination of the convulsion is more gradual than shown for the first seizure and a flat EEG does not develop after paroxysmal activity ceases as was seen with the first treatment. These observations also hold true for flurothyl as illustrated in the tracing in Figure 3 which displays the termination of seizure No. 19 in the series.

Other ictal differences have been identified with seizures induced by unilateral electrical stimulation of the right or the left side of the head. These methods also produce generalized grand mal convulsions, but EEG recordings towards the end of the clonic phase usually reveal amplitude asymmetries, sometimes with relative suppression of voltage on the ipsilateral side, and sometimes with voltage emphasis on the side of electrical stimulation. Another difference between the ictal characteristics of seizures induced with unilateral as compared to bilateral electrical stimulation or flurothyl is that postseizure isolectric EEG activity is, in our experience, rarely if ever seen. Further, the duration of unilaterally induced seizures is somewhat shorter than with bilateral ECT, although these differences were not statistically significant in our series.

Some of these observations are illustrated in Figure 4, which shows the termination of a unilaterally induced seizure, first in the treatment series.

Paroxysmal activity terminates abruptly but is not followed by a flat EEG. The ending of the 11th seizure in a series is shown in the figure. The ending is more gradual as with other forms of ECT, and there is still no electrical silence. Also shown are voltage asymmetries occurring late in the clonic phase that persist into the immediate postictal period. In the second tracing, amplitude emphasis is ipsilateral whereas the third recording shows voltage depression on the side of electrical stimulation.

Interictal Studies

The interictal EEG changes that accompany different kinds of convulsive therapy have been studied in numerous investigations. Almost everyone reports that there is diffuse slowing with increased voltage and dysrhythmic activity, as well as a decrease in fast frequencies and a slowing of persistent alpha rhythms. The degree, duration, and extent of these changes are directly related to the frequency and number of induced grand mal convulsions.

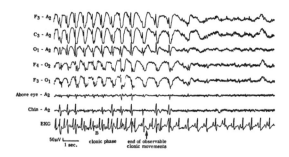

BILATERAL E C T - TREATMENT #9

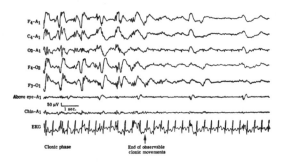

INDOKLON C T - TREATMENT # 19

FIG. 3. Termination of seizures later in the treatment series with bilateral ECT and flurothyl.

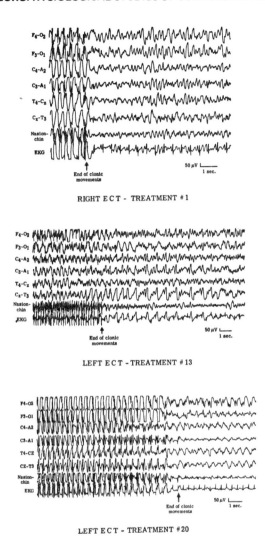

RIGHT E C T - TREATMENT #1

LEFT E C T - TREATMENT #13

LEFT E C T - TREATMENT #20

FIG. 4. Termination of unilaterally induced seizures early and late in the treatment series.

In Figure 5, visual ratings of interictal EEG changes and the grading criteria that were used are shown for flurothyl, bilateral and unilateral ECT with mean values prior to convulsive treatment, 24 hr after the 5th, 10th, and 15th seizures, and again 60 to 90 days after termination of treatment. These profiles appear much the same for the three kinds of treatment and there were no statistically significant differences between them. In this series, the mean ratings were a little higher for the unilateral group than for the others, although age and other initial group differences may have accounted for these discrepancies. There were no distinctions in terms of these ratings between right- and left-sided induction of seizures.

Interictal EEG ratings were compared for recordings done 1 to 3 hr after the seizures and the EEGs obtained 24 hr later. This was investigated in two series of patients who received unilateral convulsive treatment. Figure 6 shows that both generalized and paroxysmal EEG disturbances were more prominent 24 hr after the seizures than immediately afterwards. This was particularly true of paroxysmal characteristics, especially since the 1-3 hr group had significantly higher ratings prior to treatment than did the 24-hr patients.

We also examined the lateralization of EEG and other changes occurring with convulsive therapy. A typical example of asymmetrical slowing and paroxysmal EEG changes with unilateral ECT is shown in Figure 7 which displays interictal EEG recordings in a patient who received ECT on the left side. These recordings show progressive slowing in background and paroxysmal activity that is more pronounced on the left or ipsilateral side than on the right.

Table 2 contains tabular data expressing the percentage of cases within the four treatment groups in which a discernible lateralized emphasis of EEG slowing was noted by "blind" visual inspection. (This does not mean that such asymmetries were necessarily considered clinically abnormal; in fact significant focal or lateralized EEG disturbances prior to treatment were reasons for excluding patients from some of these studies.) There were very few of the flurothyl cases who displayed lateralized slowing prior to treatment, and these percentages remained constant throughout the series of seizures. Bilateral ECT was different. Although the group started with pretreatment EEG characteristics similar to those of the flurothyl patients, there was clearly more left-sided EEG slowing after the 5th and 10th seizures, and even more after the 15th, which persisted to some extent on followup 60 to 90 days later. Seizures induced on the right side were accompanied by right-sided emphasis of slowing in about half the cases and no lateralized features in the others after the first five seizures. More right-sided preponderance developed after more treatments. Patients receiving unilateral treatment on the left side developed EEG slowing on either side, actually more on the right than on the left, after a series of five treatments. With subsequent seizures, however, the lateralization of paroxysmal activity corresponded more to the side of electrical stimulation as shown by the percentages after 10 and 15 seizures.

More recently, our interictal EEG studies have been concerned with more subtle right-left changes that were not apparent in the visually inspected recordings. Such work has employed computer techniques to evaluate sensory evoked potentials recorded from homologous areas on each side of the head and mean voltage energy content and variability of the EEG before, during, and after convulsive therapy. Results of the former have yet to show significant lateralized differences corresponding to the side of electrical stimulation. Instead there appeared to be complicated interactions between variables such as hemispheric

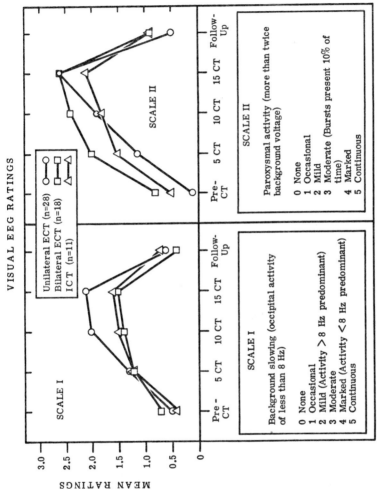

FIG. 5. Visual EEG ratings of background slowing and paroxysmal activity during bilateral and unilateral ECT and flurothyl convulsive treatment.

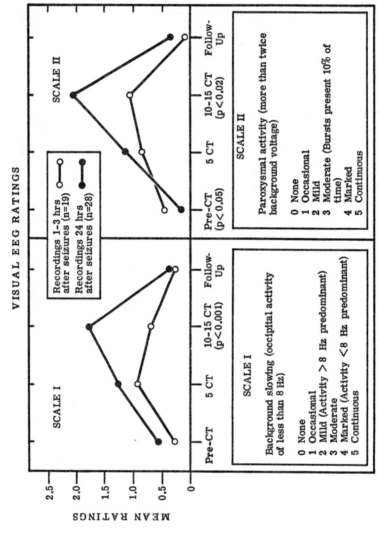

FIG. 6. Visual EEG ratings of background slowing and paroxysmal activity 1 to 3 hr and 24 hr after unilateral ECT.

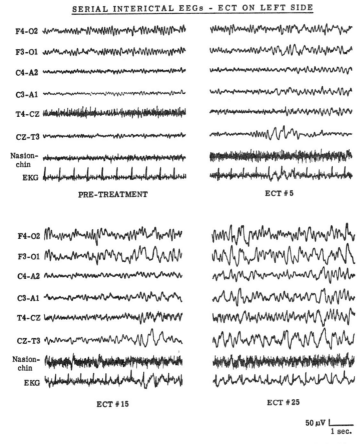

FIG. 7. Scalp EEG activity before unilateral ECT induced on the left side
and 24 hr after the 5th, 15th, and 25th seizures.

dominance, sensory stimulus modality, and area of scalp recording as well as side
of electrical stimulation.

However our work with voltage integration has been more definitive. We used
a dual channel integrator (Emde & Shipton, 1972) to measure the energy under
the EEG curve in homologous regions of the head (occiput to ipsilateral ear
linkage) in 10 patients who received right-sided ECT and 10 patients who
received stimulation on the left. Group mean profiles of relative numeric
expressions of energy content are displayed in Figure 8. Prior to treatment the
mean energy content was a little greater on the nondominant side in both
treatment groups. (This difference could be real or it might be a function of
small variations in calibration or noise levels of the two EEG and/or tape
recording channels.) However, a highly significant increase in mean energy
content appeared on the dominant (left) side 24 hr after increments of 5, 10,

TABLE 2
Lateralized EEG Slowing with Convulsive Therapies
(percent of cases within each time period)

	Number of Cases	Pre-CT O R L			Post 5 CT O R L			Post 10 CT O R L			Post 15 CT O R L			Post 20 CT O R L			Follow-Up O R L		
Flurothyl (Indoklon)	49	88	4	8	86	8	6	-	-	-	86	5	9	83	4	13	92	2	6
Bilateral ECT	49	88	4	8	73	6	21	-	-	-	63	0	37	71	4	25	86	2	12
Right Induced ECT	24	96	0	4	46	54	0	30	70	0	12	78	0	-	-	-	88	8	4
Left Induced ECT	24	96	4	0	63	21	16	20	0	80	24	6	71	-	-	-	81	6	13
		*NS			p <.01			p <.01			p <.01			p <.01			NS		

*Differences between treatment groups
(Chi Square Analysis of Raw Data)

58

SERIAL CHANGES IN MEAN ENERGY WITH ECT

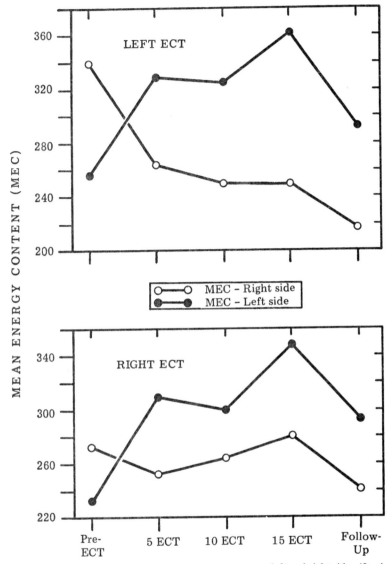

FIG. 8. Group average values of mean energy content on left and right sides (0_1-A_1, 0_2-A_2) before unilateral ECT, 24 hr after the 5th, 10th, and 15th seizures and 60–90 days after ECT.

and 15 seizures. This was true whether stimulation was administered to the right or to the left side of the head. Findings on the nondominant side were variable. There was little change in mean energy when the right side was stimulated. However in the left treatment group there was a significant decrease in mean energy on the right. Moreover these lateralized changes persisted on follow-up 60 to 90 days after ECT, at a time when the scalp EEG asymmetries had mostly resolved. We also measured the coefficient of variation, a measure that is usually included with voltage integration. It changed in the opposite direction to the mean energy content as there was no change in the variability of the data during the course of treatment. (The coefficient of variation is an expression of the standard deviation divided by the mean energy content.)

DISCUSSION

This paper has provided an overview of the EEG and neurophysiological changes accompanying convulsive treatment and has described similarities and differences of ictal and interictal characteristics of seizures induced with flurothyl, bilateral ECT, and electrical stimulation on the right or the left side of the head. Ictal differences included variations in seizure duration with flurothyl producing the longest seizure and unilateral ECT the shortest; bilateral ECT was associated with intermediate times. Seizure termination was also found to differ with the method of induction, with a flat EEG following seizures induced with bilateral ECT or flurothyl but not with unilateral ECT. Seizures terminated abruptly early in the course of treatment with each of the four kinds of convulsive therapy. Later in the treatment series, seizures ended more gradually with disappearance of EEG isoelectricity in the flurothyl and bilateral ECT groups. Lateralized voltage asymmetries in the later part of the clonic phase and postictal phase of the seizures were found with unilateral ECT but not with flurothyl or bilateral ECT. Interictal EEG studies revealed very similar quantitative changes in background and paroxysmal activity with the four kinds of treatment. Such were found to be much more prominent 24 hr after seizure induction than 1 to 3 hr after treatment, at least with unilateral electroconvulsive treatment. Lateralized asymmetries occurred with electrically induced seizures but not with flurothyl. With bilateral ECT, left-sided emphasis of slow activity was encountered, whereas early in the course of unilateral treatment slowing tended to be more on the right side. However ipsilateral emphasis of paroxysmal activity was generally the case with unilateral ECT later in the treatment series. Evoked potential data were equivocal, but evidence from voltage integration studies indicated that mean energy content increased more on the dominant than on the nondominant side with ECT induced either on the right or the left side. This was found to persist for as long as 60 to 90 days after termination of treatment.

The majority of these reported findings are in agreement with those of other workers. The longer duration of flurothyl-induced seizures has been recognized

(Chatrian & Petersen, 1960; Laurell, 1970) but different average measures have been reported, probably as a function of interindividual variability and diverse systems of measurement. Likewise shorter seizures with unilateral ECT than with bilateral electrical induction have been noted (Abrams, Fink, Dornbush, Feldstein, Volavka, & Roubicek, 1972). The latter investigators also reported an absence of EEG flattening with the unilateral form of induction, although d'Elia and Perris (1970) did not. Gradual termination of seizures after a series of treatments has been described by Blachly and Gowing (1966) in the context of multiple-monitored ECT. Slowing of EEG background and paroxysmal slowing in the interictal recordings with all forms of treatment has been reported by most workers. Likewise the findings of more left-sided slowing with bilateral ECT is in accord with Volavka, Feldstein, Abrams, Dornbush, and Fink (1972) and other observers. However the unilateral literature is somewhat contradictory with some workers describing ipsilateral emphasis of such EEG changes (Sutherland, Oliver, & Knight, 1969) and others finding no consistent lateralized differences (Bergman, Impastato, Berg, & Feinstein, 1953). However Blaurock, Lorimer, Segal, and Gibbs (1950) did report more right-sided or nondominant EEG slowing after unilaterally induced seizures on either side as was observed in our series. Our finding of increased mean energy content on the dominant hemisphere following unilateral ECT on either side of the head does not agree with d'Elia's observations of more energy on the stimulated side. However he analyzed the EEG during and immediately after the seizures and the measurements may have been affected by the recent passage of electrical current, ictal events, vascular changes, effects of anesthetics and other drugs, and other factors which may not have been operative 24 hr later. The differences in our visual ratings of the scalp EEG 1 to 3 hr after seizures versus 24 hr later also support the hypothesis that some time is required for the development of EEG changes and other CNS alterations with induced convulsions. Work with voltage integration with bilateral ECT and flurothyl has not been reported, but Marjerrison discovered a greater increase in mean energy on the dominant than on the nondominant side with bilateral ECT (Marjerrison & Bowman, in press).

This review has demonstrated that ictal and interictal EEG changes occur with convulsive treatment, and that these vary with the method of seizure induction as well as with the number of seizures administered. The topic of how such EEG and neurophysiological data relate to the psychological, behavioral, and clinical measures was not discussed in this report. This is a very important scientific question which has still been largely neglected. It is puzzling why this area of investigation has not attracted more attention recently, as present equipment for the recording and analysis of the EEG data is much improved, and standard interviews and objective rating scales of clinical phenomena are now widely used in psychiatry. Moreover there are standardized and precise psychological and behavioral methods of assessment available, and there is a large animal literature upon which to draw for ideas, hypotheses, and experimental designs.

SUMMARY

EEG data are described which compare and contrast the ictal and interictal characteristics of convulsions induced with an inhaled gas (flurothyl), or with electrical currents applied bitemporally or to the dominant or nondominant hemispheres. Data derived from a large clinical series demonstrated that grand mal convulsions had different neurophysiological characteristics depending upon the mode of seizure induction. Lateralized emphasis of slowing and paroxysmal activity in the interictal EEG recordings also varied with the kind of convulsive treatment administered. Computerized analysis of EEG data revealed increases in mean energy content on the dominant side of the head with either right or left unilateral electrical induction. These changes persisted after visual ratings of scalp EEG activity had returned to pretreatment status.

REFERENCES

Abrams, R., Fink, M., Dornbush, R. L., Feldstein, S., Volavka, J., & Roubicek, J. Unilateral and bilateral electroconvulsive therapy. *Archives of General Psychiatry*, 1972, 27, 88-91.

Bergman, P. S., Impastato, D. J., Berg, S., & Feinstein, R. Electroencephalographic changes following electrically induced focal seizures. *Confinia Neurologica*, 1953, 13, 271-277.

Blachly, P. H., & Gowing, D. Multiple monitored electroconvulsive treatment. *Comprehensive Psychiatry*, 1966, 7, 100-109.

Blaurock, M. F., Lorimer, F. M., Segal, M. M., & Gibbs, F. A. Focal electroencephalographic changes in unilateral electric convulsion therapy. *Archives of Neurology and Psychiatry*, 1950, 64, 220-226.

Chatrian, G. E., & Petersen, M. C. The convulsive patterns provoked by Indoklon, Metrazol and electroshock: Some depth electrographic observations in human patients. *Electroencephalography and Clinical Neurophysiology*, 1960, 12, 715-725.

d'Elia, G., & Perris, C. Comparison of electroconvulsive therapy with unilateral and bilateral stimulation. I. Seizure and post-seizure electroencephalographic pattern. *Acta Psychiatrica Scandinavica*, 1970, 215, 9-29.

Emde, J. W., & Shipton, H. W. A dual channel integrator for EEG studies. Presented at the Central Association of Electroencephalographers Annual Meeting, Indianapolis, April 1972.

Laurell, B. (Ed.) Flurothyl convulsive therapy. *Acta Psychiatrica Scandinavica*, 1970, 46 (Suppl. 213).

Marjerrison, G., & Bowman, R. Electroconvulsive therapy: EEG and clinical effects. *Canadian Medical Association Journal*, in press.

Small, I. F., & Small, J. G. Ictus and amnesia. *Recent Advances in Biological Psychiatry*, 1968, 10, 144-159.

Small, I. F., & Small, J. G. EEG, evoked potential and DC responses with unilateral ECT. *Journal of Nervous and Mental Disease*, 1971, 152, 396.

Small, I. F., Small, J. G., Milstein, V., & Sharpley, P. Interhemispheric relationships with somatic therapy. *Diseases of the Nervous System*, 1973, 34, 170-177.

Small, J. G., Small, I. F., Perez, H. C., & Sharpley, P. EEG and neurophysiological studies of electrically induced seizures. *Journal of Nervous and Mental Disease*, 1970, 150, 479-489.

Small, J. G., Small, I. F., Sharpley, P., & Moore, D. F. A double blind comparative evaluation of flurothyl and ECT *Archives of General Psychiatry*, 1968, 19, 79-86.

Sutherland, E. M., Oliver, J. E., & Knight, D. R. E.E.G., memory and confusion in dominant, non-dominant and bi-temporal E.C.T. *British Journal of Psychiatry,* 1969, **115**, 1059-1064.

Volavka, J., Feldstein, S., Abrams, R., Dornbush, R. L., & Fink, M. EEG and clinical change after bilateral and unilateral electroconvulsive therapy. *Electroencephalography and Clinical Neurophysiology,* 1972, **32**, 631-639.

6
INHALANT CONVULSIVE THERAPY

Iver F. Small, M.D.

Historically, flurothyl, or Indoklon, was discovered as an outgrowth of a series of investigations of the anesthetic effects of aliphatic fluorinated ethers (Krantz, Carr, Lu, & Bell, 1953; Lu, Ling, & Krantz, 1953). When inhaled by laboratory animals, hexafluorodiethyl ether was observed to elicit violent seizures that ceased when the convulsant agent was removed from the inspired air. Repeated exposures did not appear to injure the animals or to produce significant physical or laboratory test abnormalities. On the basis of such observations, the investigators thought that this chemical might be useful in the treatment of certain kinds of mentally ill patients. They surmised that the apparently harmless nature of exposures to the vapor, as well as rapid onset of seizures and ready control of the depth and duration of the convulsions, might offer some advantages in the treatment of psychiatric disorders. Accordingly, four depressed patients in whom convulsive therapy was indicated were subjected to one treatment with flurothyl administered by inhalation (Krantz, Truitt, Speers, & Ling, 1957). This was well tolerated without any untoward reactions. Then followed a series of clinical trials and experimental studies of flurothyl, by Esquibel, Krantz, Truitt, Ling, and Kurland (1958) and Krantz, Esquibel, Truitt, Ling, and Kurland (1958) with later studies by Karliner and Padula (1959a, 1959b). Since that time, there have been numerous reports of clinical trials with flurothyl and electroconvulsive treatment. There have also been several psychological and EEG studies of inhalant convulsive therapy.

In this paper some of the highlights from a large clinical study of flurothyl and electroconvulsive therapy will be described, with inclusion of some recent followup data. The literature will not be exhaustively reviewed on this occasion as such has been recently published elsewhere (Small, J. G., & Small, I. F.,

1972). However, the data from our studies will be discussed in relation to other published work and directions for future research will be considered.

METHOD AND MATERIALS

The investigation to be described was conducted at the Larue D. Carter Memorial Hospital which is a state psychiatric treatment facility situated on the Indiana University Medical School campus. Short term, intensive care is provided to hospitalized patients selected from statewide referrals in a program oriented to teaching and research. The subjects of this study were 100 adults for whom convulsive therapy had been prescribed by the clinical staff of two male and two female inpatient treatment teams. They were selected for the study in consecutive order of referral. The only exclusions were cases with serious medical problems and patients for whom convulsive treatment was ordered for more than three times weekly. Prior to convulsive treatment, all patients received comprehensive examinations, including medical, psychiatric, neurological and physical evaluations, and routine laboratory studies which included one or more EEG recordings during waking, sleep, and activation procedures. Independent research evaluations encompassed standard psychiatric diagnostic interviews (Small, I. F., Small, J. G., Gonzalez, & Gynther, 1964), with assignment of psychiatric diagnoses according to strict criteria similar to those recently compiled in a summary paper (Feighner, Robins, Guze, Woodruff, Winokur, & Munoz, 1972). Standard clinical ratings were also completed by a research psychiatrist, which included the Inpatient Multidimensional Psychiatric Rating Scale (IMPS), the Hamilton Rating Scale for Depression (HRS), and a brief rating Scale of Psychiatric Symptoms (SPS). Pretreatment psychological tests were administered, which included the Shipley-Hartford scale of intelligence, the Minnesota Multiphasic Personality Inventory (MMPI), the Institute for Personality and Ability Testing Anxiety Scale (IPAT), the Wechsler memory scale, and other tests of eye-hand coordination and visuomotor skills. Social workers, ward staff, and the patients themselves contributed ratings of mood, hospital adjustment, and socioeconomic status.

The subjects were assigned by means of a table of random numbers to receive either flurothyl convulsive treatment or bilateral ECT on alternate days, three times weekly. Although the clinical staff was responsible for deciding when convulsive treatment was initiated and also when it would be terminated, the selection of whether flurothyl or ECT was to be the treatment modality was entirely governed by the research design. The treatment assignment was not revealed to the psychiatric or nursing personnel, the research raters, or to the patients. Only a technician, who timed the phases and duration of the seizures with a stopwatch, and the psychiatric residents and nurses who administered convulsive treatment were aware of which form of treatment was utilized.

Techniques for the administration of treatment, except for the induction of seizures, were similar for flurothyl and ECT. One-fiftieth of a grain of atropine was given by injection 30 min before treatment. After insertion of a rubber mouthpiece, 80-100 mg of sodium methohexital, followed by 15-20 mg of succinylcholine chloride, were given intravenously. In patients receiving ECT, the mouthpiece was left in place, and after a 60-sec delay to allow the relaxant to become effective, a Medcraft model 5A1 shock stimulator delivered a conventional glissando modified sine wave AC electrical current by means of bitemporal electrode forceps. Parameters of the stimulus were adjusted for each patient to just above threshold levels (group mean amplitude of 120 V with a range of 110 to 150 V applied for 0.3 to 0.6 sec). For patients receiving flurothyl, the same procedures were used until after the injection of succinylcholine. At this juncture, the rubber mouthpiece was removed and an adult rubber Guedel oropharyngeal airway was inserted. The face mask of the breathing apparatus for the administration of flurothyl had been prepared in advance with 0.5 to 0.75 cc of flurothyl in the vaporizer and the breathing bag half filled with oxygen. This was placed firmly over the patient's face and the bag was gently squeezed, forcing the oxygen-flurothyl mixture into the lungs at a rate of once every 3 sec. The usual number of inflations varied from four to six, with seizures commencing within 40 to 60 sec of positioning the mask. Patients were oxygenated after the convulsion as indicated, and when respiration was reestablished, they were moved into an adjacent recovery room. Here research nurses recorded the presence or absence of signs and symptoms on a checklist. Nursing observations were repeated again 4 to 6 hr later on the day of treatment. In order to maintain the double-blind conditions of the experiment, all subjects receiving flurothyl had the electrode forceps applied to the temples without the current but with sufficient pressure to leave imprints before entry into the recovery room. Likewise, the patients who received ECT were each sprinkled with a little flurothyl so that the odor was present on all subjects.

The same psychiatrist and other research raters reevaluated the patients at specific intervals during the course of treatment with repetition of most of the clinical and psychological ratings listed before. The first such reexamination took place 24 hr after the fifth convulsive treatment; the second, the week of termination of treatment; and a third, 60 to 90 days later. In addition, global clinical assessments of response to treatment, confusion, and memory loss were made weekly during the course of convulsive treatment.

RESULTS

Table 1 shows the identifying and diagnostic characteristics of the patients who received flurothyl and ECT. There were no major differences between the groups in these variables. Likewise, the groups were equivalent in terms of the clinical and psychological ratings and EEG observations.

In general, clinical results of the two forms of treatment were very much the same. The patients in similar diagnostic categories received comparable numbers of seizures whether induced with flurothyl or electricity, and the course of

TABLE 1

Sample Characteristics of Flurothyl and ECT Groups

Psychiatric diagnosis	N	Sex		Age	Marital status		Education		
		M	F	$\bar{X}$ Years	Married	Other	<HS	HS grad.	Higher ed.
Flurothyl (Indoklon)									
Schizophrenic disorders	26	11	15	29	14	12	10	9	7
Affective disorders	16	8	8	39	14	2	5	3	8
Other disorders	8	8	0	28	6	2	4	4	0
Totals	50	27	23	32	34	16	19	16	15
ECT									
Schizophrenic disorders	28	12	16	27	15	13	8	11	9
Affective disorders	15	7	8	47	14	1	3	5	7
Other disorders	7	2	5	32	5	2	2	3	2
Totals	50	21	29	34	34	16	13	19	18

treatment was similar for each without significant complications or difficulties. Longitudinal profiles of changes in the clinical ratings of psychotic, depressive, and other symptomatology showed improvement in both groups without statistically significant differences or even trends of difference between the two treatment modalities. Clinical outcome 60 to 90 days after termination of treatment was much the same, with better results in patients with affective disorders and less improvement in patients with schizophrenia. The study confirmed that flurothyl convulsive treatment was practical, safe, and as effective as ECT.

Despite these similarities, the study also revealed a number of differences between the two forms of treatment. These had to do with the physical and EEG characteristics of the seizures, and clinical and psychological assessments of memory loss and confusion.

Figure 1 displays graphs of the mean duration of the externally timed phases of the seizures for flurothyl and ECT. *(Some of the times were checked with concurrent EEG tracings of seizure activity during the convulsions. By this means it was found that these timings were quite accurate with the exception of the duration of the clonic phase later in the course of treatment. The observer tended to underestimate the duration of the clonic phase under these circumstances.)* Figure 1 shows that the flurothyl seizures were longer, averaging 104 sec as compared to 45 sec for ECT. Also, the flurothyl seizure included a preliminary myoclonic phase which the electrically induced seizure did not.

Other differences between the two forms of treatment were noted by the nursing and clinical staff. They reported more facial flushing in the recovery period in the patients who received electrically induced seizures, as well as more confusion later in the day of treatment. The flurothyl patients were less confused; for example, they were oriented and could remember names and events, but they complained of more headaches later in the day than the ECT group.

Other clinical differences were present at termination of convulsive treatment. These are summarized in Table 2 which indicates that significantly more of the flurothyl-treated patients were rated as clinically improved with minimal or no confusion, whereas more of the ECT group were described as markedly confused, so much so that the clinical response was temporarily obscured. These differences disappeared on followup assessment 60 to 90 days later.

Only one of the psychological tests showed significant differences between the flurothyl and ECT patients. Figure 2 displays the group average values for the Weschler memory quotient and for the word association subscale of the test. After five seizures, there was a decline from pretreatment values in the total memory quotient for both groups. This was accounted for mostly by the contribution of the associate learning subtest, as shown in the upper graph. Moreover, this decrement was greater for bilateral ECT than for flurothyl. The differences between the two treatment modalities were not statistically

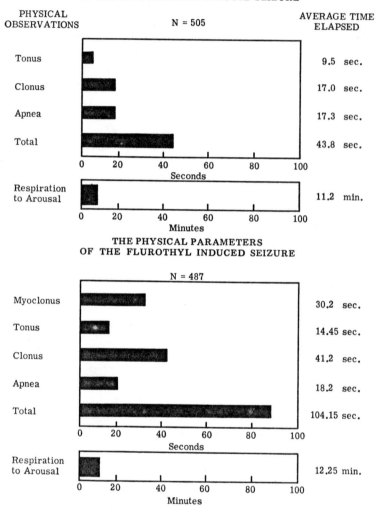

FIG. 1.   Timed observations of seizures induced with flurothyl and ECT.

significant after five seizures, but they were at termination of treatment, with better performance by the flurothyl group. This difference was more prominent on followup, with the flurothyl patients exceeding their pretreatment test performance. Other analyses indicated that there was a relationship in the flurothyl group between performance on the Wechsler scale and seizure duration, with longer seizure times associated with less memory loss, as defined clinically, and higher Wechsler memory quotient values; that is, better test performance at the time of termination of treatment. No such correlations were identified with ECT.

TABLE 2
Clinical Status at Termination of Convulsive Treatment

Number of treatments	Clinical improvement* Minimal or no confusion	Clinical improvement plus moderate confusion	Marked confusion* Obscuring clinical response	Little or no clinical improvement
Flurothyl (Indoklon)				
Less than 10	1	0	0	0
10–15	1	2	2	4
16–20	8	5	2	1
21–25	5	4	0	1
26–30	4	1	0	5
More than 30	3	0	0	1
Totals	22	12	4	12
ECT				
Less than 10	1	1	2	2
10–15	2	3	1	2
16–20	1	2	4	4
21–25	0	1	6	1
26–30	1	1	8	2
More than 30	0	2	2	1
Totals	5	10	23	12

*$p < 0.01$ for flurothyl – ECT differences (x^2).

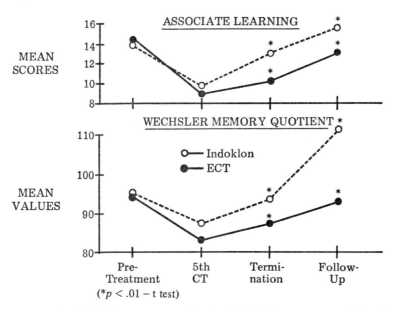

FIG. 2. Longitudinal group mean profiles for the Wechsler memory quotient and associate learning subscale.

Some of the patients who took part in this study were examined as part of a long term followup evaluation of memory functions and clinical status 2 to 5 years after convulsive therapy (Table 3). Patients who received flurothyl and bilateral ECT and another series of patients who had been given right or left unilateral ECT were included. Patients were selected who could be located for followup, with individual matching in the four groups for age, education, global pretreatment clinical ratings of severity of illness, and scores on the Wechsler memory scale. Forty-four such patients were available from the four original treatment groups with characteristics as shown in Table 3.

The only significant initial group differences were in the mean number of treatments the patients received. Some of the same clinical ratings and memory tests that were done as part of the comparative study were repeated on follow-up examination. Longitudinal mean values of the clinical ratings of psychotic features and depression were much the same in the four treatment groups. Profiles of mean values over time for the Brief Psychiatric Rating Scale (BPRS), (a condensation of the longer IMPS used in the large study), the HRS, and the SRS are shown for the four groups combined in Figure 3, which shows that values at termination of convulsive treatment and on short and long term followup were much the same. Mean Wechsler memory quotient values are shown in Table 4 for the same time periods. Statistical analysis of these values revealed no significant differences between the four types of treatment. The word association subtest differences between flurothyl and ECT identified in the large study were not at significant levels in this small sample. However, there was a trend for the patients who received unilateral ECT on either side of the

TABLE 3
Two to Five-year Follow-up of Convulsive Therapies

Treatment group	N	Sex		Age	Education	$\bar{x}$ Number seizures	Diagnosis n
		M	F	$\bar{x}$ Years	$\bar{x}$ Years		
Flurothyl (Indoklon)	9	2	7	34	12.0	21.5	Depressed (3) Schizophrenic (6)
Bilateral ECT	13	4	9	33	11.9	21.1	Depressed (2) Schizophrenic (10) Manic-depressive (1)
Unilateral ECT— Right side	12	2	10	38	12.1	16.1	Depressed (6) Schizophrenic (4) Manic-depressive (1) Schizo-affective (1)
Unilateral ECT— Left side	10	3	7	35	14.2	17.9	Depressed (3) Schizophrenic (3) Manic-depressive (2) Schizo-affective (2)

LONGITUDINAL PROFILES OF CLINICAL RATINGS

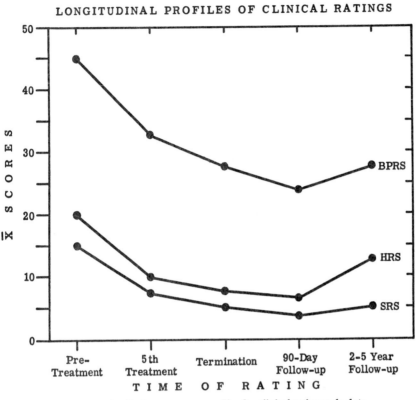

FIG. 3. Longitudinal group mean profiles for clinical rating scale data.

head to have higher mean scores on short and long term followup than the other two groups, with lowest values for bilateral ECT.

However, the patients' subjective evaluations of their memory did show some interesting associations with the method of induction of seizure several years previously. (Patients were not aware of the type of induction that had been

TABLE 4
Wechsler Memory Scale Scores

Treatment group	Pretreatment	After 5th treatment	Termination	Follow-up 60-90 days	Follow-up 2-5 years
Flurothyl (Indoklon)	102.7	88.0	85.1	105.7	103.0
Bilateral ECT	97.5	83.2	84.1	88.0	98.3
Unilateral ECT– Right side	101.0	100.6	104.2	110.1	106.7
Unilateral ECT– Left side	97.0	85.7	99.4	109.1	106.5

TABLE 5

Subjective Memory Loss on
Long Term Follow-up

Convulsive therapy	Present	Absent
Flurothyl (Indoklon)	2	7
Bilateral ECT	6	7
Unilateral ECT–Right side	1	11
Unilateral ECT–Left side	1	9

used.) More than half of the patients considered their memory to be worse on followup than it was before their illness and convulsvie therapy. Nineteen of them reported specific memory losses, particularly for the time that they received convulsive treatment. In addition, six complained of persistent memory defects lasting for several years after convulsive treatment.

Table 5 shows the association of memory loss as rated subjectively by the patients to method of seizure induction. Half of the patients who received bilateral ECT complained of these effects, whereas there were very few in the other treatment groups. It was also found that severe impairment of memory persisting long after convulsive therapy was complexly related to the severity of the index illness, as well as the number of convulsive treatments received and clinical status at the time of followup. No correlation was found between subjective assessment of memory defect and performance on the Wechsler memory test.

DISCUSSION

This paper has presented the highlights from a large double-blind comparative study of inhalant and electroconvulsive treatment that was conducted a few years ago. In addition, some long term followup information about flurothyl, ECT, and unilateral convulsive therapy have been reported. Findings from these studies are generally in accord with the experience of other investigators. Most of the early clinical studies, beginning with Krantz et al. (1958), have shown that flurothyl convulsive therapy is safe and clinically effective. Other comparative studies of flurothyl and ECT, beginning with the work of Karliner and Padula (1959a, 1959b) and additional studies by Fink, Kahn, Karp, Pollack, Green, Allan, and Lefkowits (1961) and Spreche (1964), concluded that there were no essential differences in treatment outcome between the two different methods. Some clinicians considered flurothyl too troublesome and time consuming to administer, but others did not. Further data were added by Scanlon and Mathas (1967), by Kafi, Todd, and Dennis (1967), Gander, Bennett, and Kelly (1967), and by Laurell (1970). Most authors agreed that the flurothyl convulsion was different, with a preliminary myoclonic phase and longer duration than bilateral ECT. Also, most of the studies indicated that there was less memory loss associated with the use of flurothyl than electroshock. However, both therapies affect memory, and there have been studies with opposite findings.

Apropos the followup data presented in this report, there have been no formal studies of the effects of convulsive therapies on memory several years after such treatment. Nevertheless, every clinician is aware of psychiatric patients who complain of memory deficits long after convulsive treatment, even though most of the short term followup studies indicate a restoration to pretreatment levels of performance on objective psychological tests. Case reports of long-lasting memory defects have been published (Tooth & Blackburn 1939; Levy, Serota, & Grinker 1942; Brody 1944) in which patients complained of persisting memory deficits after electroshock therapy, involving recall of long-known familiar material. The only systematic long term followup study was by Bidder, Strain, and Brunschwig (1970), in which memory and clinical status were evaluated 1 year after bilateral or unilateral ECT. There were no differences in performance on the Paired Associates Learning Tests (PALT) or the Benton visual retention test between the bilateral and unilateral groups. Moreover, results on the PALT improved over time in both groups. The patients' subjective memory experiences were not evaluated.

Other aspects about inhalant convulsive therapy are important for future scientific inquiry. As a clinically acceptable alternate to ECT, flurothyl provides a useful tool for the study of mechanisms of action and other aspects of convulsive treatment. Comparative studies of various kinds of convulsive therapy are needed to separate the therapeutic and other influences of the electrical or chemical stimulants, the duration of the seizure, oxygenation, the EEG changes, and many other aspects. It will be of particular interest to evaluate and compare seizures induced by chemical and electrical means, as there is some evidence that chemically induced seizures may be primarily subcortical, whereas electroshock evokes a cortical mechanism. (Chatrian & Petersen, 1960; Sellinger, Azcurra, Ohlsson, Kohl, & Zand, 1972) If such be the case, there might be important clinical implications of different kinds of seizure induction. Some support for such implications is provided by viewpoints of early clinicians who felt that seizures induced with pentylenetetrazol (Metrazol) were more therapeutically effective than electrically induced seizures, although they were more physically injurious and anxiety provoking for patients. These issues could be readily reopened at present since there are anesthetics and muscle relaxants which can be used to minimize the severity of pentylenetetrazol and other chemically produced seizures.

It is clear from the foregoing that much is yet to be learned about how induced convulsions exert their antidepressive and antipsychotic effects, as well as how they influence memory, performance, and the electroencephalogram. Comparative multidisciplinary studies of seizures induced by different means would appear to be a promising avenue for future investigation.

SUMMARY

The clinical and psychological concomitants of inhalant convulsant therapy are discussed in this paper. The highlights of a large double-blind comparative study of flurothyl and ECT are described with inclusion of some long term followup data. The first study showed that flurothyl and bilateral ECT yielded comparable therapeutic results, but differed in terms of the physical characteristics of the seizures and the incidence of memory loss and confusion. Flurothyl was associated with longer seizures and less amnestic effects than ECT. The followup studies revealed that persistent subjective memory defects may occur years after convulsive therapy and that these may be related to the method of seizure induction. Such observations are described in context with the literature, suggesting areas for future investigation.

REFERENCES

Bidder, T. G., Strain, J. J., & Brunschwig, L. Bilateral and unilateral ECT: Follow-up study and critique. *American Journal of Psychiatry*, 1970, 127, 737-745.

Brody, M. B. Prolonged memory defects following electro-therapy. *Journal of Mental Science*, 1944, 90, 777-779.

Chatrian, G. E., & Petersen, M. C. The convulsive patterns provoked by Indoklon, Metrazol, and electroshock: Some depth electrographic observations in human patients. *Electroencephalography and Clinical Neurophysiology*, 1960, 12, 715-725.

Esquibel, A. J., Krantz, J. C., Jr., Truitt, E. B., Jr., Ling, A. S. C., & Kurland, A. A. Hexafluorodiethyl ether (Indoklon): Its use as a convulsant in psychiatric treatment. *Journal of Nervous and Mental Disease*, 1958, 126, 530-534.

Feighner, J. P., Robins, E., Guze, S. B., Woodruff, R. A., Jr., Winokur, G., & Munoz, R. Diagnostic criteria for use in psychiatric research. *Archives of General Psychiatry*, 1972, 26, 57-63.

Fink, M., Kahn, R. L., Karp, E., Pollack, M., Green, M. A., Allan, B., & Lefkowits, H. J. Inhalant-induced convulsions. Significance for the theory of the convulsive therapy process. *Archives of General Psychiatry*, 1961, 4, 259-266.

Gander, D. R., Bennett, P. J., & Kelly, D. H. W. Hexafluorodiethyl ether (Indoklon) convulsive therapy: A pilot study. *British Journal of Psychiatry*, 1967, 113, 1413-1418.

Kafi, A., Todd, R. E., & Dennis, M. S. A comparative study of memory in patients receiving ECT and Indoklon inhalation treatment. Section 77 on Psychopharmacology, Scientific Proceedings in Summary Form, 123rd Annual Meeting of the American Psychiatric Association, Detroit, May 1967.

Karliner, W., & Padula L. Improved technique for Indoklon convulsive therapy. *American Journal of Psychiatry*, 1959, 116, 358. (a)

Karliner, W., & Padula, L. Indoklon combined with penthothal and Anectine. *American Journal of Psychiatry*, 1959, 115, 1041-1042. (b)

Krantz, J. C., Jr., Carr, C. J., Lu, G., & Bell, F. K. Anesthetic action of trifluoroethyl vinyl ether. *Journal of Pharmacology and Experimental Therapeutics*, 1953, 108, 488-495.

Krantz, J. C., Jr., Esquibel, A. J., Truitt, E. B., Jr., Ling, A. S. C., & Kurland, A. A. Hexafluorodiethyl ether (Indoklon)—an inhalant convulsant. Its use in psychiatric treatment. *Journal of the American Medical Association.* 1958, 166, 1555-1562.

Krantz, J. C., Jr., Truitt, E. C., Jr., Speers, L., & Ling, A. S. C. New pharmacoconvulsive agent. *Science*, 1957, 126, 353-354.

Laurell, B. (Ed.) Flurothyl convulsive therapy. *Acta Psychiatrica Scandinavica*, 1970, 46 (Suppl. 213).

Levy, N. A., Serota, H. M., & Grinker, R. R. Disturbances in brain function following convulsive shock therapy. Electroencephalographic and clinical studies. *Archives of Neurology and Psychiatry*, 1942, 47, 1009-1029.

Lu, G., Ling, J. S. L., & Krantz, J. C., Jr. Anesthetic properties of certain fluorinated hydrocarbons and ethers. *Anesthesiology*, 1953, 14, 466-472.

Scanlon, W. G., & Mathas, J. Electroencephalographic and psychometric studies of Indoklon convulsive treatment and electroconvulsive treatment. A preliminary report. *International Journal of Neuropsychiatry*, 1967, 3, 276-281.

Sellinger, O. Z., Azcurra, J. M., Ohlsson, W. G., Kohl, H. H., & Zand, R. Neurochemical correlates of drug-induced seizures: Selective inhibition of cerebral protein synthesis by methionine sulfoximine. *Federation Proceedings*, 1972, 31(No. 1), 160-165.

Small, I. F., Small, J. G., Gonzalez C. R., & Gynther, M. D. Content reliability of a structured psychiatric interview. *Archives of General Psychiatry*, 1964, 11, 192-196.

Small, J. G., & Small, I. F. Clinical results: Indoklon versus ECT. *Seminars in Psychiatry*, 1972, 4(No. 1), 13-26.

Spreche, D. A quantitative comparison of electroconvulsive therapy with hexafluorodiethyl ether. *Journal of Neuropsychiatry*, 1964, 5, 132-137.

Tooth, G., & Blackburn, J. M. Disturbance of memory after convulsion treatment. *Lancet*, 1939, 2, 17-20.

7
MULTIPLE ECT: WHAT HAVE WE LEARNED?[1]

Richard Abrams, M.D.

A quarter of a century has passed since the first report of the administration of multiple ECT in a single day (Milligan, 1946). This technique received sporadic attention during the ensuing 20 years, becoming known as "regressive electroshock therapy" (REST) due to the appearance in treated patients of a transient syndrome of confusion, incontinence, and inability to feed themselves. REST was introduced in the treatment of psychoneurotic patients, but subsequent workers employed REST mainly as a treatment for patients with schizophrenia (Kennedy & Anchel, 1948; Rothschild, van Gordon, & Varjabedian, 1951; Weil, 1950; Garrett & Mockbee, 1952; Glueck, Reiss, & Bernard, 1957; King, 1959; Jacoby & Van Houten, 1960; Cameron, 1960; Graber & McHugh, 1960; Cameron, Lohrenz, & Handcock, 1962; Schwartzmann & Termansen, 1967; Murillo and Exner, 1973).

The method has not flourished. Followup studies in the chronically ill patients who were treated, failed to show an advantage for REST over conventional ECT and it remains to be demonstrated that "regression" is necessary for a therapeutic effect.

In 1966, Blachly and Gowing reintroduced the administration of multiple electrically induced seizures in a single day, spacing the treatments 2 to 3 min apart, with simultaneous monitoring of the EEG and EKG ("multiple monitored ECT"). As monitoring is not required to administer multiple seizures, we adopted the term "multiple ECT" (MECT) followed by a digit for the number of seizures of a treatment session (e.g., MECT-4). Blachly and Gowing treated 46 patients with 3 to 8 bilateral ECT each session without difficulty. Memory loss

[1] Partial support for this research was provided through United States Public Health Service grant MH-15561.

and confusion were estimated to be similar to that seen after 1 to 2 conventional bilateral ECT. They observed EEG seizure activity to terminate in electrical silence (designated the "fit switch") in the first treatments, but a sharp termination became less precise with increasing numbers of seizures. This "breakdown" of the "fit switch" seemed to occur earlier in depressed than in schizophrenic patients, providing suggestive evidence for a relation to therapeutic outcome.

White, Shea, and Jonas (1968) gave bilateral MECT-5 to 28 patients, and nondominant unilateral MECT-5 to an additional patient, and reported all but one of their patients to show significant improvement or complete remission. They felt that post-ECT memory loss was less after MECT than after 6 to 8 conventionally spaced bilateral ECT, but did not assess memory changes directly.

Bidder and Strain (1970) gave two sessions of bilateral MECT-4 spaced 48 hr apart to 14 patients, with an excellent clinical response in only 1 patient, a good response in 9, and a fair or poor response in 4 patients. Minimal memory loss was noted in 4 patients on a paired-associates learning test, but the authors observed frequent prolonged postictal confusion, drowsiness, disorientation, and described one patient who became severely confused after each session of MECT. They noted that improvement after MECT was often delayed for 18 to 24 hr. In a brief case report, Strain and Bidder (1971) reported a patient who developed status epilepticus and transient neurological signs during the first session of MECT-5.

Abrams and Fink (1972) described their experiences with 38 patients who received unilateral or bilateral MECT-4 or 6. A dramatic clinical improvement after a single session of MECT occurred in only one patient, and in several patients the therapeutic effects seemed accelerated. Two patients with severe endogenous depression failed to improve with a session of bilateral MECT-6, only to recover with additional single conventionally spaced seizures. The side-effects of MECT were more pronounced than with conventional ECT, and prolonged postictal confusion, apprehension, and fearful agitation were frequently observed. Two patients developed severe, self-limited confusional states characterized by disorientation, clouding of consciousness, and increased EEG delta activity. For most patients, the memory changes 24 hr after a session of MECT-4 or 6, seemed little different from those after one or two conventional ECT. In a group of patients receiving MECT-4, paired associate learning tests obtained before and after treatment were not different from those obtained in patients tested after a single ECT with the same electrode placement.

A delayed onset of clinical improvement was frequently observed, and a similar delay often occurred for the amnestic effects of MECT.

Bridenbaugh, Drake, and O'Regan (1972) treated 17 schizophrenic patients with twice-weekly sessions of bilateral MECT-5. After an average of 4.5 sessions, 14 patients were improved and 3 were not. The authors attempted to relate clinical response with total seizure duration, but their method of data analysis is unclear. The report of seizure duration is difficult to interpret as they observed 16 seizures lasting over 15 min, and one seizure which lasted 62 min. They treated one patient who developed pulmonary aspiration and subsequent pneumonitis during the first session of MECT-5. The effects of MECT on memory function were not discussed, nor was there any mention of "regression."

In a study of EEG seizure patterns during multiple unilateral and bilateral ECT, we recorded 160 EEG seizures in 18 patients during 45 sessions of MECT (Abrams, Volavka, & Fink, 1973). Seizures in MECT with bilateral electrodes were 10 sec longer than with unilateral electrodes. Seizures increased in duration in a given session, the last seizure being longer than the first in most instances. Seizure activity with unilateral MECT tended to end in mixed alpha/beta activity, contrasting with bilateral MECT seizures which usually ended in electrical "silence." Seizure termination was not less precise with increasing number of seizures; if anything, there was a tendency for seizures to end *more* precisely as the number of seizures increased.

DISCUSSION

Observations that therapeutic outcome in convulsive therapy was related to number of seizures, and the reports of the safety of multiple seizures (MECT) led to an expectation that single sessions of multiple seizures would reduce the time for a therapeutic response. This hoped-for dramatic clinical response did not materialize. In our studies of MECT, we are left with a clinical impression only that MECT accelerates the treatment course in some patients, requiring fewer ECT sessions and a shorter stay in hospital.

Equally unfounded was the apprehension that MECT would elicit severe organic confusional states and "regression." We do observe an increase in undesirable side-effects with MECT (e.g., organic confusional states, increased postictal sleep and cognitive disorganization, status epilepticus, and pulmonary aspiration), and the physician must weigh these advantages and disadvantages in choosing between conventional ECT and MECT. Unilateral MECT may find wider use due to a low incidence of such side-effects.

Several questions raised by MECT may contribute to our understanding of the mechanism of action of convulsive therapy.

Why is "regression" not seen with MECT? What is the distinction from REST? Regression is not generally reported with MECT although 3/143 patients[2] developed transient organic confusional states.

Patients receiving REST were treated several times a day, but not in the same treatment session. For example, four seizures spaced in a period of 8 hr elicited more memory difficulties than the same number of seizures given in 20 to 30 min. The difference in memory effects between MECT and REST may lie in the

---

[2] This figure is the number of patients who received MECT in the reports cited earlier.

use of forced oxygenation throughout MECT, a procedure not routinely used for REST. Succinylcholine, which was also not used with REST, reduces oxygen consumption by the musculature and helps maintain high circulating oxygen levels. The distinction between MECT and REST may lie in the factor of oxygenation.

Why is there no therapeutic equivalence for MECT and conventional thrice-weekly ECT when an equal number of seizures are given? The difference in therapeutic and memory effects of MECT and REST suggests that cerebral processes maturing between seizures are essential to the therapeutic effect. One suggestion of the difference in time course is that the time reflects alterations in turnover and synthesis rates of cerebral amines. Support for this hypothesis derives from the studies of Pryor (this volume) who reported that ECT given in 1 week alters cerebral monoamine oxidase activity less than an equal number of seizures spread out over 2 weeks. The possibility that the memory alterations with ECT also require development over time, finds support in the recent work of Hargreaves, Fischer, Elashoff, & Blacker (1972), who found that the memory dysfunction with conventional bilateral ECT was more pronounced the day *after* ECT than on the afternoon of the treatment day.

Why is memory loss less after MECT than after an equal number of seizures given on alternate days? General anesthesia and any loss of consciousness may be followed by retrograde amnesia. Conventional ECT requires separate anesthesia inductions and separate episodes of unconsciousness to deliver the same number of convulsions which are given in a single session with MECT. The memory effects of MECT as well as the therapeutic effects, may also require development over time, accompanied by alterations in the turnover rates of cerebral amines. This was shown by Essman (1970) to have a direct relation to retrograde amnesia in animals receiving ECS.

SUMMARY

MECT has been more rewarding for the questions it raises concerning the convulsive therapy process than for an enhancement of clinical efficacy of convulsive therapy. It is generally not possible to give a therapeutic course of ECT for a depressive illness in a single treatment session. While many patients treated with MECT show an acceleration of the therapeutic process, this occurs with an increased incidence of undesirable treatment side-effects.

Cerebral oxygenation may account for the difference in memory alterations between REST and MECT. The present use of succinylcholine prevents muscular utilization of oxygen during the seizure, and with forced oxygenation throughout, hemoglobin oxygen saturation levels remain high.

The memory loss with 4 or 6 ECT in one session is less than with the same number given on alternate days. It is possible that the cognitive effects of induced seizures require a period of consolidation, and an elapsed time for the appearance of the amnesic effects.

Therapeutic effects may also require evolution, accounting for the failure of most patients to recover after a single session of MECT. This evolution may depend on the chemical processes induced by the seizures, and the delayed clinical response noted in some patients after a single session of MECT suggests that such processes, once established, may proceed independently.

REFERENCES

Abrams, R., & Fink, M. Clinical experiences with multiple electroconvulsive treatments. *Comprehensive Psychiatry*, 1972, 13, 115-121.

Abrams, R., Volavka, J., & Fink, M. EEG seizure patterns during multiple unilateral and bilateral ECT. *Comprehensive Psychiatry*, 1973, 14, 25-28.

Bidder, T. G., & Strain, J. J. Modifications of electroconvulsive therapy. *Comprehensive Psychiatry*, 1970, 11, 507-517.

Blachly, P. H., & Gowing, D. Multiple monitored electroconvulsive treatment. *Comprehensive Psychiatry*, 1966, 7, 100-109.

Bridenbaugh, R. H., Drake, F. R., & O'Regan, T. J. Multiple monitored electroconvulsive treatment of schizophrenia. *Comprehensive Psychiatry*, 1972, 13, 9-17.

Cameron, D. E. Production of differential amnesia as a factor in the treatment of schizophrenia. *Comprehensive Psychiatry*, 1960, 1, 26-34.

Cameron, D. E., Lohrenz, J. G., & Handcock, K. A. The depatterning treatment of schizophrenia. *Comprehensive Psychiatry*, 1962, 3, 65-76.

Essman, W. B. Some neurochemical correlates of altered memory consolidation. *Transactions of the New York Academy of Sciences*, 1970, 32, 948-973.

Garrett, E. S., & Mockbee, C. W. New hope for far advanced schizophrenia: Intensive regressive therapy in treatment of severely regressed schizophrenics. *Ohio State Medical Journal*, 1952, 48, 505-509.

Glueck, B. C., Jr., Reiss, H., & Bernard, L. E. Regressive electric shock therapy. *Psychiatric Quarterly*, 1957, 31, 117-136.

Graber, H. K., & McHugh, R. B. Regressive electroshock therapy in chronic schizophrenia: A controlled study. *Lancet*, 1960, 30, 24-27.

Hargreaves, W. A., Fischer, A., Elashoff, R. M., & Blacker, K. H. Delayed onset of impairment following electrically induced convulsions. *Acta Psychiatrica Scandinavica*, 1972, 48, 69-77.

Jacoby, M. C., & Van Houten, Z. Regressive shock therapy. *Diseases of the Nervous System*, 1960, 21, 582-583.

Kennedy, C. J. C., & Anchel, D. Regressive electric shock in schizophrenics refractory to other shock therapies. *Psychiatric Quarterly*, 1948, 22, 317-320.

King, P. D. A comparison of REST and ECT in the treatment of schizophrenics. *American Journal of Psychiatry*, 1959, 116, 358-359.

Milligan, W. L. Psychoneuroses treated with electrical convulsions: Intensive method. *Lancet*, 1946, 215, 516-520.

Murillo, L. G., & Exner, J. E. The effects of regressive ECT with process schizophrenics. *American Journal of Psychiatry*, 1973, 130, 269-273.

Pryor, G. T. Effects of repeated ECS on brain weight and brain enzymes. This volume.

Rothschild, D., van Gordon, D. J., & Varjabedian, A. Regressive shock therapy in schizophrenia. *Diseases of the Nervous System*, 1951, 12, 147.

Schwartzmann, A. E., & Termansen, P. E. Intensive electroconvulsive therapy: A follow-up study. *Canadian Psychiatric Association Journal*, 1967, 12, 217-218.

Strain, J. J., & Bidder, T. G. Transient cerebral complication associated with multiple monitored electroconvulsive therapy. *Diseases of the Nervous System*, 1971, 32, 95-100

Weil, P. L. "Regressive" electroplexy in schizophrenics. *Journal of Mental Science,* 1950, 96, 514.

White, R. K., Shea, J. J., & Jonas, M. A. Multiple monitored electroconvulsive therapy. *American Journal of Psychiatry,* 1968, 125, 622-626.

8
ELECTROCONVULSIVE SHOCK: EFFECTS ON LEARNING AND MEMORY IN ANIMALS[1]

James L. McGaugh, Ph.D.[2]

Shortly after electroconvulsive shock was introduced as a therapeutic treatment for mental disorders, clinicians observed that patients given a series of treatments often had impaired memory. Extensive clinical and experimental studies have confirmed these observations (Mayer-Gross, 1943; Williams, 1966; Cronholm, 1969; Dornbush, 1972; Dornbush & Williams, this volume). Patients treated with electroshock have difficulty remembering events, names, and even some aspects of personal life history. Memories of recent experiences are particularly affected by the treatments. Although there were early suggestions that the memory impairment might contribute to the therapeutic effectiveness of electroshock treatments (Janis & Astrachan, 1951), there is now much evidence that memory impairment is not essential for the therapeutic effect of electroshock (d'Elia, 1970; this volume). Consequently, recent studies of electroshock effects on patients have focused on attempts to find conditions under which the treatments have maximal therapeutic effects with minimal memory impairment.

From this perspective, the effects of electroshock stimulation on memory are regarded as undesirable side-effects. From another perspective, however, the observations that electroshock stimulation affects memory suggested that electroshock stimulation might be useful as an experimental procedure in studies on memory. The results of studies conducted over the past 25 years provide

[1] The research was supported by Research Grant MH-12526 from the National Institute of Mental Health, United States Public Health Service.
[2] I thank Paul Gold, John Haycock, Roderick Van Buskirk and Steven Zornetzer for their contributions to this paper.

extensive experimental evidence that electroshock stimulation affects memory. The experimental findings are generally consistent with the clinical evidence suggesting that the conditions which produce memory impairment are different from those required for the therapeutic effects. This paper summarizes some of the findings of studies of the effects of electroshock stimulation on memory in laboratory animals. Since many summaries of research in this area are available (cf. Glickman, 1961; Hunt, 1965; McGaugh & Dawson, 1971; McGaugh & Herz, 1972), this paper focuses only on a few of the major issues and emphasizes recent research findings.

EFFECTS OF A SERIES OF ECS TREATMENTS

Electroshock stimulation is therapeutically effective only when given repeatedly (Fink, 1972). Usually the treatment is administered to patients several times each week. Because of this, many of the early studies of the effect of electroconvulsive shock (ECS) on learning and memory in animals examined the effect of a series of ECS treatments (Russell, 1948). In general, the findings of such studies indicate that, in rats and monkeys, the learning and retention of complex tasks are impaired following a series of ECS treatments (McGaugh, 1968). However, the impairment typically lasts only for a few weeks. The impairment seems to be due to the convulsions, since the treatments are ineffective if the convulsions are prevented by administering the ECS while the animals are anesthetized with ether. Thus, the results of these early studies of the effects of ECS on animals' behavior are generally consistent with the clinical observations: Repeated ECS treatments produce a general impairment of learning and memory.

In an extensive series of studies, Hunt and his colleagues (Hunt, 1965) demonstrated that a series of ECS treatments was particularly effective in attenuating a learned emotional response. In these experiments, rats were first trained to press a lever for a water reward and were then given a series of trials in which a click was followed by a footshock. After a few trials the click elicited a conditioned emotional response (CER) consisting of crouching and urinating and cessation of the lever pressing. The rats were then given three ECS treatments each day for 7 days. Following the ECS treatments, the click failed to elicit the CER. However, the effect of ECS on the CER, like those on other learning tasks, was temporary. The CER typically reappeared within a month if no additional ECS treatments were given. Again, as was found with other types of learning, the convulsions appear to be critical for the impairment: A series of ECS treatments did not attenuate the CER in animals given the treatments while anesthetized with ether. The 21 treatments were maximally effective when given at 8- or 24-hr intervals. The treatments had no effect if given every 30 min or one per second and were only partially effective when given only at 2- or 3-day intervals. It is important to note that the ECS treatments did not impair the lever pressing response; the treatments selectively affected the retention of the CER. Further, as is discussed below, conditions which do not affect the retention of a well-learned CER (e.g., a single ECS or a series of massed treatments) are highly effective in producing other effects on memory. Experimental studies of the effects of a series of ECS treatments in infrahuman animals are important primarily because the procedures used in such studies are somewhat comparable to those used in early clinical studies. These findings support the general conclusion that under some conditions memory is impaired by a series of ECS treatments. Such studies, however, provide little understanding of the bases of the effects.

EFFECTS OF A SINGLE ECS TREATMENT

Patients treated with electroshock seem to have particular difficulty remembering experiences occurring just prior to each treatment. Systematic studies of retention of patients treated with electroshock have generally confirmed the clinical impressions that electroshock produces retrograde amnesia (RA) in human patients (Mayer-Gross, 1943; Williams, 1966; Cronholm, 1969). Further, findings of early studies (cf. Duncan, 1949; Gerard, 1955; Thompson & Dean, 1955) provide strong evidence that ECS treatments selectively interfere with recently acquired memory in laboratory animals. Animals given training followed by an ECS treatment subsequently perform poorly on retention tests. The degree of retention generally varies directly with the length of the interval between the training and the ECS treatment.

These findings are commonly interpreted as suggesting that ECS treatments produce alterations in brain activity that interfere with the consolidation or storage of memory (Glickman, 1961; McGaugh & Herz, 1972). However, the interpretation that ECS interferes with memory consolidation has been questioned by several investigators, and a number of alternative interpretations of the ECS effects on retention performance have been offered. Since many of these controversial issues have been examined in detail in other reviews (cf. Lewis & Maher, 1965; McGaugh & Petrinovich, 1966; Spevack & Suboski, 1969; Lewis, 1969; Dawson, 1971; McGaugh & Dawson, 1971; McGaugh & Herz, 1972), only two major issues will be discussed here: (a) the nature of the RA gradient, and (b) the permanence of the RA.

THE NATURE OF THE RA GRADIENT

There is little disagreement concerning the conclusions that the degree of the impairing effect of ECS on retention decreases as the length of the interval between the training and ECS treatment is increased. Retrograde amnesia gradients are readily obtained with many treatments which affect central nervous system functioning, including convulsant drugs (Cherkin, this volume) and protein synthesis inhibitors (Agranoff, 1972; Barondes & Squire, 1972). In general, the RA gradients obtained with other treatments are comparable to those obtained with ECS (McGaugh & Herz, 1972). The controversy has centered on the question of the length of the RA gradient. Specifically, what is the longest training-treatment interval that produces a significant retention deficit? If it is assumed that the RA gradient reflects only the time required for memory consolidation or permanent storage and that memory storage time does not vary, then it might be expected that all RA studies would obtain similar gradients. However, estimates of "consolidation time" based on studies employing posttraining treatments have ranged from a few seconds (Chorover & Schiller, 1965; Weiskrantz, 1966) to several days (Kopp, Bohdanecky, & Jarvik, 1966; Jamieson, 1972; Cherkin, this volume). Most recent evidence indicates that the assumption that RA gradients reflect only consolidation time is unwarranted. The RA gradient depends upon the particular experimental conditions used in any particular study, including the strain of animal,[3,4] the time of day at which the experiment is conducted (Stephens, McGaugh, & Alpern, 1967), the criterion used for retention (Robustelli, Geller, & Jarvik, 1969; Schneider, Kapp, Aron, & Jarvik, 1969), and the particular treatment used to produce RA (Cherkin, 1969; Dorfman & Jarvik, 1968).

Thus, RA curves are curves of "susceptibility;" the nature of the gradient obtained depends both upon the neural processes underlying memory which are susceptible to disruption as well as the procedures used to produce and assess the disruption. For example, Schneider et al. (1969) showed that, when all other conditions are held constant, the length of the RA gradient depends upon the retention measure used. In their study, rats and mice were trained on a one-trial inhibitory (passive) avoidance task. They received a footshock as they stepped from one chamber into the other chamber of a two-compartment apparatus and were tested a day later. The measure of retention used in inhibitory avoidance tasks is the latency of response of entering the compartment where they had received shock. Short latencies are considered as evidence of amnesia and long latencies as evidence of retention. On the retention test, animals remaining in the starting chamber for an arbitrary period of time are assumed to retain the response. Schneider et al. (1969) found, however, that the results of RA studies depend upon the maximum length of the retention period used. If mice were allowed only a 30-sec period in which to respond on the retention test, the RA gradient was short (only a few seconds). If a 600-sec retention criterion was used, the RA gradient was extended to approximately 1 hr. That is, the longer test provided an opportunity for assessing memory that was not provided by the shorter criterion. In many gradient studies a 30-sec criterion has been used. Frequently, such studies have obtained evidence of short gradients. Such evidence, of course, does not mean that the "true" RA gradient is 30 sec. The short gradient may have been an artifact of the "ceiling effect" resulting from the arbitrary short cutoff time on the retention test.

Other studies have shown that when the retention criterion is held constant the degree of amnesia produced by ECS depends upon the parameters of the current used. When ECS treatments are given at one specific delay interval following training, the degree of retention decreases as the ECS current intensity is increased (Dorfman & Jarvik, 1968; Miller, 1968; Zornetzer & McGaugh, 1971a, 1971b). Further, the length of the RA gradient varies directly with current intensity and duration (Alpern & McGaugh, 1968; Buckholtz & Bowman, 1972; Haycock & McGaugh, 1973). Jamieson (1972) found that the length of the gradient can be extended by giving animals a series of five ECS treatments (each 0.5 sec) at one of several intervals following training on a one-trial inhibitory avoidance task. A fairly short gradient was obtained with a single 2.5-sec treatment, a 1-hr gradient was produced by five treatments spaced 5 sec apart, and a 48-hr gradient was produced by five ECS treatments spaced 1 min apart. Thus, the effect on memory obtained with a single ECS treatment is not necessarily an adequate estimate of the maximal degree of disruption that it is possible to obtain. Obviously then, any particular treatment cannot provide a measure of "consolidation time." These findings are consistent with evidence from Cherkin's studies (1969; this volume) which indicate that the RA gradient produced by the convulsant flurothyl depends upon the concentration of the drug (which is inhaled) as well as the duration of exposure to the drug. The findings are also consistent with the findings of Gold, Macri, and McGaugh (1973) that in rats the degree of amnesia produced by direct electrical stimulation of the cortex depends upon the cortical region stimulated as well as the intensity of the current. Rats in the study by Gold et al. (1973) were trained on a one-trial inhibitory avoidance task, given bilateral cortical stimulation at one of several posttrial intervals and then given a retention test a day later. When current intensity was held constant, the RA gradient obtained with frontal cortex stimulation was shorter than that obtained with posterior cortex stimulation. For both electrode placement sites, degree of RA varied directly with the current intensity. For example, a brief (less than 5 sec) gradient was obtained with 2.0 mA current administered to frontal cortex. At the other extreme, a 1-hr gradient was obtained with 4 mA current applied to posterior cortex. It seems likely that even longer gradients might be obtained with currents of greater intensity. There are probably brain sites which are more effective (in producing RA) than either of those used by Gold et al. (1973). This problem is considered further below.

Studies of the RA gradient have provided strong evidence that memory processes become decreasingly susceptible to interfering treatments as the training-treatment interval is increased. The studies have not provided support for the view that there is a "true" RA gradient of any particular length, whether long or short. RA gradients are a product of the experimental conditions used to define them. However, it is important to note that there are conditions under which retention impairment can be produced with long training-treatment intervals. Such findings suggest that memory storage or consolidation involves processes which are active for perhaps even days. The temporal limits of the consolidation process have not yet been defined.

THE PERMANENCE OF RA

According to the hypothesis that ECS and other treatments improve retention by interfering with memory consolidation processes, the amnesia produced by ECS should be permanent. Memory should not return when the animals recover from the acute effects of the amnesic treatment. Although some investigators have reported finding that the memory impairment produced by ECS is only temporary (e.g., Zinkin & Miller, 1967; Nielson, 1968), most studies investigating this problem have found that the RA is permanent, at least over intervals of time ranging from 12 hr to 1 month (Chevalier, 1965; Luttges & McGaugh, 1967; Geller & Jarvik, 1968; Greenough; Schwitzgebel, & Fulcher, 1968; Herz & Peeke, 1968; Zornetzer & McGaugh, 1969). Overall, there is very little evidence to support the view that ECS produces only temporary RA.

However, evidence that RA is permanent is not sufficient to allow the conclusion that ECS causes RA by interfering with the storage of information. Several investigators have argued that amnesic treatments may interfere with retention by impairing the processes underlying the retrieval of memory processes rather than their storage. The findings of a number of recent experiments are consistent with the "impaired retrieval" interpretation (Lewis, Misanin, & Miller, 1968; Quartermain, McEwen, & Azmitia, 1972; Springer & Miller, 1972). In these studies, animals are typically trained on an inhibitory avoidance task and then given an ECS or other amnesic treatment and a retention test a day or so later. The animals are then given an aversive treatment, such as a footshock, in a different apparatus and a second retention test a day after receiving the noncontingent aversive treatment. In comparison with controls given only the amnesic treatment, animals given the noncontingent treatment show better retention on the second test. The noncontingent aversive treatment appears to attenuate the ECS-induced amnesia. The noncontingent treatment is thought to act as a "reminder" and thus remove the conditions blocking retrieval and enable the animals to remember the original training experience.

Thus, the findings of reminder studies such as those cited above are consistent with the view that ECS-induced amnesia is due to blocked retrieval rather than to impaired storage. However, the results of several recent studies suggest that the reminder stimulus may increase retention simply because it constitutes a training experience whose effects can add to a "weak" memory produced by the amnesic treatment. For example, Cherkin (1972) reported that a reminder is effective in increasing the retention of chicks rendered amnesic by flurothyl only if a weak amnesic treatment is used. Further, Gold, Haycock, Macri, and

McGaugh (1973) found that the retention of rats given training on a one-trial inhibitory avoidance task followed by direct bilateral electrical stimulation of the posterior cortex was improved by a noncontingent reminder footshock only if the animals displayed some evidence of retention on the first retention test. Comparable findings were obtained by Haycock, Gold, Macri, and McGaugh (1973) in a study using mice and transcorneal ECS: In animals given a nonspecific reminder shock, retention (measured by response latencies) on the second retention test was greatest in animals which showed partial retention on the first retention test. These results strongly suggest that reminders are effective because their effects add, through generalization, to weak memories which survive the ECS treatment. Additional support for this alternative interpretation of reminder effects is provided by other findings of the experiments by Gold et al. (1973) and Haycock et al. (1973). Noncontingent reminder footshocks were also effective in increasing the retention performance in animals that were poorly trained on the inhibitory avoidance task (i.e., the animals received a weak footshock on the training trial). Thus, reminder treatments are effective in increasing retention of either partially amnesic or poorly trained animals. The essential condition required for the effectiveness of the reminder treatment appears to be that the animals have poor retention (for whatever reason) of the original experience. The evidence from these recent studies indicates that while reminder treatments clearly affect retention, it is not necessary to assume that they do so by removing ECS induced processes blocking the retrieval of stored information. The evidence from the reminder studies is consistent with the view that ECS and other treatments produce amnesia because they interfere with memory storage processes.

BRAIN STIMULATION AND RA

It is generally assumed that ECS impairs memory storage because the treatment alters brain activity. Although ECS was first used in studies of RA over 25 years ago, there were, until recently, few studies attempting to investigate the neural alterations underlying the amnesic effects of ECS. Recent experiments have attempted to find out (a) what changes in neural activity are essential for producing RA, and (b) whether specific brain regions differ in thresholds for RA produced by electrical stimulation.

It is quite clear that in laboratory animals, ECS need not produce behavioral convulsions in order to produce RA. RA is readily produced at current levels below tonic convulsion thresholds (Jarvik & Kopp, 1967; Lee-Teng, 1969). Further, retrograde amnesia can be produced when convulsions are prevented by lightly anesthetizing the animals with depressant drugs prior to administration of the current (Weissman, 1965; McGaugh & Alpern, 1966; McGaugh, Dawson, Coleman, & Rawie, 1971; Zornetzer & McGaugh, 1972). Thus, the effects of a single ECS treatment on memory appear to differ from the effects of a series of ECS treatments. As noted earlier, in rats, a series of ECS treatments does not impair retention if the convulsions are prevented by ether anesthesia. The issue is complicated by the finding that ether raises both RA and brain seizure thresholds. If animals are deeply anesthetized with ether, the ether prevents the brain seizures and no RA results (McGaugh & Zornetzer, 1970). The level of ether anesthesia used in earlier studies was not reported.

In unetherized mice the current threshold for producing brain seizures is approximately the same as that for producing RA for an inhibitory avoidance response. Further, under some conditions, light ether anesthesia produces comparable increases in both the brain seizure and RA thresholds. For example, Zornetzer and McGaugh (1971a), found that in untreated mice given a 200-ms transcorneal ECS, the brain seizure threshold and the RA threshold were both approximately 3 mA. In mice lightly anesthetized with ether the RA and brain seizure thresholds were both elevated to approximately 13 mA. These findings would seem to suggest that brain seizures are essential for producing RA. However, other evidence indicates that, under other conditions, RA can be obtained in mice with current intensities below the brain seizure threshold (Zornetzer & McGaugh, 1971b). Further, in some strains of mice, animals lightly anesthestized with ether do not have RA even though the current is well above the brain seizures threshold (Van Buskirk and McGaugh, see Footnote 3).

Thus, the findings of studies using mice treated with transcorneal ECS indicate that, while brain seizure thresholds are often correlated with RA thresholds, the elicitation of brain seizures is apparently neither a necessary nor sufficient condition for producing RA. In view of this, it is interesting to note that in untreated, as well as ether anesthestized mice, ECS produces significant interference with brain protein synthesis only at current intensities which produce RA and brain seizures (Cotman, Banker, Zornetzer, & McGaugh, 1971). These findings are generally consistent with other evidence that ECS treatments produce an inhibition of brain protein synthesis, and that the degree of inhibition varies directly with the ECS current intensity (Dunn, Giuditta, Wilson, & Glassman, this volume).

In most of the research using electroshock stimulation, the current is delivered through electrodes applied transpinneally or transcorneally. Further, in order to insure that the treatment affects the brain, the current used in most studies is usually of an intensity sufficient to produce convulsions. In the past few years a number of experiments have examined the amnesic effects produced by direct stimulation of the brain. In a series of experiments Zornetzer and McGaugh (1969, 1971a, 1971b, 1972; Zornetzer, this volume) have shown that the degree of RA produced by direct stimulation of the frontal cortex varies directly with the current intensity. Further, under some conditions, the degree of RA is correlated with degree of brain seizure activity. Other findings indicate that the degree of amnesia produced by cortical stimulation depends upon the region of the cortex stimulated (Gold & McGaugh, in press; Gold et al., in press), as well as the specific training task and procedures used (Gold, Bueno, & McGaugh, 1973). Under some conditions, the elicitation of brain seizures by cortical stimulation is not a sufficient condition for producing RA (Gold & McGaugh, 1973). Further, the elicitation of brain seizures by subcortical stimulation does not appear to be a sufficient condition for producing RA in rats (Zornetzer, 1972).

These findings, considered together with those of brain seizures and RA in mice treated with ECS indicate that RA is probably not caused by generalized brain seizure activity. The results of studies using subcortical stimulation provide additional support for this conclusion. Recent research indicates that RA can be produced by stimulation of a number of subcortical regions, including the caudate nucleus (Wyers, Peeke, Williston, & Herz, 1968; Deadwyler & Wyers, 1972), hippocampus (Shinkman & Kaufman, 1972; Zornetzer, Chronister, & Ross, in press), and amygdala (Kesner & Doty, 1968; McDonough & Kesner, 1971; Bresnahan & Routtenberg, in press; Gold, Macri, & McGaugh, in press). Under some conditions the stimulation appears to produce RA at intensities that are below the seizure thresholds. These findings are important since they suggest that RA may be produced by subtle alterations in brain activity. Further, by using low intensity current, it should be possible to "map" the brain regions sensitive to brain stimulation as indicated by RA effects. On the basis of present evidence, however, it can only be concluded that RA can be produced by low intensity electrical stimulation of some regions of the brain. Whether the RA is due to alterations in the stimulated structures, or to effects produced elsewhere in the brain by stimulation of the structures, remains to be determined.

CONCLUDING COMMENTS

The findings of experimental studies of ECS in infrahuman animals are highly consistent with clinical observations suggesting that ECS impairs memory. The extensive studies of the characteristics of ECS effects on memory have increased our understanding of experimentally induced retrograde amnesia and have stimulated investigations of the effects of direct electrical stimulation of the brain on memory. The results of recent research suggest that the effects of ECS on memory may be due to subtle alterations of neural activity in specific brain regions. An understanding of the organization of "sensitive" brain regions could be useful in the development of brain stimulation procedures which produce minimal effects on memory and maximal therapeutic effectiveness. Further, studies of this kind should eventually increase our understanding of the anatomical differentiation of processes underlying memory and affect. If the effects of brain stimulation on memory are restricted to specific brain regions, it may also be that there are specific brain regions which, when stimulated, produce maximal antidepressant effects. Such understanding would seem to be essential for developing a rational basis for therapeutic use of electrical stimulation of the brain in the treatment of affective disorders.

REFERENCES

Agranoff, B. W. Further studies on memory formation in the goldfish. In J. L. McGaugh (Ed.), *The Chemistry of mood, motivation and memory.* New York: Plenum Press, 1972.

Alpern, H. P., & McGaugh, J. L. Retrograde amnesia as a function of duration of electroshock stimulation. *Journal of Comparative and Physiological Psychology,* 1968, 65, 265-269.

Barondes, S. H., & Squire, L. D. Slow biological processes in memory storage and "recovery" of memory. In J. L. McGaugh (Ed.), *The chemistry of mood, motivation and memory.* New York: Plenum Press, 1972.

Bresnahan, E., & Routtenberg, A. Memory disruption by low level, non epileptogenic stimulation of the medial amygdaloid nucleus. *Physiology and Behavior,* 1972, 9, 513-526.

Buckholtz, N. S., & Bowman, R. E. Incubation and retrograde amnesia studies with various ECS intensities and durations. *Physiology and Behavior,* 1972, 8, 113-117.

Cherkin, A. Kinetics of memory consolidation: Role of amnesic treatment parameters. *Proceedings of the National Academy of Sciences of the United States of America,* 1969, 63, 1094-1101.

Cherkin, A. Retrograde amnesia in the chick: Resistance to the reminder effect. *Physiology and Behavior,* 1972, 8, 949-955.

Cherkin, A. Effects of flurothyl (Indoklon) upon memory in the chick. This volume.

Chevalier, J. A. Permanence of amnesia after a single posttrial electroconvulsive seizure. *Journal of Comparative and Physiological Psychology,* 1965, 59, 125-127.

Chorover, S. L., & Schiller, P. H. Short-term retrograde amnesia in rats. *Journal of Comparative and Physiological Psychology,* 1965, 59, 73-78.

Cotman, C. W., Banker, G., Zornetzer, S. F., & McGaugh, J. L. Electroshock effects on brain protein synthesis: Relation to brain seizures and retrograde amnesia. *Science,* 1971, 173, 454-456.

Cronholm, B. Post ECT amnesias. In G. A. Talland & N. C. Waugh (Eds.), *The pathology of memory.* New York: Academic Press, 1969.

Dawson, R. G. Retrograde amnesia and conditioned emotional response: A further evaluation. *Psychological Bulletin,* 1971, 75, 278-285.

Deadwyler, S. A., & Wyers, E. J. Disruption of habituation by caudate nuclear stimulation in the rat. *Behavioral Biology,* 1972, 7, 55-64.

d'Elia, G. Unilateral electroconvulsive therapy. *Acta Psychiatrica Scandinavica,* 1970, 46 (Suppl. 215), 1-98.

Dorfman, L. F., & Jarvik, M. E. A parametric study of electroshock-induced retrograde amnesia in mice. *Neuropsychologia,* 1968, 6, 373-380.

Dornbush, R. L. Memory and induced ECT convulsions. *Seminars in Psychiatry,* 1972, 4, 47-54.

Dornbush, R. L., & Williams, M. Memory and ECT. This volume.

Duncan, C. P. The retroactive effect of electroshock on learning. *Journal of Comparative and Physiological Psychology,* 1949, 42, 32-44.

Fink, M. The therapeutic process in ECT. *Seminars in Psychiatry,* 1972, 4, 39-46.

Geller, A., & Jarvik, M. E. Electroconvulsive shock induced amnesia and recovery. *Psychonomic Science,* 1968, 10, 15-16.

Gerard, R. W. Biological roots of psychiatry. *Science,* 1955, 122, 225-230.

Glickman, S. E. Perseverative neural processes and consolidation ot the memory trace. *Psychological Bulletin,* 1961, 58, 218-233.

Gold, P. E., Bueno, O. F., & McGaugh, J. L. Training and task-related differences in retrograde amnesia thresholds determined by direct electrical stimulation of the cortex in rats. *Physiology and Behavior,* 1973, 11, 57-63.

Gold, P. E., Haycock, J. W., Macri, J., & McGaugh, J. L. Retrograde amnesia and the "reminder effect": An alternative interpretation. *Science*, 1973, 180, 1119-1201.

Gold, P. E., Macri, J., & McGaugh, J. L. Retrograde amnesia gradients: Effects of direct cortical stimulation. *Science*, 1973, 180, 1199-1201.

Gold, P. E., Macri, J., & McGaugh, J. L. Amnesic effects of subseizure stimulation of the amygdala. in press, *Behavioral Biology.*

Gold, P. E., & McGaugh, J. L. Relationship between amnesia and brain seizures in rats. *Physiology and Behavior*, 1973, 10, 41-46.

Greenough, W. T., Schwitzgebel, R. L. & Fulcher, J. K. Permanence of ECS-produced amnesia as a function of test conditions. *Journal of Comparative and Physiological Psychology*, 1968, 66, 554-556.

Haycock, J. W., & McGaugh, J. L. Retrograde amnesia gradients as a function of ECS-intensity. *Behaviorial Biology*, 1973, 9, 123-127.

Haycock, J. W., Gold, P. E., Macri, J., & McGaugh, J. L. Noncontingent footshock "attenuation.' of retrograde amnesia: A generalization effect. *Physiology and Behavior*, 1973, 11, 99-102.

Herz, M. J., & Peeke, H. V. S. ECS-produced retrograde amnesia: Permanence vs. recovery over repeated testing. *Physiology and Behavior*, 1968, 3, 517-521.

Hunt, H. F. Electroconvulsive shock and learning. *Transactions of the New York Academy of Sciences*, 1965, 27, 923-945.

Jamieson, J. L. Temporal patterning of electroshock retrograde amnesia. Unpublished doctoral dissertation, University of British Columbia, 1972.

Janis, I. L., & Astrachan, M. The effects of electroconvulsive treatments on memory efficiency. *Journal of Abnormal and Social Psychology*, 1951, 46, 501-511.

Jarvik, M. E., & Kopp, R. Transcorneal electroconvulsive shock and retrograde amnesia in mice. *Journal of Comparative and Physiological Psychology*, 1967, 64, 431-433.

Kesner, R. P., & Doty, R. W. Amnesia produced in cats by local seizure activity initiated from the amygdala. *Experimental Neurology*, 1968, 21, 58-68.

Kopp, R., Bohdanecky, Z., & Jarvik, M. E. Long temporal gradient of retrograde amnesia for a well-discriminated stimulus. *Science*, 1966, 153, 1547-1549.

Lee-Teng, E. Retrograde amnesia in relation to subconvulsive and convulsive currents in chicks. *Journal of Comparative and Physiological Psychology*, 1969, 67, 135-139.

Lewis, D. J. Sources of experimental amnesia. *Psychological Review*, 1969, 76, 461-472.

Lewis, D. J., & Maher, B. A. Neural consolidation and electroconvulsive shock. *Psychological Review*, 1965, 72, 225-239.

Lewis, D. J., Misanin, J. R., & Miller, R. R. Recovery of memory following amnesia. *Nature*, 1968, 220, 704-705.

Luttges, M. W., & McGaugh, J. L. Permanence of retrograde amnesia produced by electroconvulsive shock. *Science*, 1967, 156, 408-410.

Mayer-Gross, W. Retrograde amnesia. *Lancet*, 1943, 2, 603-605.

McDonough, J. H., Jr., & Kesner, R. P. Amnesia produced by brief electrical stimulation of amygdala or dorsal hippocampus in cats. *Journal of Comparative and Physiological Psychology*, 1971, 77, 171-178.

McGaugh, J. L. Electroconvulsive shock. *International Encyclopedia of Social Science*, 1968, 5, 21-25.

McGaugh, J. L., & Alpern, H. P. Effects of electroshock on memory: Amnesia without convulsions. *Science*, 1966, 152, 665-666.

McGaugh, J. L., & Dawson, R. G. Modification of memory storage processes. In W. K. Honig & P. H. R. James (Eds.), *Animal memory*. New York: Academic Press, 1971.

McGaugh, J. L., Dawson, R. G., Coleman, R., & Rawie, J. Electroshock effects on memory in diethyl ether-treated mice: Analysis of the CER-incubation hypothesis of retrograde amnesia. *Communications in Behavioral Biology*, 1971, 6, 227-232.

McGaugh, J. L., & Herz, M. J. *Memory consolidation*. San Francisco: Albion, 1972.

McGaugh, J. L., & Petrinovich, L. F. Neural consolidation and electroconvulsive shock reexamined. *Psychological Review*, 1966, 73, 382-387.

McGaugh, J. L., & Zornetzer, S. Amnesia and brain seizure activity in mice: Effects of diethyl ether anesthesia prior to electroshock stimulation. *Communications in Behavioral Biology*, 1970, 5 (Pt. A), 243-248.

Miller, A. J. Variations in retrograde amnesia parameters of electroconvulsive shock and time of testing. *Journal of Comparative and Physiological Psychology*, 1968, 66, 40-47.

Nielson, H. C. Evidence that electroconvulsive shock alters memory retrieval rather than memory consolidation. *Experimental Neurology*, 1968, 20, 3-20.

√Quartermain, D., McEwen, B. S., & Azmitia, E. C., Jr. Recovery of memory following amnesia in the rat and mouse. *Journal of Comparative and Physiological Psychology*, 1972, 79, 360-370.

Robustelli, F., Geller, A., & Jarvik, M. E. Temporal gradient of 23 hours with electroconvulsive shock and its implications. *Communications in Behavioral Biology*, 1969, 4, 79-84.

Russell, R. W. Contributions of research in infrahuman animals to the understanding of electric convulsive shock phenomena. *Journal of Personality*, 1948, 17, 16-28.

Schneider, A. M., Kapp, B., Aron, C., & Jarvik, M. E. Retroactive effects of transcorneal and transpinnate ECS on step-through latencies of mice and rats. *Journal of Comparative and Physiological Psychology*, 1969, 69, 506-509.

Shinkman, P. G., & Kaufman, K. P. Posttrial hippocampal stimulation and CER acquisition in the rat. *Journal of Comparative and Physiological Psychology*, 1972, 80, 283-292.

Spevack, A. A., & Suboski, M. D. Retrograde effects of electroconvulsive shock on learned responses. *Psychological Bulletin*, 1969, 72, 66-76.

Springer, A. D., & Miller, R. R. Retrieval failure induced by electroconvulsive shock: Reversal with dissimilar training and recovery agents. *Science*, 1972, 177, 628-630.

Stephens, G., McGaugh, J. L., & Alpern, H. P. Periodicity and memory in mice. *Psychonomic Science*, 1967, 8, 201-202.

Thompson, R., & Dean, W. A further study of the retroactive effect of ECS. *Journal of Comparative and Physiological Psychology*, 1955, 48, 488-491.

Weiskrantz, L. Experimental studies of amnesia. In C. W. M. Whitty & O. L. Zangwill (Eds.), *Amnesia*. London: Butterworths, 1966.

Weissman, A. Effects of anticonvulsant drugs on electroconvulsive shock-induced retrograde amnesia. *Archives Internationales de Pharmacodynamie et de Therapie*, 1965, 154, 122-130.

Williams, M. Memory disorders associated with electroconvulsive therapy. In C. W. M. Whitty & O. L. Zangwill (Eds.), *Amnesia*. London: Butterworths, 1966.

Wyers, E. J., Peeke, H. V. S., Williston, J. S., & Herz, M. J. Retroactive impairment of passive avoidance learning by stimulation of the caudate nucleus. *Experimental Neurology*, 1968, 22, 350-366.

Zinkin, S., & Miller, A. J. Recovery of memory after amnesia induced by electroconvulsive shock. *Science*, 1967, 155, 102-104.

Zornetzer, S. F. Brain stimualtion and retrograde amnesia in rats: A neuroanatomical approach. *Physiology and Behavior*, 1972, 8, 239-244.

Zornetzer, S. F., Chronister, R. B., & Ross, B. The hippocampus and retrograde amnesia: Localization of some positive and negative memory disruptive sites. *Behavioral Biology*, 1973, 8, 507-518.

Zornetzer, S. F., & McGaugh, J. L. Effects of electroconvulsive shock upon inhibitory avoidance: The persistence and stability of amnesia. *Communications in Behavioral Biology*, 1969, 3 (Pt. A), 173-180.

Zornetzer, S. F., & McGaugh, J. L. Retrograde amnesia and brain seizures in mice. *Physiology and Behavior*, 1971, 7, 401-408. (a)

Zornetzer, S. F., & McGaugh, J. L. Retrograde amnesia and brain seizures in mice: A further
analysis. *Physiology and Behavior,* 1971, 7, 841-845. (b)

Zornetzer, S. F., & McGaugh, J. L. Electrophysiological correlates of frontal cortex-induced
retrograde amnesia in rats. *Physiology and Behavior,* 1972, 8, 233-238.

9

RETROGRADE AMNESIA AND BRAIN SEIZURES IN RODENTS: ELECTROPHYSIOLOGICAL AND NEUROANATOMICAL ANALYSES[1]

Steven Zornetzer[2]

Electroconvulsive therapy (ECT), the treatment of choice in severe depressive illness, is poorly understood at the mechanistic level. It is known that the effective therapeutic use of ECT for depressive illness appears to depend upon the production of brain seizure activity resulting from the delivery of current. Subconvulsive current levels appear to reduce the effectiveness of the treatment. In addition to the therapeutic effects of ECT, impairment of recent memory, associated with brain seizure activity, is a very common clinical sign. The relationship between ECT-produced alterations in memory storage systems and the therapeutic effects of ECT is poorly understood. It is possible, for example, that the modification of memory processes by ECT is in some way related to its clinical effectiveness in reducing severe depressive illness.

One approach in exploring this possible relationship has been to administer current to the brains of laboratory animals in order to study the effects of the current on alterations in brain chemistry, brain physiology, and memory storage processes. An understanding of the psychobiological bases of memory storage and memory disruption processes may provide a basis for understanding the relationship between the modification of memory processes by ECT and the amelioration of certain forms of mental illness.

More than two decades of animal research using electroconvulsive shock (ECS) supported the idea that recently acquired information is subject to

[1] The work in this paper was supported by Research Grant MH-12526 to James L. McGaugh, and Predoctoral Fellowship No. 5-F01 MH-36372 from the National Institute of Mental Health, and Biomedical Sciences Support Grant no. US PHS PR-07008-05.

[2] Special thanks to Dr. James McGaugh for his support and encouragement.

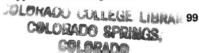

disruption and often permanent loss. This ECS-produced loss of memory, or retrograde amnesia (RA), was the subject of intensive descriptive analyses by experimental psychologists for a number of years. Briefly, this research indicated that the magnitude of ECS-produced RA was a function of ECS current parameters (intensity and duration), route of ECS administration, animal genotype, nature of the learning tasks, circadian influences, and other seemingly subtle experimental manipulations (see McGaugh & Herz, 1972, for a detailed review).

What have we learned from this research? Was it simply performed to describe a phenomenon or was there a more fundamental purpose associated with it? Much of this research on memory *disruption* was designed, paradoxically, to understand, in some way, the nature of memory *storage*. Thus, at the behavioral level investigators believed that ECS was a useful tool in an analysis of the temporal dissociation between recently formed memories, held in short term storage, and older memories somehow held in permanent or long term storage. By definition, memories that were subject to ECS-produced disruption had not yet been "consolidated," or placed into long term memory. Further, this research indicated that new memories were not all equally vulnerable to ECS-produced disruption. Hidden in its simplicity, this is an important point. Finally, recent research indicates that the disruption of memory by ECS does not result in immediate loss of memory. Rather, it appears that recently acquired memory (short term memory) is unaffected by ECS and can be retrieved for a period of time following ECS administration (Geller & Jarvik, 1968; McGaugh & Landfield, 1970). This short term memory then decays, apparently not able to achieve a successful transformation into long term memory. It is at this point that animals appear amnesic. This parcellation of the susceptibility of different hypothetical memory storage systems to ECS is an important contribution to our understanding of memory processes.

It should be made clear exactly what the limitations of ECS research are in providing an understanding of memory-storage processes. At one level, the behavioral one, ECS is useful in determining the temporal characteristics of memory *susceptibility* to disruption. Additionally, ECS is useful in identifying the complex interactions that a number of experimental variables have with it. Thus, research at this level does not provide information about the mechanism of memory storage per se, the location of storage in the brain, or the mechanisms of memory disruption. Such questions must be dealt with at another level of analysis.

How is memory storage studied at a more mechanistic level? What changes occur and persist in brain indicating that memories are formed and maintained? Where can these changes be found? Why are some memories labile to disruption while other memories are not? There are, at present, no definite answers to these basic questions. Recent evidence suggests that the effectiveness of an amnesic agent may depend upon its ability to affect critical brain sites. This is not to suggest that there is a specific amnesic "center" in the brain, but rather that critical structures and systems within brain must function properly during a critical period of time following the reception of information by the organism. If these structures or systems are interfered with by an appropriate experimental treatment then events will not be properly stored in long term memory.

There is evidence that some brain sites are more involved than others in the production of RA. Although a complete review of this literature will not be attempted here, the following structures have been implicated in electrical stimulation-produced RA: amygdala (Lidsky, Levine, Kreinick, & Schwartzbaum, 1970; Kesner & Doty, 1968); caudate nucleus (Wyers, Peeke, Williston, & Herz, 1968; Wyers & Deadwyler, 1971; Peeke & Herz, 1971; Herz & Peeke, 1971); hippocampus (McDonough & Kesner, 1971; Vardaris & Schwartz, 1971; Kesner & Conner, 1972); medial thalamus (Mahut, 1962; 1964; Wilburn & Kesner, 1972). These findings suggest that there may be at least regional, if not structural specificity involved in one or more aspects of the memory disruption process produced by the administration of "whole head" massive current administration, i.e., ECS.

If we are destined to descend into the depths of the brain in our search for the engram, surely there must be some helpful hints we can take along from our experience with ECS. Perhaps the single most obvious hint, though long ignored, is that typically, ECS results not only in subsequent RA, but is immediately accompanied by severe behavioral convulsions. These convulsions are but a sign that extensive brain (or spinal) seizure activity is occurring. Since the brain is generally believed to be the target organ for ECS, it seems logical to begin a more mechanistic analysis of ECS-produced memory disruption by investigating its relationship to brain seizure activity. I would like to emphasize that this type of research approach is specifically designed to study various aspects of electroshock-produced memory disruption. Its relationship to memory storage processes is indirect and at best inferential. Nonetheless, a clearer understanding of the ways in which memories are disrupted should be useful in providing insights into how memories are stored.

My approach to the problem of ECS-produced memory disruption incorporated both electrophysiological and behavioral analyses. Since the most obvious and striking effect of ECS upon the central nervous system is the seizure discharge, I began by asking whether there was a systematic relationship between brain seizure activity and RA.

The experiments reported here attempted to answer the following questions: First, is there a quantifiable relationship between the parameters of seizure-producing frontal cortex brain stimulation, and the EEG changes produced by such stimulation? Second, is direct cortical brain stimulation effective in producing retrograde amnesia, and if so, how does its effectiveness compare with extracranially delivered transpinneal ECS? Third, is there a relationship between the magnitude of EEG changes produced by direct cortical stimulation and the magnitude of retrograde amnesia? And finally, if frontal cortex is found to be an effective amnesia-producing site when stimulated, what other neuroanatomical regions are directly associated with frontal cortex? Do these other regions also participate in a memory disruption system in brain?

METHODS

Naive male albino rats (Simonsen Laboratories) weighing 200 to 300 g were used. Four cortical electrodes (stainless steel screws (1/8 in. X 0/80) were implanted in the skull. The two anterior electrodes were located 3.0 mm anterior to Bregma and 3.0 mm lateral. The posterior electrodes were located 5.0 mm posterior to Bregma and 3.0 mm lateral. Specific details of the surgical procedures have been reported elsewhere (Zornetzer & McGaugh, 1970.)

Following postoperative recovery, each animal was administered a series of frontal cortex stimulation trials in order to determine (a) brain seizure threshold and, (b) electrographic characteristics of the brain seizure as a function of current intensity. Brain stimulation was administered only once during each test session. Test sessions were 48 hr apart. During test sessions each rat was placed in an isolation chamber. Electrocorticogram (ECoG) recordings were taken from four electrode pair combinations: left frontal-right frontal, left posterior-right posterior, left frontal-left posterior, right frontal-right posterior.

Brain stimulation was delivered from a Grass Model SD5 stimulator and consisted of 1.0 msec biphasic pulses delivered to the two frontal electrodes at 100 Hz for 1.0 sec. Stimulus intensity was monitored on an oscilloscope. The following determinations were made for each animal: (a) the lowest level of brain stimulation sufficient to produce a primary afterdischarge (PAD), i.e., sustained iterative spiking producing a coherent envelope of paroxysmal events lasting at least 3.0 sec; (b) the mean spike frequency of the PAD as a function of current intensity; (c) the duration of the PAD as a function of current intensity; (d) the presence or absence of a subsequent spontaneous secondary afterdischarge (SAD), an afterdischarge not directly elicited by the cortical stimulus; and (e) the duration of the postictal period of ECoG quiescence beginning at the termination of the PAD and lasting either until a SAD occurs, or until normal ECoG patterns are reinstated. Following the PAD threshold determination, suprathreshold levels of stimulation were delivered over a period of 2 weeks.

Characterization of Brain Seizures Produced by
Frontal Cortex Stimulation

The brain's response to different intensities of frontal cortex stimulation is shown in Figure 1. At subthreshold intensities, stimulation (i.e., insufficient to result in a PAD) cortical desynchrony was produced (Figure 1A) and most animals responded by a cessation in ongoing behavior. At higher intensities of stimulation, but still subthreshold for PAD production, animals responded to the brain stimulation with vocalization, nondirected escape behavior, defecation, and urination. In other words, at these higher levels of subthreshold frontal cortex stimulation, the animals respond to the stimulus as if it were noxious.

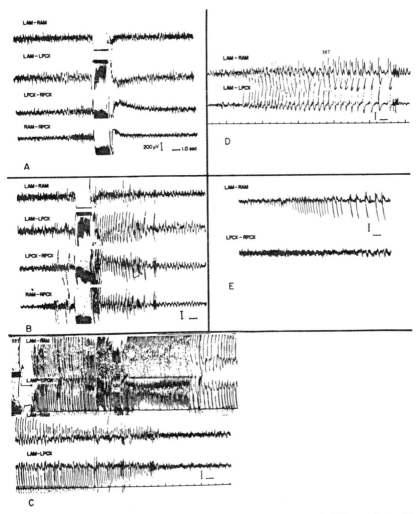

FIG. 1. EEG recordings following frontal cortex stimulation of different intensities. LAM=Left amygdala, RAM=Right amygdala, LPCX-Left posterior cortex, RPCX=Right posterior cortex, Calibrations: 200 μV and 1.0 sec. (A) subthreshold level of frontal cortex stimulation; (B) threshold level of frontal cortex stimulation; (C) suprathreshold level of frontal cortex stimulation; (D) continuation of seizure shown in (C). Spontaneous secondary afterdischarge (SAD) begins 52 sec after termination of the primary afterdischarge (PAD). (E) SAD elicited by stimulation of frontal cortex which was limited to subcortical structures only. (From Zornetzer & McGaugh, 1970)

Brain seizure threshold was marked by a brief (generally less than 6.0 sec) period of biphasic afterdischarge activity recorded in all recording leads (Figure 1B). These biphasic spikes occurred with a frequency of approximately 3 to 4 per second, and a peak to peak amplitude of 300 to 600 μV. The PAD ended simultaneously and abruptly in all recording channels. The mean PAD threshold elicited by frontal cortex stimulation was 1.3 mA (range = 0.7-2.2 mA). Typically, the behavioral manifestations of such a brain seizure included slight clonic twitching of the forepaws, rearing on the hind legs, and twitching jaw movements. Frequently, low frequency synchronization was present for a brief period following the termination of the PAD. Normal ECoG patterns reappeared usually within a minute or two following the PAD, and the animals appeared behaviorally alert.

The duration of the PAD was directly related to the stimulus intensity (Figure 2A) over the intensity range tested (0.5-10.0 mA). Concomitant with the increased PAD duration as a function of current intensity was a similar increase in the severity of the clonic movements as well as the duration of the postictal depression period. An important breaking point occurred in the data when the stimulus intensity reached about 3.0 mA. At this intensity level and above (up to 10 mA) spontaneous secondary afterdischarges (SAD) regularly occurred following the PAD and a period of postictal depression lasting 30-70 sec (Figure 1C). In addition, once this SAD threshold was reached for each animal, the clonic convulsoid concomitants of the brain seizure were preceded by a tonic phase of convulsoid activity with increasing current application to frontal cortex. Similarly, once this SAD threshold range was reached, there appeared to be no further relationship between stimulus intensity and the duration of the postictal period of cortical depression following the PAD.

At stimulus intensities above PAD threshold levels the mean frequency of paroxysmal spikes increased linearly as a function of current intensity until the SAD threshold (about 3.0 mA) was reached. Above this current level the mean PAD spike frequency remained constant up to 10.0 mA (Figure 2B). Thus, the duration of the PAD and the mean spike frequency of the PAD have very different relationships to current intensity over the range of 1.0-10.0 mA. PAD duration and frontal cortex stimulation were linearly related throughout this intensity range, while PAD spike frequency was linearly related to current intensity up to about 3.0 mA and then reached an asymptote.

Figures 1C and 1D show a typical example of a PAD followed by a SAD. During the initial tonic phase of the behavioral convulsion large amplitude (800 μV to 1700 μV) biphasic waves of 4 to 10 hz appeared. At current intensities around 3.0 mA the PAD typically lasted for 50-100 sec. During the later states of the PAD the initial biphasic waveform was replaced by a monophasic wave. The PAD always ended simultaneously and abruptly in all recording leads. PAD termination marked the beginning of the variable (30-70 sec) duration postictal depression period. The end of this postictal period was indicated either by a gradual reinstatement of slow waves leading eventually to a normal ECoG (this occurred at lower stimulus intensities) or the development of a SAD. The onset of the SAD was very stereotyped in all cortical leads. The SAD consisted of monophasic waves which grew in amplitude with successive spike events. This recruitmentlike phenomenon lasted until peak amplitude was reached, at which

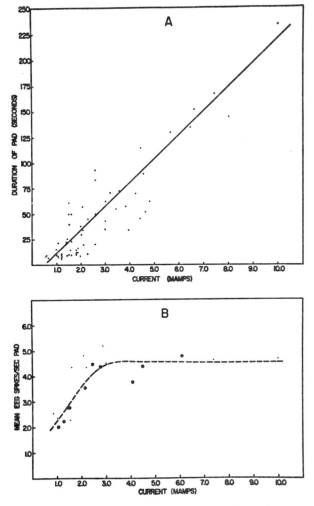

FIG. 2. (A) Relationship between PAD duration and current intensity of frontal cortex stimulation. (B) The mean number of EEG spikes in the PAD was calculated for each animal at each stimulus intensity. The relationship between mean spike frequency and stimulus intensity is direct up to about 3.0 mA, but then spike frequency reaches an asymptotic level. (From Zornetzer & McGaugh, 1970)

point the spikes remained at peak amplitude for a short period before abruptly terminating. The total discharge duration of the SAD did not usually exceed 30 sec. There was rarely any behavioral indication that a second brain seizure was occurring, although about 15% of the SADs were accompanied by mild clonic movements of the forepaws.

To summarize, the above findings indicate that as a function of current intensity the electroencephalographic response to frontal cortex stimulation varies in at least two ways: (*a*) it is linear with regard to PAD duration and, (*b*) it is asymptotic with regard to mean PAD frequency. In addition, spontaneous SADs develop at higher stimulus intensities.

The characterization of the brain's seizure response to frontal cortex stimulation, while interesting in its own right, has not yet been shown to be a meaningful research approach in the understanding of retrograde memory disruption produced by electrical stimulation. In order to begin such an analysis it was first necessary to demonstrate that frontal cortex stimulation could produce retrograde amnesia.

Evaluation of the Memory-disrupting Effects of Frontal Cortex Stimulation

Experiment 1. This first experiment was designed to compare directly the efficacy of direct frontal cortex stimulation with extracranial clip ECS in disrupting memory. The animals were 30 naive male albino rats of the same age and strain as used in the electrophysiological determinations. Each of 9 rats was implanted with four cortical screw electrodes as described above. In addition, all rats (the 9 implanted and the 21 nonimplanted rats) had two stainless steel wound clips attached to an area of shaved skin immediately subadjacent to each pinna. Conventional ECS (50 mA, 60 Hz, 800 msec) was subsequently delivered to the nonimplanted rats via these clips. Each rat was individually caged and placed on a water deprivation schedule. Body weights were reduced to 80% of initial weights.

Animals were trained to bar press for water reward in a long (91.5 cm) trough-shaped Plexiglas alley (Zornetzer & McGaugh, 1970). Animals were trained to bar press for 100 reinforced presses each day on a continuous reinforcement schedule. The total approach latency to the bar, i.e., the time from first being placed in the apparatus until the first lever press, and the total time to make 100 presses were automatically recorded each day.

Fourteen days of bar-press training resulted in very stable and predictable performance in both the approach latency score and the total time to complete 100 presses each day. Midway through the training (i.e., on Day 7) a cable was attached to each animal just prior to the training session. For the implanted animals the cable was a standard electrophysiological recording cable plus two small shielded alligator clips that were attached to the wound clips behind each ear. For the nonimplanted animals the cable consisted of only the alligator clip leads to be connected to the wound clips.

The animals were divided into four groups, one implanted group and three nonimplanted groups. Group 1 animals (MS-CXS) received 2.0 mA of mouth shock (MS) following the 10th lever press on Day 15. The mouth shock duration was that of a single lick. Immediately following MS these animals received 3.0 mA of biphasic frontal cortex stimulation for 1.0 sec. ECoG records were made after the brain stimulation was delivered. Group 2 animals (MS-ECS) were treated in exactly the same way as animals in Group 1, except instead of receiving cortical stimulation following MS, Group 2 animals received conventional ECS (50 mA, 60 Hz, 800 msec). Group 3 animals (MS-NECS) received MS but no ECS, and Group 4 animals (NMS-ECS) received no MS but did receive ECS following the 10th lever press on Day 15. These last two groups, Groups 3 and 4, were used as controls in order to evaluate, respectively, the effectiveness of the MS in effecting a learned behavior, and the effects of ECS alone upon an already well-established behavior pattern.

The behavioral results were expressed in terms of two suppression ratios calculated for each animal. These ratios (the first for latency to make the first bar press, and the second for total latency to complete 100 presses following the first press) indicated the amount of behavioral inhibition produced by the treatment on Day 15 as measured on Day 16. Low values for the suppression ratio indicate no change in behavior following the treatment on Day 15; high values indicate an inhibition in behavior.

An analysis of suppression ratios indicated that both conventional clip-ECS as well as frontal cortex stimulation produced complete RA (no behavioral suppression following mouth shock) for the inhibitory avoidance response (Figure 3). Animals in Group MS-CXS showed total amnesia, on both behavioral indices, when compared to Group MS-NECS ($p < 0.001$, Mann-Whitney U test, two-tailed). There was no significant difference in amnesia produced by frontal cortex stimulation (3.0 mA) and by conventional clip-ECS (50 mA). Data from the ECS control group (NMS-ECS) indicated that ECS alone, i.e., not preceded by MS, had no effect upon either behavioral measure 24 hr later. Thus, when measured 24 hr following ECS administration, the highly trained bar pressing behavior was not affected.

Since complete retrograde amnesia resulted from both clip-ECS and frontal cortex stimulation, it was not possible to relate degrees of memory loss to the electrophysiological changes produced by the two types of memory disruptive treatments.

These results indicate that biphasic pulses delivered to rat frontal cortex at 100 Hz with an intensity of 3.0 mA for 1.0 sec produce memory disruption at least as effectively as a much more intense current (50 mA for 800 msec) applied extracranially. These results are interesting in view of the results of a number of studies (Dorfman & Jarvik, 1968; Pagano, Bush, Martin, & Hunt, 1969; Alpern & McGaugh, 1968) indicating that the amnesia-producing effects of ECS are related to the intensity and/or duration of ECS. Although a precise formulation of this relationship has not yet been achieved (see Cherkin, 1969) it is not unlikely that the magnitude of RA is in some limited way related, in part at least, to the total amount of electrical charge, i.e. the number of coulombs actually reaching critical brain regions.

In the present experiment 3.0 mcoul of charge delivered directly to frontal cortex was sufficient to produce as much memory disruption as 40 mcoul

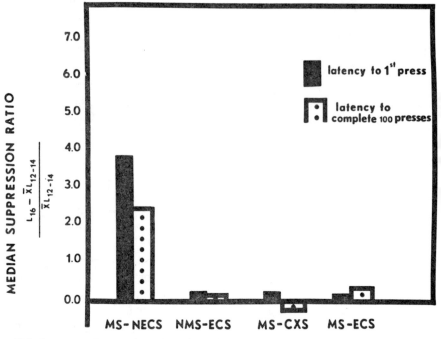

FIG. 3. The effects of either frontal cortex stimulation or clip ECS upon mouth-shock-induced inhibitory avoidance behavior. A high suppression ratio indicates an unimpaired memory for the mouth shock, a low suppression ratio for animals receiving mouth shock indicates retrograde amnesia. MS-NECS mouth shock followed by no ECS, NMS-ECS no mouth shock followed by ECS, MS-CXS mouth shock followed by 3.0 mA frontal cortex stimulation, MS-ECS mouth shock followed by 50 mA of clip ECS. (Adapted from Zornetzer & McGauch, 1970)

applied through external clip electrodes. Furthermore, the duration of the PAD following the 3.0 mcoul of charge is longer than the PAD produced by 40 mcoul delivered to external clips (unpublished findings). Interestingly, however, it should be noted that the duration and severity of the behavioral tonic-clonic convulsion produced by clip-ECS was greater than that produced by frontal cortex stimulation. Taken together, these data suggest that the route of current flow through the central nervous system is quite different in the two stimulus situations. If one or more critical brain regions, whose normal functions are necessary for the incorporation of labile memory into long term memory, is differentially affected by the two types of stimulation then this could help explain why a relatively low level of current administered directly to frontal cortex is as potent a memory disrupting agent as much higher current delivered extracranially and more posterior.

Sufficient current levels reached these critical brain regions in the present study for complete amnesia to result in both stimulated groups. These data indicate, for the frontal cortex group at least, that 3.0 mcoul of charge is already at asymptote in terms of the hypothetical coulomb-amnesia relationship for the rat. This behavioral datum is in agreement with the electrophysiological data presented in Figure 2B showing the relationship between paroxysmal spike frequency in the PAD and current intensity. These data further suggest that the threshold for susceptibility of labile memory, to disruption produced by current applied to frontal cortex, lies somewhere along the rising portion of the sigmoidal curve shown in Figure 2B.

In recent behavioral studies using mice (Dorfman & Jarvik, 1968) and chicks (Lee-Teng, 1969) it has been reported that there is a threshold level of current, below which no RA for an inhibitory avoidance response is produced. As the current intensity is increased above this threshold the amount of memory disruption also increases in a graded manner until a plateau is reached. Additional increases in current intensity above this level do not produce additional memory disruption. These behavioral data correspond closely with the relationship found in the present study between paroxysmal spike frequency in the PAD and current intensity.

Finally, the presence of spontaneous SADs at the higher levels of current intensity, i.e., around 3.0 mA, leads to the speculation that these SADs may serve to reinforce, or act as a "booster" for, the initial memory disruption associated with the PAD. If one reasons that the PAD, when elicited by lower levels of current, does not completely disrupt the incorporation of labile memory into long term memory, then it may be the case that a residual memory trace can develop and even be restored over an extended period (Pagano et al., 1969; Zinken & Miller, 1967). However, if the initial disrupting treatment is of sufficient intensity to result in both a PAD and a SAD, then additional and probably complete amnesia can be obtained. The behavioral data of Pagano et al. support this speculation.

Experiment 2. In the previous experiment an electrophysiological relationship was reported between the intensity of frontal cortex stimulation and the mean frequency of cortical paroxysmal events. The shape of this relationship was very similar to the behavioral relationship between ECS current intensity and the magnitude of RA (Dorfman & Jarvik, 1968; Lee-Teng, 1969; Miller, 1968; Zornetzer & McGaugh, 1971a, 1971b). In addition, the data from Experiment 1 also indicated that 3.0 mA applied to frontal cortex of rats represented a point both at the beginning of the asymptote of the maximal ECoG response of spike frequency and maximal RA in an inhibitory avoidance task.

The present experiment was designed to examine in more detail the relationship between memory disruption, current intensity to frontal cortex, and electrophysiological changes.

Rats of the same strain and sex as used in Experiment 1 were used. All rats were implanted with cortical screw electrodes as described above. Following surgery animals were returned to their home cages and maintained on food and water ad lib for 2 weeks. Following this 2-week period of postoperative recovery, a series of frontal cortex stimulation trials was administered to each animal.

The purpose of these trials was to determine the PAD and SAD threshold for each animal. Animals received frontal cortex stimulation only once during any given test session. Test sessions were 48 hr apart. The method of testing for seizure threshold was the same as described earlier. In no case did any animal receive more than 10 stimulation trails over a 3-week test period.

The training apparatus and training procedures were the same as described in Experiment 1 above. On Day 15 animals were divided into five groups. Animals in each group received a single pulse of mouth shock (MS) following the 10th lever press. Immediately following MS, animals in four of the groups received electrical stimulation of frontal cortex. Groups received either 1.5 mA, 2.5 mA, 3.5 mA, or 6.0 mA of brain stimulation. Group 5 was an implanted control group, and animals in this group received no cortical stimulation following MS. ECoG data was recorded from all experimental animals throughout the experimental session on Day 15. Following the treatment on Day 15 animals were returned to their home cages. Retention testing for the MS experience was carried out 24 hr later, i.e., Day 16.

As in Experiment 1, amnesia was evaluated on Day 16 by two measures, the latency to make the first bar press and the total latency to complete 100 presses once the first press had been made. Two suppression ratios, one for each of these behavioral measures, were determined for each animal. A positive ratio indicates a latency increase (memory for the MS event) and a zero ratio indicates no change between pre-mouth shock and post-mouth shock behavior.

Figure 4 shows the median group suppression ratios for both behavioral measures for all groups. An analysis of the suppression ratios indicated that Groups 2.5 mA, 3.5 mA, and 6.0 mA had significantly lower suppression ratios than did control animals ($p = 0.001$ in each case, Mann-Whitney U test, two tailed). All animals in each of these groups developed either PADs or PADs followed by SADs in response to frontal stimulation. Animals in Groups 1.5 mA received the threshold level of current for eliciting brain seizures from frontal cortex. Consequently, 40% ($N = 4$) of these animals failed to develop a PAD following frontal cortex stimulation. Based upon this distinction among the animals in Group 1.5 mA, the group was further divided into two subgroups: Group 1.5 mA-PAD and Group 1.5 mA-NoPAD. It is important to note that animals in both groups received the same amount of current to frontal cortex; only the brain's response to the stimulation was different. An analysis of the suppression ratios for these two subgroups indicated that animals in Group 1.5 mA-PAD had significantly lower suppression ratios than control animals ($p < 0.001$) and animals in Group 1.5 mA-NoPAD ($p < 0.001$). There were no significant differences between any of the animals that developed brain seizures following cortical stimulation, regardless of current intensity to frontal cortex. Bar press performance for these animals on Day 16 was indistinguishable from pre-MS performance.

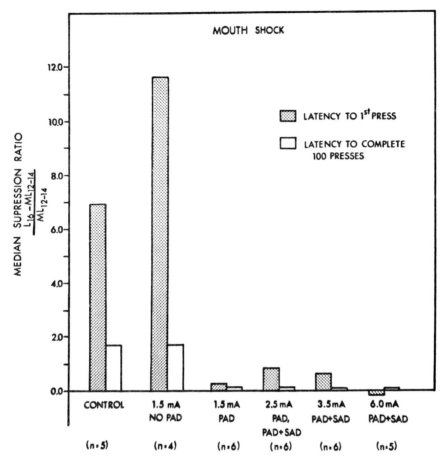

FIG. 4. Median group suppression ratio following mouth shock (MS) for both the latency to make the first bar press on Day 16 and the latency to complete 100 presses once the first press was made. (From Zornetzer & McGaugh, 1972)

These data suggest that the mere presence of a brain seizure was sufficient to produce complete amnesia. There was no graded effect of stimulus intensity and RA. These data are not in agreement with the findings of a number of studies which have reported a graded relationship between ECS current intensity and the magnitude of RA. What could account for this apparent discrepancy?

Further analysis of the data indicates that animals in Groups 1.5 mA-NoPAD had significantly *higher* suppression ratios (for latency to just press only) than did control animals ($p < 0.01$). This high initial suppression ratio indicated either that subseizure threshold frontal cortex stimulation facilitated memory for the MS experience, or that such stimulation is in itself noxious, and combined with the immediately preceding aversive MS experience to increase the total noxious quality of the entire experience. Either possibility would produce a higher latency on Day 16. Observation of 1.5 mA-NoPAD animals following brain stimulation suggested that subseizure stimulation was noxious. If we assume that subseizure threshold stimulation increased the total aversiveness of the learning experience, then we can conclude the noxious properties of the single-pulse mouth shock itself were not maximally effective in producing inhibition of bar pressing as indicated on Day 16. An alternative way of stating this, perhaps, is that the motivational intensity of the learning experience, i.e., mouth shock, was low in this experiment. Since all animals developing brain seizures, regardless of stimulation intensity, were amnesic, it appears that under conditions of low motivational intensity learning, labile memory is maximally susceptible to disruption.

There was no significant difference in suppression ratios for the latency to complete 100 presses between animals in Group 1.5 mA-NoPAD and control animals ($p > 0.30$). These data suggest that the fear of the prior MS experience extinguished rapidly on Day 16 once the initial bar presses were made. The suppression ratio for the latency to complete 100 presses is apparently not as sensitive a measure of memory as is the suppression ratio for latency to make the first bar press.

Experiment 3. The results of Experiment 2 suggest that labile information in brain, recently acquired under conditions of low motivational intensity, is highly susceptible to disruption by such insults as frontal cortex stimulation. It was shown that under such conditions, any level of frontal cortex stimulation leading to sufficient change in normal neuronal activity (i.e., afterdischarge activity) resulted in complete amnesia. Can the susceptibility of labile information to disruption be lowered by increasing the motivational intensity of the learning experience? Experiment 3 was designed to test this hypothesis.

The animals were the same as those used in Experiment 2. Following the end of Experiment 2 all animals remained in their home cages for 2 weeks. Throughout this period animals were maintained at 80% of their original weight by means of a water deprivation schedule. Retraining began for each animal at the end of this 2-week period. Training continued for 8 days, at which time the same stable level of performance was achieved as obtained in Experiment 2. On Day 9 all animals received 2.0 mA of footshock (FS) for 1.0 sec in the apparatus immediately following the 10th lever press. Frontal cortex stimulation was delivered upon termination of the FS. Animals were randomly assigned to five groups, with the only restriction being that animals from Experiment 2, not made amnesic for the mouth shock, were equally distributed among the five groups. Control animals received FS followed by no cortical stimulation. Experimental groups received either 1.5 mA, 2.5 mA, 3.5 mA or 6.0 mA to frontal cortex following FS. ECoG recordings were made following the delivery of frontal stimulation.

Retention testing for the FS experience occurred on Day 10. The suppression ratio for each animal was calculated as described earlier. Only the suppression ratio for the latency to make the first press was calculated. The suppression ratio for the latency to complete 100 presses was not calculated, since the data of Experiment 2, above, indicated that this measure was not as sensitive a measure of retention as the suppression ratio for the first bar press latency.

Figure 5 shows the results of Experiment 3. The median suppression ratio of control animals was very high, indicating that motivational intensity associated with the learning experience was much greater than when a brief pulse of MS was delivered (Experiment 2). The experimental groups were divided into subgroups based upon each animal's brain response to frontal stimulation. Thus, animals in Group 1.5 mA were subdivided into two groups on the basis of the presence (1.5 mA PAD) or absence (1.5 mA NoPAD) of afterdischarge activity following frontal cortex stimulation. Similarly, animals in Group 2.5 mA were subdivided into two groups, based on the development of a PAD only (2.5 mA PAD) or a PAD followed by a SAD in response to the stimulation (2.5 mA PAD + SAD). All animals in Group 3.5 mA and Group 6.0 mA developed both a PAD and a SAD in response to frontal cortex stimulation.

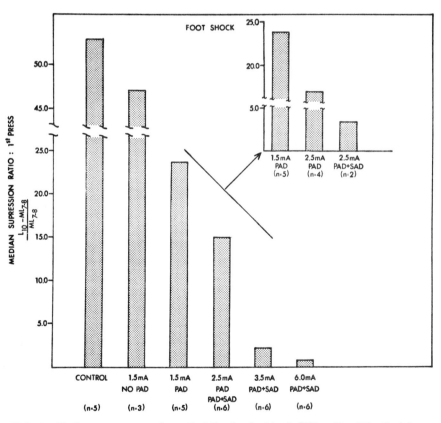

FIG. 5.   Median group suppression ratio following footshock (FS) on Day 9 for the latency to make the first bar press on Day 10. (From Zornetzer & McGaugh, 1972)

Rats in Group 1.5 mA-NoPAD did not differ significantly from control animals ($p > 0.10$), while rats in Group 1.5 mA PAD had significantly lower suppression ratios than controls ($p < 0.05$). Similarly, animals in Groups 2.5 mA PAD, 3.5 mA, and 6.0 mA had significantly lower suppression ratios than control animals ($p < .01$, all cases).

Unlike the data of Experiment 2, these data indicated that amnesia increased as current intensity increased. Maximum amnesia occurred in this experiment with 3.5 mA, since 3.5 mA and 6.0 mA produced levels of amnesia that were not significantly different. Each of these groups, however, had significantly lower suppression ratios than animals in either Group 2.5 mA PAD ($p < 0.05$) or animals in Group 1.5 mA PAD ($p < 0.01$). Similarly, animals in Group 2.5 mA PAD had significantly lower suppression ratios than animals in Group 1.5 mA-PAD ($p < 0.05$). Interestingly, animals in Group 2.5 mA PAD + SAD had very similar suppression ratios to animals in Group 3.5 mA and Group 6.0 mA. This finding suggests two things: First, the SAD does contribute to the memory disruption associated with the PAD only; and second, current intensity per se may not be the important determinant of memory disruption, but rather the brain's response to the current determines the magnitude, if any, of amnesia.

The results of Experiments 2 and 3 indicate that factors other than current intensity per se, and the response of the brain to current administration, can dramatically influence the susceptibility of labile memory to disruption. Our own earlier work (Zornetzer & McGaugh, 1970) as well as a number of other studies (Alpern & McGaugh, 1968; Dorfman & Jarvik, 1968; McGaugh & Zornetzer, 1970; Ray & Barrett, 1969; Lee-Teng, 1969; Zornetzer & McGaugh, 1971a, 1971b) reported that electroshock-produced memory disruption was directly related to current intensity and/or duration. These data provided a basis upon which to formulate the hypothesis that a similar gradient of memory disruption could be obtained when stimulation was delivered directly to frontal cortex. The findings of the present studies suggest that this hypothesis failed to consider the role of additional determinants of memory susceptibility to disruption. The magnitude of disruption resulting from a given level of frontal cortex stimulation is a complicated function of both the brain's response to the stimulating current as well as the motivational properties of the learning experience. Earlier work provided evidence that the motivational properties of an aversive experience (Ray & Bivens, 1968), or an appetitive experience (Peeke, McCoy, & Herz, 1969) was an important factor in determining the ECS-produced RA gradient. The susceptibility of labile memory to experimental modification is thus partially determined by the intensity of the stimulus events in the environment which comprise the learning experience. Whether this implies that different, or simply more, neural elements participate in the memory encoding process is not known. Nevertheless, the efficacy of a given level of brain stimulation in disrupting a labile memory is not a constant.

The results of Experiment 3 also indicated that the memory disruption produced by cortical stimulation resulting only in a PAD was not complete. As current intensity increased or as the brain's response to the current increased, the magnitude of amnesia increased. Maximal amnesia resulted when frontal cortex stimulation produced both a primary and a secondary afterdischarge in brain. No additional amnesia resulted when current intensity increased above the level required to produce these brain responses. These data support the idea that electrophysiological events occurring after the termination of the PAD contribute to memory disruption produced by the PAD. These post-PAD events, however, contribute to the amnesia only when the susceptibility of the labile memory to disruption is low. Thus, in Experiment 2, where susceptibility of labile memory to disruption was high due to a low motivational intensity learning experience, the development of post-PAD electrophysiological events did not contribute to the magnitude of amnesia.

The two most prominent post-PAD events are postictal depression and the SAD. McIntyre (1970) has suggested that postictal depression interfered with CER acquisition. McGaugh and Zornetzer (1970) on the other thand, found that postical depression could be dissociated from RA in mice. Lee-Teng and Giaquinto (1969) reached a similar conclusion from work with the chick. The present data do not indicate which of these post-PAD events might contribute to additional memory disruption. Postictal depression usually followed the elicitation of a PAD, but wasn't necessarily followed by a SAD. In those animals where SADs did develop during the postictal depression period, greater amnesia resulted. These findings suggest that the occurrence of the SAD was the important brain response associated with the additional amnesia.

Thus it appears that a number of factors can influence the degree to which labile information in the central nervous system is susceptible to experimental manipulation. Furthermore, it seems likely that these multiple factors covary in complex ways. Regardless of the influence of these factors, the basic question of whether or not there is neuroanatomical specificity underlying memory disruptive systems in brain remains unanswered.

Experiment 4. In recent years a number of studies have investigated the effects of more localized electrical stimulation of the brain (Glickman, 1961; Goddard, 1964; Gold, Farrell, & King, 1971; Kesner & Doty, 1968; Mahut, 1962, 1964; McIntyre, 1970; Wyers, Peeke, Williston, & Herz, 1968). Generally, these studies attempted to determine whether there is regional or structural specificity associated with the production of experimental amnesia. One assumption of these studies, though not explicitly stated, is that the identification of those brain regions participating in the disruption of memory should provide useful information for understanding neural systems involved in memory storage per se.

Electrical stimulation of anterior cortex in the rat produces retrograde amnesia for an aversive experience (Zornetzer & McGaugh, 1970, 1972). Gold et al. (1971) recently reported that stimulation of anterior cortex in rats produces more severe amnesia than stimulation in more posterior regions. These data suggest that various brain regions are not equipotential in terms of their participation in the disruption of memory. An additional finding of these studies is that the minimal disturbance of normal brain function sufficient to produce RA via cortical stimulation is the elicitation of a self-sustained primary afterdischarge (PAD). Once elicited from a defined locus in the brain, the PAD spreads rapidly to many brain regions. This widespread involvement of multiple brain regions in afterdischarge activity has precluded, as yet, precise anatomical localization of brain systems mediating the amnesic effect.

Experiment 4 was designed to determine the fiber connections of the region of anterior cortex previously shown to result in RA when stimulated with sufficient current. If anterior cortex in the rat represents one portion of a more extensive neuroanatomical system related to the disruption and/or storage of labile information, then will electrical stimulation of other regions within such a system also result in memory disruption? Further, is it necessary to produce an afterdischarge within this to-be-uncovered neural system in order to disrupt memory?

In order to answer these questions, animals used in Experiment 3 received electrolytic lesions of anterior cortex via the chronically indwelling stainless steel electrodes. Twelve animals received bilateral lesions; six animals received unilateral lesions. Four animals served as controls and received no cortical lesions.

Postlesion survival time varied from 6-14 days. Animals were killed with an overdoes of Nembutal and perfused transcardially with saline followed by 10% formalin. Brains were frozen on a freezing microtome and sectioned at 40 μ. Alternate sections were serially ordered and stained with cresyl violet. The Nauta-Gygax (1954) method for silver impregnation of degenerating axons was used to determine the fiber connections of anterior cortex. In addition, some brains were stained according to the method of Fink-Heimer (1967) to determine the synaptic terminals of the degenerating axons. Figure 6 shows the location of the frontal cortex lesions.

Degenerating fibers descended from the area of the lesion and entered the body of the corpus callosum, below and slightly posterior to the lesion site. The fibers coursed medially and entered the ipsilateral caudate nucleus filling the fascicles of the caudate (Figure 7). Degenerating axons passing through the caudate rarely separated from these fascicles. These degenerating fibers then collected in the internal capsule, where massive fiber degeneration was found. Degenerating axons continued in a caudal direction via the cerebral peduncle to the pons, apparently terminating in the spinal cord.

A substantial projection of fibers originating in the cerebral peduncle collateralized and ascended from the peduncle into the midbrain at the level of the rostralmost portion of the substantia nigra. These collaterals from the cerebral peduncle, described by Cajal (1966) as the bundle of Forel and by Knook (1965), left the peduncle at right angles to the main stream of descending fibers and projected dorsomedially (see Figure 7). Some of these ascending collaterals were seen terminating in the midbrain, just dorsal to the nigra. Many

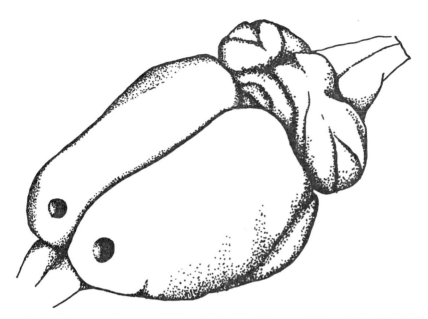

FIG. 6. Diagrammatic representation of the stimulation and lesion site in frontal
cortex of the rat brain. (From Zornetzer, 1972)

fibers from the bundle of Forel appeared to terminate in the ventral tegmental
area just medial to the nigra. As degenerating fibers ascended into the midbrain
they fanned out and became diffuse. Some fibers were seen terminating in the
area just rostral to the nucleus ruber. In animals with unilateral lesions only
ipsilateral degeneration was seen in the path described above.

The results of this experiment indicate that the area of tissue in contact with
the stimulating electrodes overlying frontal cortex was in part, at least, motor
cortex in the rat. Webster (1961) reported similar degenerative changes following
anterior cortical lesions in rats. Thus, these findings suggest that the experimental retrograde amnesia reported in Experiments 2 and 3 above, was obtained
largely from stimulation of motor cortex with consequent spread of afterdischarge activty. No a priori reason exists to assume that memory disruption
cannot be mediated by motor systems. A more conventional view, however,
would hold that complex associational systems in brain would be more likely
involved in the disruption of memory. If this view is correct, then an intriguing
possibility arises when we consider the degenerating axon collaterals comprising
the bundle of Forel and ascending into the ventral tegmental midbrain after
leaving the cerebral peduncle. These collaterals appear to terminate in the region
of the substantia nigra, nucleus ruber, and ventral tegmental area of Tsai. This
entire region, often referred to as the limbic midbrain region (Nauta, 1958), has
extensive interconnections with limbic forebrain structures and mesencephalic
reticular formation (Nauta & Whitlock, 1954). On an a priori basis, then, this

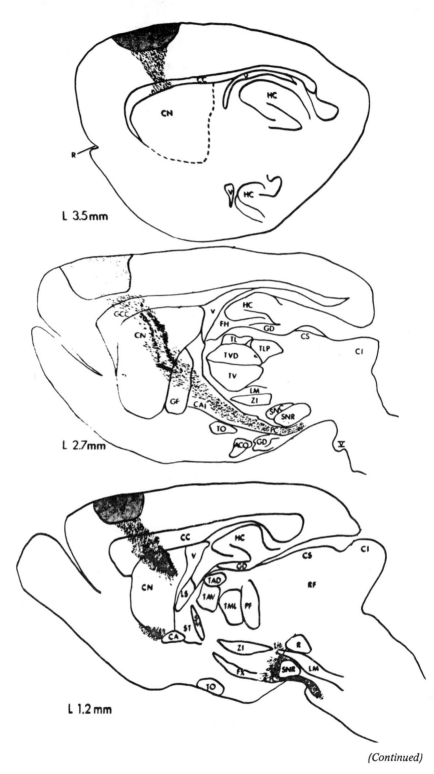

L 3.5mm

L 2.7mm

L 1.2 mm

(Continued)

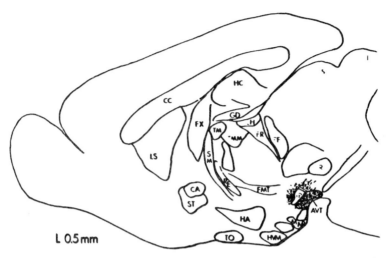

FIG. 7. Schematic representation of sagittal sections through the lesion site in frontal cortex. Stippled areas indicate pathway of major degeneration. Abbreviations: ACO: Nucleus amygdaloideus corticalis; AVT: Area ventralis tegmenti (TSAI); CA: Commissura anterior; CAI: Capsula interna; CC: Crus cerebri; CI: Colliculus inferior; CN: Nucleus caudatus; CS: Colliculus superior; FH: Fimbria hippocampi; FR: Fasciculus retroflexus; FX: Fornix; GCC: Genu Corporis callosi; GD: Gryus dentatus; GP: Globus pallidus; HA: Anterior hypothalamus; HC: Hippocampus; HVM: Nucleus ventromedialis hypothalami; I: Nucleus interstitialis; IP: Nucleus interpeduncularis; LH: Nucleus lateralis habenulae; LM: Lemniscus medialis; LS: Nucleus septi lateralis; MN: Nucleus mammaliaris; PC: Cerebral peduncle; PF: Nucleus parafascicularis; R: Nucleus ruber; RE: Nucleus reuniens; RF: Reticular formation; SM: Stria medularis; SNC: Substantia nigra, zona compacta; SNR: Substantia nigra, zona reticulata; ST: Stria terminalis; TAD: Nucleus anterior dorsalis thalami; TAV: Nucleus anterior ventralis thalami; TL: Nucleus lateralis thalami; TLP: Nucleus lateralis thalami, pars posterior; TM: Nucleus medialis thalami; TML: Nucleus medialis thalami, pars lateralis; TMM: Nucleus medialis thalami, pars medialis; TO: Tractus opticus; TV: Nucleus ventralis thalami; TVD: Nucleus ventralis thalami, pars dorsalis; V: Ventriculus lateralis; ZI: Zona incerta. (From Zornetzer, 1972)

region would seem ideally situated to play a hypothetical role in affecting complex associational systems related to memory storage processes. Furthermore, this region of midbrain, so intimately connected with both forebrain and brainstem structures, receives a direct projection from the region of frontal cortex shown to result in RA when stimulated. Experiment 5 examined the effect of stimulating this midbrain region upon RA.

Experiment 5. There is no evidence to suggest that the ventral tegmental region of the midbrain is in any way involved in a memory disruption system within brain. The question still remains, however, can direct stimulation of a region of brain, known to be anatomically connected with a known amnesia-producing site, elicit similar amnesic effects?

Thirty rats of the same strain, age, and sex as used in previous experiments were used. Bilateral bipolar twisted wire electrodes were implanted in the ventral tegmental region of the midbrain. In addition, four stainless steel screw electrodes were implanted over anterior and posterior cortex. Following surgery animals were returned to their home cages for 2 weeks of postoperative recovery.

Following the recovery period each animal received a series of brain stimulation trials during which the brain seizure threshold was determined following bilateral stimulation of the midbrain. The procedure for seizure threshold determination was similar to that described in Experiment 1 for cortical afterdischarge activity.

Following threshold determinations, animals were placed on a water deprivation schedule. All rats were gradually reduced to 80% of their original weight and were maintained at that level for the duration of the experiment.

The training apparatus was the same as described in Experiment 2. All animals reached a rapid and stable level of performance by Day 13. On Day 14 animals were divided into four groups. All animals received a brief pulse of mouth shock (MS) following the 10th lever press. Immediately following MS rats in Group MS-Stim received sham brain stimulation, were removed from the apparatus and returned to their home cages. These animals served as implanted controls. Three groups of rats received bilateral midbrain stimulation (60 Hz, 1.0-sec duration). Animals in Group MS-LStim (low stimulation) received a level of brain stimulation previously determined to be below the threshold for the elicitation of a cortical primary afterdischarge (PAD). Animals in Group MS-IStim (intermediate stimulation) received a level of midbrain stimulation sufficient to produce an afterdischarge which spread to both frontal and posterior cortical recording electrodes (PAD). Finally, animals in Group MS-HStim (high stimulation) received a level of midbrain stimulation higher than cortical PAD threshold. Animals were selected for these groups based upon their individual electrophysiological response to midbrain stimulation during the threshold testing period. With careful matching of the animals it was possible to establish the three experimental groups so that the median current intensity delivered to Group MS-LStim, Group MS-IStim, and Group MS-HStim, was 2.3 mA, 2.2 mA, and 2.7 mA respectively. Following stimulation and a brief period of time sufficient to record EEG activity, each animal was removed from the apparatus and returned to its home cage.

On Day 15, 24 hr after training and treatment, animals were returned to the apparatus for retention testing. A suppression ratio indicated the amount of behavioral inhibition produced by the treatment on Day 14 as measured on Day 15.

For most animals the following data were obtained after stimulation: a current level sufficient to produce a local midbrain afterdischarge (MAD) with no detectable seizure spread to the cortex; a current level sufficient to produce both a MAD and a cortical PAD; a current level sufficient to produce a MAD followed by both a cortical PAD and spontaneous SAD. Figure 8 shows typical examples of each of these conditions.

Behavioral observations indicated that MADs usually resulted in forelimb and hindlimb clonus. Spread of afterdischarge to the cortex was often associated with forelimb tonic convulsions followed by whole-body clonus. PADs followed by SADs always resulted in forelimb tonic convulsion and occasionally whole body tonic extension followed by clonus. There was rarely any behavioral indication that SAD was occurring.

Figure 9 shows the median suppression ratio for latency to the first bar press for all groups. An analysis of the suppression ratios indicated that MS was an effective treatment in producing bar press inhibition in nonstimulated implanted control animals (Group MS-NStim). Bilateral bipolar midbrain stimulation, producing only a localized MAD, did not result in memory disruption; i.e., there was no significant difference between Group MS-LStim and Group MS-NStim ($p > 0.30$). Similarly midbrain stimulation producing a MAD coupled with a

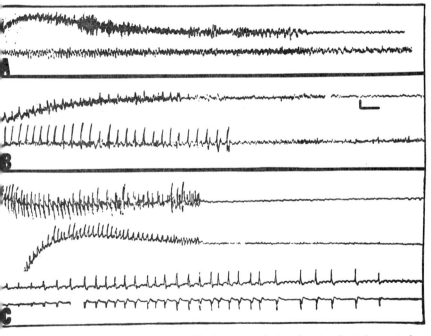

FIG. 8. EEG recorded from midbrain (bipolar electrodes) and cortex (anterior-posterior cortex) immediately following one of three levels of bilateral midbrain stimulation. (A) Midbrain stimulation resulting in a midbrain afterdischarge (MAD) but not cortical seizure activity. (B) Midbrain stimulation resulting in both an MAD and a cortical primary afterdischarge (PAD). (C) Midbrain stimulation resulting in an MAD, a PAD, and a spontaneous secondary afterdischarge (SAD). Calibrations: 100 μV and 1.0 sec. (From Zornetzer, 1972)

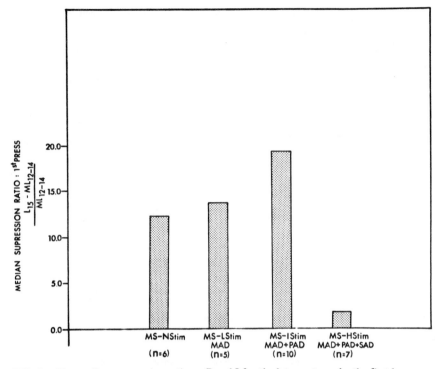

FIG. 9. The median suppression ratio on Day 15 for the latency to make the first bar press following mouth shock on Day 14. (From Zornetzer, 1972)

cortical PAD did not result in memory disruption; i.e., there was no significant difference between Group MS-IStim and Group MS-NStim ($p > 0.10$). Midbrain stimulation producing a MAD coupled with a cortically recorded PAD and followed by a spontaneous cortical and midbrain SAD resulted in significant memory disruption; i.e., animals in Group MS-HStim had significantly lower suppression ratios than animals in Group MS-NStim, Group MS-LStim, and Group MS-IStim ($p < 0.001$, all cases).

Table 1 shows the median raw score latencies to the first bar press for all groups, both prior to MS (Day 14) and following MS (Day 15).

Histological verification of electrode placements in all animals was made at the termination of the experiment. Figure 10 shows a photomicrograph through the electrode tracts and small electrolytic lesions made at the tip of each electrode for verification purposes.

The results of this experiment indicate that bilateral stimulation of the limbic midbrain region can result in amnesia for a single trial inhibitory avoidance response. Limbic midbrain-produced amnesia, measured 24 hr following stimulation, only occurred if the brain's response to stimulation included the development of both propagated primary and secondary afterdischarge activity. Elicitation of a local midbrain afterdischarge or a midbrain afterdischarge followed by a propagated cortical primary afterdischarge was not sufficient to result in retrograde amnesia.

In view of the earlier experiments described, these findings were quite unexpected. Experiments 2 and 3 suggested that cortical afterdischarge activity, elicited from frontal cortex, was at least a sufficient antecedent condition for the production of RA. Taken together, the data of these experiments and the present data suggest that the effects of electrical stimulation in an area of cortex containing cells projecting to limbic midbrain, has a different amnesia-producing effect than does electrical stimulation in the region of axonal termination of these same cells. These data further indicate that the mere alteration in normal cell function, vis à vis afterdischarge activity, is not always sufficient to cause amnesia. Both frontal cortex stimulation and sufficiently intense midbrain stimulation result in primary afterdischarge activity recorded on the cortex. Only the former, however, results in amnesia. It appears that there must be some other aspect of these two types of electrical stimulation which accounts for their differential effects upon memory storage processes.

One possible difference is the sequential ordering of induced malfunction in brain structures resulting from the spread of afterdischarge activity. For example, the sequential disturbance of normal cell function in cortex, caudate, and midbrain respectively, induced by frontal cortex-initiated afterdischarge activity, may have a very different effect upon the storage of labile information than a similar disturbance in normal cell function sequentially progressing through those same structures in the reverse order.

A second possible difference between seizure-producing stimulation of these two neuroanatomically related regions of brain is that either propagated or volume-conducted current spread from the stimulating electrodes differentially affects some other key structure or structures involved in memory storage. These possibilities are currently under investigation.

TABLE 1

Median Raw-score Latency (Sec)
to First Bar Press[a]

Group	Day 14 (Prior to mouth shock)	Day 15 (24 hr after mouth shock)
MS-NStim	31	396
MS-LStim	34	456
MS-IStim	14	411
MS-HStim	18	28

[a] From Zornetzer (1972).

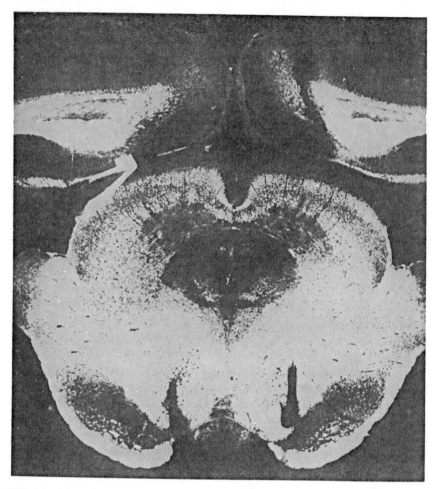

FIG. 10. Photomicrograph of bilateral electrode placements in the ventral tegmental area of the midbrain. (From Zornetzer, 1972)

The important amnesia-producing effects of the SAD were demonstrated in this experiment. These data support and extend earlier speculation (Experiment 3) that the SAD contributed to the amnesia associated with the PAD. Taken together these data suggest that the paroxysmal spiking activity, or some other abnormal physiological condition with PADs and/or SADs, appear more closely associated with the disruption of labile memory than the electrographic period of quiescence produced following a seizure discharge.

The SAD appears to have electrophysiological characteristics quite distinct from the PAD (i.e., monophasic recruitment in amplitude with a nearly constant frequency of 2.0 Hz). Since it appears to contribute in an independent way to the disruption of labile information, it seems likely that the SAD represents the firing of an independent seizure generator in brain capable of propagating to widespread regions. Further, this generator appears to be triggered only after sufficiently intense electrical stimulation causing maximum generating output of the PAD. The anatomical and/or physiological distinctness of the hypothetical seizure generator is unknown, although medial thalamic regions would be a likely candidate. The importance of the secondary afterdischarge to the clinical application of ECT cannot be discounted. Dr. Fink (personal communication) has reported some evidence that such secondary spontaneous epileptiform events may occur following ECT in patients.

Finally, experiments investigating brain structures involved in memory storage and memory disruption processes have generally approached the problem by looking for "hot spots," i.e., brain regions strongly implicated with some aspect of the memory process. Conceptually and experimentally, it is equally important to discover "cold spots" in brain as well. If no cold spots existed or, for example, if all regions of brain were equally capable of producing amnesia following electrical stimulation, then there would be little point in continuing the search for hot spots. We could then conclude that the brain was truly equipotential with regard to brain structure and memory systems. Experiment 5 identified what appears to be a cold spot, at least when the effects of stimulation in the midbrain region upon memory disruption are measured 24 hr after learning. Recently, Kesner and Conner (1972) reported that stimulation of the midbrain reticular formation produced retrograde amnesia for an aversive experience when tested shortly after the learning experience but not when tested 24 hr later. These data suggest that the hot spot-cold spot analysis of brain structure and memorial processes should be tempered with temporal considerations so as to include the possibility that brain structures may participate differentially in long and short term memory.

CONCLUSIONS

The data reported here hopefully provide a small glimpse of the complexities inherent in understanding the "hows" and "whys" of memory susceptibility to experimental modification. Perhaps more importantly, for the purpose of this discussion, the data I have described suggest that if the modification of memory storage processes, as a result of ECT, are in any way related to the clinical efficacy of ECT, than careful electroencephalographic analyses of brain changes following ECT should be studied. For example, if both the primary afterdischarge (PAD) and the spontaneous secondary afterdischarge (SAD) are involved independently in the disruption of labile memories, and if the SAD serves as a "booster" to the PAD in terms of the magnitude of this memory disruption, then one hypothesis that could be tested in the clinic is whether or not patients developing both PADs and SADs following ECT show greater or more rapid improvement than patients developing only PADs in response to ECT.

The hypothesis that the clinical effectiveness of ECT is in any way related to memory disruption per se, might be quite independent from the hypothesis that the clinical efficacy of ECT is related simply to the magnitude of brain seizure activity resulting from the application of large quantities of current to the brain. Systematic and quantitative analyses of electroencephalographic characteristics of afterdischarge activity following ECT would provide a straightforward test of such an electrophysiological hypothesis. Such analyses should include not only PAD activity but SAD activity as well.

Finally, while the psychobiological basis of ECT is still not completely understood, complimentary research in both the basic and clinical science spheres has been, and will continue to be, the most useful approach to understanding the complexities of ECT.

REFERENCES

Alpern, H. P., & McGaugh, J. L. Retrograde amnesia as a function of electroshock stimulation. *Journal of Comparative and Physiological Psychology*, 1968, 65, 265-269.

Cajal, S. R. *Studies on the diencephalon.* Springfield, Ill.: Charles C Thomas, 1966.

Cherkin, A. Kinetics of memory consolidation: role of amnesic treatment parameters. *Proceedings of the National Academy of Sciences of the United States of America*, 1969, 63, 1094-1101.

Dorfman, L. F., & Jarvik, M. E. A parametric study of electroshock-induced retrograde amnesia in mice. *Neuropsychologia*, 1968, 6, 373-380.

Fink, R. P., & Heimer, L. Two methods for selective silver impregnation of degenerating axons and their synaptic endings in the central nervous system. *Brain Research*, 1967, 4, 369-374.

Geller, A., & Jarvik, M. E. The time relations of ECS-induced amnesia. *Psychonomic Science*, 1968, 10, 15-16.

Glickman, S. E. Perseverative neural processes and consolidation of the memory trace. *Psychological Bulletin*, 1961, 58, 218-233.

Goddard, G. V. Amygdaloid stimulation and learning in the rat. *Journal of Comparative and Physiological Psychology*, 1964, 58, 23-30.

Gold, P. E., Farrell, W., & King, R. A. Retrograde amnesia after localized brain shock in passive avoidance learning. *Physiology and Behavior*, 1971, 7, 709-712.

Herz, M. J., & Peeke, H. V. S. Impairment of extinction with caudate nucleus stimulation. *Brain Research*, 1971, 33, 519-522.

Kesner, R. P., & Conner, H. S. Independence of short and long-term memory: A neural system analysis. *Science*, 1972, 176, 432-434.

Kesner, R. P., & Doty, R. W. Amnesia produced in cats by local seizure activity initiated from the amygdala. *Experimental Neurology*, 1968, 21, 58-68.

Knook, H. L. *The fibre-connections of the forebrain.* Philadelphia: F. A. Davis, 1965.

Lee-Teng, E. Retrograde amnesia in relation to subconvulsive and convulsive currents in chicks. *Journal of Comparative and Physiological Psychology*, 1969, 67, 135-139.

Lee-Teng, E., & Giaquinto, D. Electrocorticograms following threshold transcranial electroshock for retrograde amnesia in chicks. *Experimental Neurology*, 1969, 23, 485-490.

Lidsky, T. I., Levine, M. S., Kreinick, C. J., & Schwartzbaum, J. S. Retrograde effects of amygdaloid stimulation on conditioned suppression (CER) in rats. *Journal of Comparative and Physiological Psychology*, 1970, 73, 135-149.

Mahut, H. Effects of subcortical electrical stimulation on learning in the rat. *Journal of Comparative and Physiological Psychology,* 1962, 55, 472-477.

Mahut, H. Effects of subcortical electrical stimulation on discrimination learning in cats. *Journal of Comparative and Physiological Psychology,* 1964, 58, 390-395.

McDonough, J. H. Jr., & Kesner, R. P. Amnesia produced by brief electrical stimulation of amygdala or dorsal hippocampus in cats. *Journal of Comparative and Physiological Psychology,* 1971, 77, 171-178.

McGaugh, J. L., & Herz, M. J. *Memory consolidation.* San Francisco: Albion, 1972.

McGaugh, J. L., & Landfield, P. W. Delayed development of amnesia following electroconvulsive shock. *Physiology and Behavior,* 1970, 5, 1109-1113.

McGaugh, J. L., & Zornetzer, S. F. Amnesia and brain seizure activity in mice: Effects of diethyl ether anesthesia prior to electroshock stimulation. *Communications in Behavioral Biology,* 1970, 5, 243-248.

McIntyre, D.C. Differential amnestic effect of cortical vs. amygdaloid elicited convulsions in rats. *Physiology and Behavior,* 1970, 5, 747-753.

Miller, A. J. Variations in retrograde amnesia with parameters of ECS and time of testing. *Journal of Comparative and Physiological Psychology,* 1968, 66, 40-47.

Nauta, W. J. H. Hippocampal projections and related neural pathways to the midbrain in the cat. *Brain,* 1958, 81, 319-340.

Nauta, W. J. H., & Gygax, P. A. Silver impregnation of degenerating axons in the central nervous system. *Stain Technology,* 1954, 29, 91.

Nauta, W. J. H., & Whitlock, D. G. An anatomical analysis of the nonspecific thalamic projection system. In Delafresnaye, J. F. (Ed.), *Brain Mechanisms and consciousness.* A symposium organized by the council for the International Organization of Medical Science, Oxford, 1954.

Pagano, R. R., Bush, D. F., Martin, G., & Hunt, E. B. Duration of retrograde amnesia as a function of electroconvulsive shock intensity. *Physiology and Behavior,* 1969, 4, 19-21.

Peeke, H. V. S., & Herz, M. J. Caudate nucleus stimulation retroactively impairs complex maze learning in the rat. *Science,* 1971, 173, 80-82.

Peeke, H. V. S., McCoy, F., & Herz, M. J. Drive consummatory response effects on memory consolidation for appetitive learning in mice. *Communications in Behavioral Biology,* 1969, 4 (Pt. A), 49-53.

Ray, O. S., & Barrett, R. J. Disruptive effects of electroconvulsive shock as a function of current level and mode of delivery. *Journal of Comparative and Physiological Psychology,* 1969, 67, 110-116.

Ray, O. S., & Bivens, L. W. Reinforcement magnitude as a determinant of performance decrement after electro-convulsive shock. *Science,* 1968, 160, 330-332.

Vardaris, R. M., & Schwartz, K. E. Retrograde amnesia for passive avoidance produced by stimulation of dorsal hippocampus. *Physiology and Behavior,* 1971, 6, 131-135.

Webster, K. E. Cortico-striate interrelations in the albino rat. *Journal of Anatomy,* 1961, 95, 532-544.

Wilburn, M. W., & Kesner, R. P. Differential amnesic effects produced by electrical stimulation of the caudate nucleus and nonspecific thalamic system. *Experimental Neurology,* 1972, 34, 45-50.

Wyers, E. J., & Deadwyler, S. A. Duration and nature of retrograde amnesia produced by stimulation of caudate nucleus. *Physiology and Behavior,* 1971, 6, 97-103.

Wyers, E. J., Peeke, H. V. S., Williston, J. S., & Herz, M. J. Retroactive impairment of passive avoidance learning by stimulation of the caudate nucleus. *Experimental Neurology,* 1968, 22, 350-366.

Zinkin, S., & Miller, A. J. Recovery of memory after amnesia induced by electroconvulsive shock. *Science,* 1967, 155, 102-103.

Zornetzer, S. F. Brain stimulation and retrograde amnesia in rats: A neuroanatomical approach. *Physiology and Behavior,* 1972, 8, 239-244.

Zornetzer, S. F., & McGaugh, J. L. Effects of frontal brain electroshock stimulation on EEG activity and memory in rats: Relationship to ECS-produced retrograde amnesia. *Journal of Neurobiology*, 1970, 1, 379-395.

Zornetzer, S. F., & McGaugh, J. L. Retrograde amnesia and brain seizures in mice. *Physiology and Behavior*, 1971, 7, 401-408. (a)

Zornetzer, S. F., & McGaugh, J. L. Retrograde amnesia and brain seizures in mice: A further analysis. *Physiology and Behavior*, 1971, 7, 841-845. (b)

Zornetzer, S. F., & McGaugh, J. L. Electrophysiological correlates of frontal cortex-induced retrograde amnesia in rats. *Physiology and Behavior*, 1972, 8, 233-238.

10
EFFECTS OF FLUROTHYL
(INDOKLON) UPON MEMORY
IN THE CHICK

Arthur Cherkin[1]

Indoklon convulsive therapy (ICT) with flurothyl (Indoklon; $CF_3CH_2OCH_2CF_3$), a potent inhalant convulsant, was introduced as an alternative to electroconvulsive therapy (ECT) for the treatment of depression and schizophrenia (Krantz, Esquibel, Truitt, Ling, & Kurland, 1958). The remarkable antidepressive effects of ICT and ECT are comparable, as are memory disturbances, the most serious side-effect of ICT and ECT (Fink, Kahn, Karp, Pollack, Green, Alan, & Lefkowits, 1961; Laurell, 1970; Small & Small, 1972). Although some memory dysfunctions persist for months or years, most of the controlled psychometric studies of ICT and ECT patients have emphasized the dysfunctions observed during a relatively short period, of a few minutes to a few days, before and after convulsive treatment. The same is true of most laboratory studies of flurothyl and of electroconvulsive shock (ECS), including the experiments summarized in this report.

Flurothyl causes marked retrograde amnesia (RA) in the mouse (Alpern & Kimble, 1967; Bohdanecky, Kopp, & Jarvik, 1968) and the chick (Cherkin, 1969b, 1970a, 1970b, 1972). The strong, reproducible RA effect of flurothyl in mice and chicks contrasts with the weaker, more variable amnesic effects reported in man (Dolenz, 1965; Fink et al., 1961; Krantz et al., 1958; Laurell, 1970; Small & Small, 1972). The contrast could presumably reflect any of the numerous differences between clinical and laboratory convulsive treatments, including: species; age; use of anesthetics, muscle relaxants, and oxygen in the clinic but not in the laboratory; and dosage of flurothyl. The present report

[1]The author thanks Mayme Y. Bailey, Mary W. Garman, and Richard O. Meinecke for excellent technical assistance.

summarizes experiments that quantitate the dose-dependence, effect of a concurrent anesthetic, and other determinants of flurothyl-induced amnesias in the neonate chick.

The rationale for the experimental use of flurothyl vapor, in addition to its clinical relevance and its controllable amnesic potency, is its rapid uptake into all regions of the brain, a characteristic of volatile compounds of high lipid solubility and low water solubility. Thus, flurothyl obviates the uncertain pathways of current flow (Rush & Driscoll, 1968) and sites of action that complicate the effects of experimental electroshock applied through external electrodes. The rationale of the neonate chick for flurothly studies is a set of advantages, including: the economic feasibility of using large numbers of subjects to improve statistical reliability; the availability of a simple one-trial avoidance learning procedure, which utilizes a natural defensive response; the unusual resistance of the chick to the toxic effects of flurothyl (Cherkin, 1969a), which permits studies over high dose ranges; and the possibility of generalizing to Mammalia some of the flurothyl effects observed in Aves. Chicks inhaling high concentrations of flurothyl (0.85%-1.7%) show a pattern of convulsions (Herz, Spooner, & Cherkin, 1970) with features comparable to those seen in rodents receiving ECS (Chorover & DeLuca, 1969; Zornetzer & McGaugh, 1970) and in patients receiving ICT or ECT (Laurell, 1970), e.g., rapid onset of unconsciousness, tonic extension within 25 to 60 sec, clonic movements, postictal depression, behavioral lethargy, and recovery of consciousness within 30 min after removal of the flurothyl vapor.

According to Gerbrandt (personal communication 1971), the patterns of EEG activity in chicks receiving flurothyl (Herz et al., 1970) are also similar in temporal sequence to the patterns observed in mammals receiving cortical stimulation or ECS (Zornetzer & McGaugh, 1970) and in humans receiving ICT or ECT (Chatrian & Petersen, 1960; Laurell, 1970), e.g., primary seizure discharge of 10- to 20-sec duration, a postictal depression of variable duration (10 to 90 sec in most subjects), clonus-related recurrent seizure discharges, and prolonged delta wave activity (several minutes) eventually phasing into a preictal EEG pattern. The primary seizure discharge is very similar in duration in spite of wide variation in "dosage" of flurothyl or electrical current and type of animal, while the length of postictal depression, secondary seizure activity, and delta activity appear to vary widely as a function of the type of convulsant and dosage.

Flurothyl in high doses is sufficiently potent to impair memory of a prior learning experience given 24 hr earlier in the chick (Cherkin, 1969b) or 4 to 6 hr earlier in the mouse (Alpern & Kimble, 1967; Bohdanecky et al., 1968). Such prolonged RA effects are not observed in the chick with lower flurothyl doses nor do they ordinarily occur in man with the near-threshold doses used clinically (Laurell, 1970; Small & Small, 1972). The prolonged loss of old memories that occurs in some patients appears to reflect a different phenomenon.

METHODS AND MATERIALS

General procedure. The one-trial avoidance learning experiment has been described in detail (Cherkin, 1969b). It was based on the observation that chicks pecked an attractive target repeatedly, whenever it was presented. But once they pecked the target coated with a "distasteful" liquid, they ceased to peck and they then avoided the target on sight, at future presentations. We quantitated this peck suppression behavior for use as an index of memory retention.

Method for one-trial training. The chicks were 2-day-old White Leghorn cockerels weighing about 35 g, housed in individual quart cartons (8.5 cm diameter X 16.5 cm deep) in a controlled environment (32.5-34.5°C; 40%-46% RH; 194 lux illumination; 76 dB white noise background). The training target was a 3 x 5-mm microminiature lamp bulb, fixed to a 3.5 X 200-mm plastic handle. The distasteful liquid was pure methyl anthranilate (MeA), a known bird repellant. The lamp was dipped into the MeA, then presented to the chick for 10 sec. Two behavioral measures were used: (*a*) the peck latency, i.e., the time required for the first peck, and (*b*) the number of pecks. Control chicks were treated identically except that the target coating was distilled water (DW) instead of MeA. The MeA-trained groups had the same median latency of peck as the DW controls (0.8-1.9 sec) but they emitted fewer mean pecks (2 compared to 8). This reduced peck rate during the 10-sec training trial demonstrated the aversiveness of the stimulus liquid. The intensity of the avoidance training was reduced when desired, simply by using a dilute aqueous solution of MeA (Cherkin, 1971a), or absolute ethanol, as the stimulus liquid.

Method for testing retention. The 10-sec test for memory retention was identical with the training trial, except that the target was dry, i.e., not coated with any liquid. MeA-trained chicks typically showed a prolonged latency of peck (> 10 sec) and made few pecks whereas DW controls showed a short latency and made many pecks, as they did during training. Chicks trained on dilutions of MeA, e.g., 0.25% MeA in water, showed intermediate peck behavior. The retention test was "blind", i.e., the experimenter was unaware of the previous history of any chick.

Method for flurothyl treatment. The selected volume of liquid flurothyl was dispensed into each chick carton from a microliter syringe fitted with a repeating dispenser and the carton was closed. The vapor concentration (% *v/v*) under our conditions was calculated from the relationship:

$$C\left(\%\frac{v}{v}\right) = \frac{vd}{M.W.} \times V_m \times \frac{100}{V} = 20.32 \, v,$$

where v = volume of liquid flurothyl (ml); d = liquid density at 20°C (1.4146 g/ml); $M.W.$ = 182.07; V_m = mol volume at 33.5°C (25,163 ml); and V = free space of chick carton (962 ml). The flurothyl vaporized within 10 sec and induced tonic convulsions and opisthotonos with mean induction times of 25 to

59 sec, depending upon the flurothyl concentration. After a predetermined interval, the flurothyl vapor was sucked out and replaced by room air. The parameters manipulated were: the intervals between flurothyl treatment, training and testing; the concentration of flurothyl vapor; and the length of time the chicks were in the vapor. To determine the effect of an inhalant anesthetic, liquid methoxyflurane was dispensed into the cartons in the same way, alone or simultaneously with flurothyl. Observation of chick behavior during the vapor treatments was made through a transparent Plexiglas cover.

Method for determining effect of increased stress upon convulsions. The effect of behavioral "arousal" by an aversive stimulus upon susceptibility to convulsions at a near-threshold level of flurothyl treatment was studied in two groups. Group MeA ($N = 80$) pecked the MeA-coated lamp; 2 min later, 42 μl of liquid flurothyl was dispensed into each carton to form 0.85% v/v flurothyl in air. One minute later, the flurothyl vapor was replaced by room air. Group DW ($N = 80$) was a control group treated identically except that the training lamp was coated with distilled water. All chicks were under the stress of physical and visual isolation from other chicks; in addition, Group MeA chicks were subjected to the stressful gustatory effects of the aversive MeA in their beaks. Each chick was observed for convulsive movements at the end of the flurothyl treatment. Half of each group was tested for retention 6 hr after training and half was tested 72 hr after training.

Method for determining convulsant and lethal doses of flurothyl. The flurothyl procedure above was used in chicks and mice to compare the CD_{50} (convulsant dose, vapor concentration convulsing 50% of subjects within 10 min) and the LD_{50} (lethal dose, vapor concentration killing 50% of subjects within 24 hr). The CD_{50} and LD_{50} values were for a 10-min exposure to the flurothyl (Cherkin, 1969a).

Method for hypoxia and hyperoxia experiments. Cerebral hypoxia is a candidate common denominator for RA induced by various convulsive agents, as well as by cranial trauma, cerebral ischemia, and hypoxic hypoxia. We therefore studied the effect of inspired oxygen levels upon memory retention. Chicks were trained in room air, then immediately provided with a continuous flow (75 cc/min) of an oxygen-nitrogen mixture for the next 30 hr, to span the consolidation period (Cherkin, 1971b). The hypoxic oxygen levels were 50-80 torr (6.6%–10.5% O_2), the hyperoxic level was 742 torr (100% O_2), and the control level was that of normal air (O_2 at 159 torr; 20.9% O_2). After 30 hr, the carton lids were removed, the gas flow was stopped, and the chicks were allowed to breathe room air thereafter. The retention test occurred 18 hr after cessation of gas flow.

RESULTS

Results of training. Chicks strongly trained on 100% MeA retained the peck-suppression response well. Nine days after training, the longest interval tested (Cherkin, 1970b), 92.5% of MeA-trained chicks (N = 40) suppressed pecking for the full 10-sec test period, compared to 28.2% of DW controls (N = 39); the difference was highly significant (χ^2 = 31.6, $p < 0.0001$). In contrast, chicks weakly trained on 0.25% MeA lost their peck-suppression response within 24 hr (Cherkin, 1971a). The proportion of chicks that avoided pecking for 10 sec was termed the "avoidance score."

Results of flurothyl treatments (overall). We found that flurothyl did not have an all-or-none effect upon memory processing even in chicks that had full tonic convulsions. Rather, the effects upon our index of memory retention were critically dependent upon three major parameters: (*a*) flurothyl vapor concentration; (*b*) duration of exposure to the vapor; and (*c*) temporal relations among training, flurothyl treatment, and testing. Under appropriate conditions, flurothyl could exert an amnesic, a neutral, or an enhancing effect upon retention of a training trial.

Results of flurothyl treatment (anterograde). After exposure to a strong treatment (with 1.7% flurothyl for 8 min) chicks were behaviorally depressed for 2 hr (Cherkin, 1970b). During the first 0.5 hr they were comatose. One hour after treatment they were lethargic and oriented poorly to the peck target. Two hours after treatment they could be MeA trained but they showed slightly impaired 24-hr retention, compared to chicks trained 48 hr after flurothyl treatment (χ^2 = 8.3, $p < 0.01$). No significant impairment was observed in chicks trained 4 or 24 hr after treatment, compared to the 48-hr group. Thus, the proactive impairment of motor performance by flurothyl persisted for 2 hr and confounded effects upon acquisition with effects upon sensory or motor systems.

A similar proactive deficit was observed when the strong flurothyl treatment was applied 4 min after training and retrieval was tested 1 or 2 hr later; the deficit was observed in both the DW-control group and in the MeA-trained group. Again, the deficit was not observed when the interval between treatment and testing was 4, 24, or 48 hr. Similar proactive performance deficits have been reported in mice tested within 4 hr after ECS (Ray & Barrett, 1969).

Results of flurothyl treatment (retrograde amnesia). Chicks that suppressed their peck response displayed retention of their MeA training. An effective amnesic treatment should reverse the learned suppression, i.e., it should restore normal pecking. Thus, a measure of amnesic effectiveness was the "induced peck score" (Cherkin, 1969b), which normalized the proportion of MeA-trained, flurothyl-treated chicks that pecked during the retention test, to the proportion of MeA-trained, non-flurothyl-treated chicks that pecked during the retention test. For complete amnesia, the induced peck score would be 100%; for perfect retention the score would be zero.

The major determinant of retention was the time elapsing between training and flurothyl treatment (Figure 1; chick, 4, 8, 16 min). The longer the time interval, the more retention (less RA) was observed after a given flurothyl treatment; when the interval reached 48 hr, no RA was observed. When the flurothyl vapor was removed from the carton 1 min after opisthotonos, the extent of RA was markedly reduced (Figure 1; chick, 1 min). The lower effectiveness of flurothyl in the mouse (Figure 1; mouse, 0 min) may reflect the constraint on flurothyl exposure time because of lethality (Alpern & Kimble, 1967).

We found that in our experiment the RA effect could not be increased by increasing the flurothyl concentration above 1.7% or the exposure time above 8 min. All chicks exposed to 0.85% or 1.7% flurothyl for 1 min (plus 1 min to allow for uptake of flurothyl into the brain) underwent full tonic convulsion with opisthotonos. Under weaker flurothyl conditions, neither convulsions nor RA were observed. Convulsions per se, however, were insufficient to induce

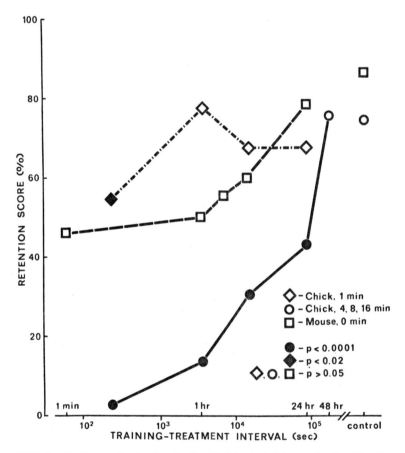

FIG. 1. Gradients of retention in flurothyl-treated chicks and mice. The RA effect in mice was statistically significant at the 0-, 1- and 4-hr intervals, when the median latency measure was used (Alpern & Kimble, 1967). These time intervals represent the times of exposure to flurothyl vapor after onset of tonic convulsions. Note that retention is the inverse of RA.

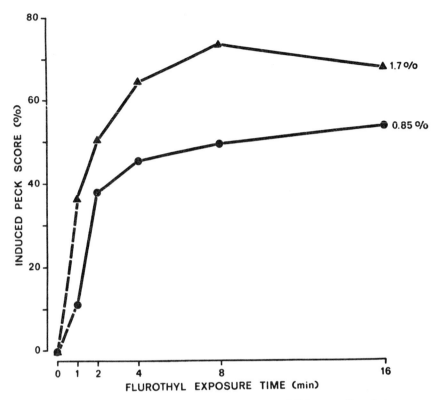

FIG. 2. Dependence of induced peck score, a measure of RA, upon flurothyl exposure time for pooled training-treatment intervals of 4-, 64-, 256- and 1440-min. Each point represents 160 chicks. (The maximum scores are below 80% because of the decreased RA effect at the longer intervals.)

amnesia. For example, exposure for 1 min to 0.85% or 1.7% flurothyl, starting 64 min after training, caused no amnesia (Cherkin, 1969b). Furthermore, the longer the convulsed chicks were exposed to flurothyl vapor, the more severe was their RA (Figure 2). Thus, full tonic convulsions per se were not a sufficient condition for RA and continued flurothyl exposure after the onset of convulsions exerted an increasing RA effect, for 8 min.

Results of flurothyl treatment (retrograde enhancement). Flurothyl at concentrations of 0.85%, 1.7% or 3.0% was strongly amnesic, whereas at 0.43% no RA was detected, even when the treatment was applied shortly after training. When we reduced the concentration to 0.2%, we observed an *enhancement* of peck suppression following training with ethanol, a weak aversant. Chicks ($N = 37$) trained on ethanol and exposed to 0.2% flurothyl for 8 min had an avoidance score of 54.0%, compared to a score of 17.9% for ethanol-trained controls ($N = 39$) not exposed to flurothyl; the difference was highly significant ($\chi^2 = 9.29, p < 0.003$). The same flurothyl treatment did not significantly raise the avoidance score of chicks trained on a stronger aversant, 10% MeA in ethanol (73.7% avoidance when treated, 67.5% when untreated; χ^2 = 0.08, $p > 0.7$); this was anticipated as a ceiling effect. The 0.2% flurothyl also had no effect on the avoidance score of DW controls (2.6% avoidance when treated; 2.6% when untreated).

Results of effect of increased stress upon convulsions. MeA training just before flurothyl treatment reduced the incidence of convulsions from 91.3% in DW controls to 67.5% in the chicks that experienced MeA training (χ^2 = 12.4, $p < 0.001$). The 72-hr avoidance score of MeA-trained chicks was 64.0% for the convulsed chicks ($N = 25$) and 73.0% for the nonconvulsed chicks ($N = 15$); this difference was not significant (χ^2 = 0.07, $p > 0.8$).

Results of combined flurothyl-methoxyflurane treatment. The conditions used, exposure to 1.7% flurothyl for 8 min, induced convulsions in 100% of the chicks ($N = 80$). The 0.94% methoxyflurane alone caused no convulsions but caused anesthesia in 42.5% of chicks ($N = 80$), as evidenced by closed eyes, sleeping posture, and nonresponse to stimuli. Adding 0.94% methoxyflurane to the 1.7% flurothyl reduced the incidence of convulsions from 100% to 45.0%, a highly significant effect (χ^2 = 69.8, $p < 0.0001$).

The avoidance scores when treatment was applied 4 min after training were: 5.0% for the flurothyl group, indicating nearly complete RA; 85.0% for the methoxyflurane group, indicating no RA; and 52.5% for the flurothyl-methoxyflurane group, indicating significant RA (χ^2 = 5.82; $p < 0.02$) but less than the RA of the flurothyl group (χ^2 = 14.1; $p < 0.0005$). The chicks ($N = 18$) that convulsed under flurothyl-methoxyflurane had more RA than the chicks ($N = 22$) that did not convulse but the difference was not significant; the avoidance scores were 38.8% versus 63.5% (χ^2 = 1.54, $p > 0.2$). The results for the 64-min interval between training and treatment were similar to the results for the 4-min interval. In sum, methoxyflurane reduced both the incidence of convulsions and the extent of RA caused by a high concentration of flurothyl.

Results of determining convulsant and lethal doses of flurothyl. In the chick, the CD_{50} was 0.49% and the LD_{50} was 10.1%; in the mouse, the CD_{50} was 0.32% and the LD_{50} was 0.33% (Cherkin, 1969a). The "factor of safety" was 20.6 (10.1/0.49) for the chick and only 1.03 (0.33/0.32) for the mouse, therefore the chick tolerated a closer approach to a maximal RA dose of flurothyl. Toxicity is a critical parameter in RA studies because it is the limiting factor controlling the maximal strength of an RA treatment that can be used experimentally. This limitation often prevents attainment of a maximal amnesic effect. I suggest that submaximal treatments may permit memory consolidation to persist in the survivors of treatments that kill some of the animals.

Results of hypoxia and hyperoxia experiments. Chicks that inspired low O_2 mixtures gave evidence of cerebral hypoxia by their marked behavioral depression; chicks in 6.6% to 10.5% O_2 were lethargic and those in 6.6% O_2 could not be aroused by tapping stimuli. In addition, the 0.3% mortality rate in air (20.9% O_2) rose to 13.3% in 6.6% O_2. Surprisingly, the 30-hr exposure to low oxygen did not decrease the avoidance scores of chicks that were weakly trained on 0.25% MeA or strongly trained on 100% MeA. On the contrary, the avoidance of both trained groups was increased by the hypoxic treatment, suggesting an enhanced retention. Under hyperoxic conditions (100% O_2), no significant changes in retention occurred, as compared with controls inhaling air.

DISCUSSION

It is a long leap from the laboratory to the clinic and a chick is not a man, needless to say. Such obvious differences render plausible any differences that may be found between chick and man in memory processing. By the same token, they augment the interest of any similarities that may emerge. In the discussion that follows, it must be kept in mind that the aim of ECT or ICT is to set off the brain seizure with minimal electrical energy or flurothyl dosage. In contrast, most laboratory experiments aim for a maximal RA effect and therefore use high ECS currents or flurothyl dosage.

Proactive effects. Chicks showed impaired orientation and impaired pecking at a target for 2 hr after a strong flurothyl treatment. In man, postseizure recovery of recall of six simple facts (name, age, hospital, department, day, date) required a mean of 50 min after ICT and 40 min after ECT (Laurell, 1970). The chick and human values appear reasonably comparable, in view of the stronger treatment given to the chick.

The anterograde amnesic effect of flurothyl subsided in the chick within 4 hr after a single treatment; in man, some evidences of impairment were still present 3 to 7 days after a series of 3 to 10 ICT or ECT treatments (Laurell, 1970).

Retrograde amnesia. The period after training during which memory processing appeared to be vulnerable to flurothyl could be increased from 4 min to 24 hr, simply by increasing the flurothyl vapor concentration and exposure time (Cherkin, 1969b). The longer chicks were exposed to flurothyl vapor after convulsing, the more amnesia they had, rising to a plateau after an 8-min exposure (Figure 2). This finding contradicted the conventional criterion used to predict a full RA effect from ECS, namely, full tonic convulsion, but it has since been confirmed using ECS in the rat (Zornetzer & McGaugh, 1970). At 48-hr posttraining, the highest flurothyl concentration and exposure no longer caused RA; stronger treatments were forbidden by toxicity constraints. We have developed in detail the argument that a major source of the wide variation in so-called consolidation times is the use of incompletely effective RA treatments, which permit consolidation to continue at a reduced rate after treatment (Cherkin, 1969b).

As Jarvik (1972, p. 458) points out, it is unfortunate that the opportunity has not been seized to determine the RA gradient in man. Laurell (1970) presented information to patients 1 hr before administering a single ICT or bilateral ECT; significant RA was observed on testing 5 hr after treatment. RA was significantly less after ICT than after ECT, despite the longer duration of seizure during ICT (114 sec versus 89 sec). This finding was held to support the view that the electric current contributes to RA, beyond the seizure itself. This view appears to be consistent also with our finding that prolonging the exposure of chicks to flurothyl vapor increases RA, despite a constant initial seizure (Figure 2).

Transcranial electroshock has proved ineffective in producing RA in chicks when applied more than 0.5 min after training, even with high convulsive currents (Lee-Teng, 1970). With direct brain stimulation, RA was induced 4 min after training. It appears that flurothyl is a far more potent RA agent than ECS, in the chick.

Memory enhancement. The enhanced retention observed when weak flurothyl (0.2%) was administered shortly after training is consistent with the finding that small doses of several "amnesic" compounds have retrograde enhancing effects. This phenomenon has been reported with pentylenetetrazol (McGaugh, 1968), ether (Wimer, 1968), and pentobarbital (Steinberg & Tomkiewicz, 1968) and may be related to the enhancement of memory consolidation by reticular stimulation (Bloch, 1970) and to the controversial notion of "countershock" after ECT (Cronholm & Ottosson, 1961).

Role of psychological state. We found that chicks are more resistant to flurothyl convulsions when in a state of increased stress shortly after pecking an aversive liquid. This result is consistent with other experiments in animals and man (Pinel & Chorover, 1972). The effect of stress upon cortical seizure patterns is more complex; Chorover and DeLuca (1969) reported that footshock blocked ECS-induced seizures in the rat whereas Gold and McGaugh (1972) found only slight alterations.

It has been suggested that information is most vulnerable to a given ECS when it is brought to active consciousness (Misanin, Miller, & Lewis, 1968). Rubin (1969) has proposed clinical application of this concept, by applying ECT immediately after directing the patient's attention to his most disturbing feelings.

Concurrent anesthesia. The antagonistic effect of methoxyflurane and other anesthetics upon flurothyl are well known (Cascorbi & Loecher, 1967; Perez & Pittinger, 1967; Schuck & Shulman, 1971). We have demonstrated that methoxyflurane reduces both the convulsive and the amnesic effect of flurothyl. The use of anesthetics in conjunction with ICT or ECT is accepted procedure today. Neki and Kishore (1968) employed a combination of thiopental and pentylenetetrazol that produced CNS stimulation without convulsions and antidepressive effects comparable to those with ECT, with less amnesia. Light anesthesia with ether, trifluroethyl vinyl ether, or thiopental slightly decreased the amplitude of discharge activity produced by flurothyl in the rhesus monkey; deep surgical anesthesia blocked the cortical dysrhythmia (Ling, Truitt, & Krantz, 1959). The ability to control by graded anesthesia the degree of seizure activity resulting from a given intensity of ICT or ECT, would appear to be a potential research tool in achieving maximal antidepressive effect with minimal memory disturbance. It may be asked if one direction of future research might include

ICT combined with anesthesia at an anticonvulsant level, that might also obviate the need for a muscle relaxant. Obviously, the anesthetic must be appropriate for repeated use; perhaps nitrous oxide could be considered, since it antagonizes flurothyl in the mouse (Perez & Pittinger, 1967). The choice of anesthetic and dosage may prove critical, in view of the report that lidocaine modification of ECT reduced memory disturbance only sightly, with the disadvantage of reducing the antidepressive effect (Ottosson, 1962).

Hypoxia. Meyer (1963) suggested that the prolonged memory deficits sometimes observed in convulsive therapy patients may be associated with minimal brain damage. Our finding that prolonged moderate hypoxia after training had no RA effect suggests that where acute hypoxia does cause RA (Sara & Lefevre, 1972) it may do so by causing irreversible damage to brain regions involved with memory storage or retrieval or both. If so, regional hypoxic damage would provide a plausible interpretation of the prolonged loss of well-consolidated memories seen after ICT and ECT; a cautious investigation of convulsive therapy under conditions of cerebral hyperoxygenation might prove illuminating.

Additional directions of future research. It may be expected that future animal studies will pay more attention to the role of the conditions used in ICT and ECT, including: oxygen level, anesthesia, muscle relaxation, and *repeated* treatments with near-threshold levels of flurothyl or ECS. It is also possible that clinical researchers may become interested to explore the gradient of RA in man under given conditions of ICT or ECT, and the differences between two types of RA, the first observed over a short time period (minutes to days) and the second observed over a long time period (weeks to years).

SUMMARY

The effects of flurothyl (Indoklon) upon retention of one-trial avoidance learning in the neonate chick were found to be highly dose dependent. A high convulsive dose (exposure to 1.7% v/v flurothyl vapor for 8 min) caused proactive impairment for 2 hr, anterograde amnesia for 2 hr, and retrograde amnesia (RA) extending over 24 hr. Full tonic convulsions were not a sufficient condition for RA. Rather, RA increased as the duration of postconvulsion exposure to flurothyl increased, reaching an asymptote in 8 to 16 min under our conditions. A lower concentration of flurothyl (0.85%) caused less RA and 0.43% caused none. A subconvulsive concentration of flurothyl (0.2%) enhanced retention of prior training.

The convulsive effect of flurothyl was reduced in chicks aroused by an aversive training during which a distasteful liquid was introduced into the beak. Both the convulsive effect and the RA effect of flurothyl were attenuated by simultaneous administration of 0.94% methoxyflurane, approximately the AD_{50} level. Flurothyl is a more potent amnesic agent than ECS in the chick and the mouse. Prolonged moderate hypoxia (30 hr in 6.6% O_2) did not cause RA in the chick model.

Indoklon convulsive therapy differs from the experimental model in many obvious respects, including: species; lower flurothyl dose and exposure time; multiple administrations; and concurrent use of oxygen, anesthesia, and muscle relaxation. Nevertheless, the superficial similarities in proactive and retrograde effects, despite these differences, suggest that insights from the chick model may prove useful in understanding some of the memory deficits associated with ICT and perhaps ECT.

REFERENCES

Alpern, H. P., & Kimble, D. P. Retrograde amnesic effects of diethyl ether and bis (trifluoroethyl) ether. *Journal of Comparative and Physiological Psychology,* 1967, **63,** 168-171.

Bloch, V. Facts and hypotheses concerning memory consolidation processes. *Brain Research,* 1970, 24, 561-575.

Bohdanecky, Z., Kopp, R., & Jarvik, M. E. Comparison of ECS and flurothyl-induced retrograde amnesia in mice. *Psychopharmacologia,* 1968, 12, 91-95.

Cascorbi, H. F., & Loecher, C. K. Antagonism and synergism of six volatile anesthetic agents and flurothyl, a convulsant ether. *Anesthesia and Analgesia,* 1967, 46, 546-550.

Chatrian, G. E., & Petersen, M. C. The convulsive patterns provoked by Indoklon, Metrazol and electroshock: Some depth electrographic observations in human patients. *Electroencephalography and Clinical Neurophysiology,* 1960, 12, 715-725.

Cherkin, A. Flurothyl toxicity: A remarkable species difference between chick and mouse. *Psychopharmacologia,* 1969, 15, 404-407. (a)

Cherkin, A. Kinetics of memory consolidation: Role of amnesic treatment parameters. *Proceedings of the National Academy of Sciences of the United States of America,* 1969, **63,** 1094-1101. (b)

Cherkin, A. Effects of flurothyl on memory processing. In W. L. Smith (Ed.), *Drugs and cerebral function,* Springfield, Ill.: Charles C Thomas, 1970. (a)

Cherkin, A. Retrograde amnesia: Impaired memory consolidation or impaired retrieval? *Communications in Behavioral Biology,* 1970, 5, 183-190. (b)

Cherkin, A. Biphasic time course of performance after one-trial avoidance training in the chick. *Communications in Behavioral Biology,* 1971, 5, 379-381. (a)

Cherkin, A. Memory consolidation in the chick: Resistance to prolonged post-training hypoxia. *Communications in Behavioral Biology,* 1971, 5, 325-330. (b)

Cherkin, A. Retrograde amnesia in the chick: Resistance to the reminder effect. *Physiology and Behavior,* 1972, 8, 949-955.

Chorover, S. L., & DeLuca, A. M. Transient change in electrocorticographic reaction to ECS in the rat following footshock. *Journal of Comparative and Physiological Psychology,* 1969, 69, 141-149.

Cronholm, B., & Ottosson, J. -O. "Countershock" in electroconvulsive therapy. *Archives of General Psychiatry,* 1961, 4, 254-258.

d'Elia, G. Unilateral electroconvulsive therapy. *Acta Psychiatrica Scandinavica,* 1970, 46 (Suppl. 215), 1-98.

Dolenz, B. J. Indoklon: A clinical review. *Psychosomatics,* 1965, 6, 200-205.

Fink, M., Kahn, R. L., Karp, E., Pollack, M., Green, M. A., Alan, B., & Lefkowits, H. J. Inhalant-induced convulsions. *Archives of General Psychiatry,* 1961, 4, 259-266.

Gold, P. E., & McGaugh, J. L. Effect of recent footshock on brain seizures and behavioral convulsions induced by electrical stimulation of the brain. *Behavioral Biology,* 1972, 7, 421-426.

Herz, M. J., Spooner, C. E.. & Cherkin, A. Effects of the amnesic agent flurothyl on EEG and multiple-unit activity in the chick. *Experimental Neurology,* 1970, **27,** 227-237.

Jarvik, M. E. Effects of chemical and physical treatments on learning and memory. *Annual Review of Psychology,* 1972, **23,** 457-478.

Krantz, J. C., Jr., Esquibel, A. J., Truitt, E. B., Jr., Ling, A. S. C., & Kurland, A. A. Hexafluorodiethyl ether (Indoklon) - an inhalant convulsant. *Journal of tne American Medical Association,* 1958, **166,** 1555-1562.

Laurell, B. (Ed.) Flurothyl convulsive therapy. *Acta Psychiatrica Scandinavica,* 1970, **46** (Suppl. 213), 1-79.

Lee-Teng, E. Retrograde amnesia gradients by subconvulsive and high convulsive transcranial currents in chicks. *Proceedings of the National Academy of Sciences of the United States of America,* 1970, **65,** 857-865.

Ling, A. S. C., Truitt, E. B., & Krantz, J. C., Jr., Anesthesia LIX: Effect of anestheia with ether, Fluoromar, and thiopental sodium on Indoklon-induced cerebral cortical seizures. *Anesthesiology,* 1959, **20,** 173-176.

McGaugh, J. L. Drug facilitation of memory and learning. In D. H. Efron (Ed.), *Psychopharmacology. A review of progress.* (US PHS Publ. No. 1836) Washington, D.C.: United States Government Printing Office, 1968.

Meyer, A. Epilepsy. In W. Blackwood et al. (Eds.), *Greenfield's Neuropathology,* Edward Arnold Ltd., London, 1963.

Misanin, J. R., Miller, R. R., & Lewis, D. J. Retrograde amnesia produced by electroconvulsive shock after reactivation of a consolidated memory trace. *Science,* 1968, **160,** 554-555.

Neki, J. S., & Kishore, B. Narcostimulation in depressive states. *American Journal of Psychiatry,* 1968, **124,** 1196-1201.

Ottosson, J. -0. Seizure characteristics and therapeutic efficiency in electroconvulsive therapy: An analysis of the antidepressive efficiency of grand mal and lidocaine-modified seizures. *Journal of Nervous and Mental Disease,* 1962, **135,** 239-251.

Perez, R. E., & Pittinger, C. B. Xenon, nitrous oxide and oxygen antagonism of flurothyl. *Federation Proceedings,* 1967, **26,** 504.

Pinel, J. P. J., & Chorover, S. L. Inhibition by arousal of epilepsy induced by chlorambucil in rats. *Nature,* 1972, **236,** 232-234.

Ray, O. S., & Barrett, R. J. Step-through latencies in mice as a function of ECS-test interval. *Physiology and Behavior,* 1969, **4,** 583-586.

Rubin, R. D. New application of ECT. In R. D. Rubin & C. M. Franks (Eds.), *Advances in behavior therapy,* New York: Academic Press, 1969.

Rush, S., & Driscoll, D. A. Current distribution in the brain from surface electrodes. *Anesthesia and Analgesia,* 1968, **47,** 717-723.

Sara, S. J., & Lefevre, D. Hypoxia-induced amnesia in one-trial learning and pharmacological protection by Piracetam, *Psychopharmacologia,* 1972, **25,** 32-40.

Schuck, S. L., & Shulman, A. A study of the central action of flurothyl and methoxyflurane. *Australian Journal of Experimental Biology and Medical Science,* 1971, **49,** 501-512.

Small, J. G., & Small, I. F. Clinical results: Indoklon versus ECT. *Seminars in Psychiatry,* 1972, **4,** 13-26.

Steinberg, H., & Tomkiewicz, M. Drugs and memory. In D. H. Efron (Ed.), *Psychopharmacology. A review of progress.* (US PHS Publ. No. 1836) Washington, D.C.: United States Government Printing Office, 1968.

Wimer, R. E. Bases of a facilitative effect upon retention resulting from posttrial etherization. *Journal of Comparative and Physiological Psychology,* 1968, **65,** 340-342.

Zornetzer, S. F., & McGaugh, J. L. Effects of frontal brain electroshock stimulation on EEG activity and memory in rats: Relationship to ECS-produced retrograde amnesia. *Journal of Neurobiology,* 1970, **1,** 379-394.

11

EFFECTS OF ELECTROCONVULSIVE SHOCK ON NOREPINEPHRINE TURNOVER AND METABOLISM: BASIC AND CLINICAL STUDIES[1]

Joseph J. Schildkraut, M.D., and Paul R. Draskoczy, M.D.[2]

The changes in norepinephrine metabolism produced by drugs that alter affective state in man have been extensively studied. The findings of these studies suggest the hypothesis that stimulants, euphoriants, or antidepressants which elevate affective state increase norepinephrine at receptors in brain, whereas drugs which depress affective state decrease norepinephrine (Schildkraut, 1970a). Utilizing the techniques previously applied in the study of the effects of various psychoactive drugs, the effects of electroconvulsive shock on the release and metabolism of tritiated norepinephrine have been examined in rat brain. Initially, it was observed that acutely administered electroconvulsive shocks increase the rate of discharge of intracisternally administered norepinephrine-H^3 in rat brain resulting in a transient increase in levels of normetanephrine-H^3 (Schildkraut, Schanberg, Breese, & Kopin, 1967). These findings would be consistent with several earlier observations that levels of endogenous norepinephrine in animal brain were decreased immediately after the administration of one or more electroconvulsive shocks (Shatalova & Antonov, 1961; Breitner, Picchioni, & Chin, 1964) but this has not been found in all studies (Kato, Gozsy, Roy, & Groh, 1967). This paper will summarize the findings of the studies of the effects of electroconvulsive shock on

[1] This work was supported in part by United States Public Health Service Grant no. MH-15413 from the National Institute of Mental Health.

[2] We wish to thank Edwin L. Grab, M.S., Pallas Sun Lo, M.S., Patricia A. Platz, B.S., and Hans Scharen, B.A., who assisted with these experiments and chemical determinations; Malcolm Rogers, M.D., and Barbara Keeler, M.S.W., who collaborated in the clinical study; and Gladys Rege who assisted in the preparation of this manuscript.

norepinephrine turnover and metabolism which have been conducted in our laboratory during the past several years.

METHODS

Studies in Animals

Male Sprague-Dawley rats (180-200g) were used in the course of these experiments. Racemic or 1-norepinephrine-H^3 (5 μCi; 7 to 12 Ci per millimole) was administered by intracisternal injection as described elsewhere (Schanberg, Schildkraut, & Kopin, 1967). Norepinephrine-H^3 and its metabolites as well as endogenous norepinephrine were determined in brain or various regions of the brain (Whitby, Axelrod, & Weil-Malherbe, 1961; Kopin, Axelrod, & Gordon, 1961; Anton & Sayre, 1962; Schanberg, Schildkraut, Breese, & Kopin, 1968b; Schildkraut, 1970b). Electroconvulsive shocks (115 V for 0.2 to 0.3 sec) were administered through earclip electrodes. Student's t test was used to determine the statistical significance of differences. Individual experiments are described in detail in the text or in the captions to figures.

Clinical Studies

The urinary excretion of norepinephrine, epinephrine, and metabolites were studied before, during, and after a course of eight modified electroconvulsive treatments (ECT) in a patient with a severe recurrent depressive disorder. Bilateral ECT was employed in the first five treatments utilizing bitemporal electrode placements; in the three subsequent treatments, unilateral ECT was administered to the nondominant hemisphere. Sodium methohexital (Brevital) (60 to 70 mg i.v.) and succinylcholine chloride (Anectine) (40 to 60 mg i.v.) were administered prior to each electroconvulsive treatment. The Reiter Mol-Ac II electrostimulator was used at medium setting with current applied for 2 sec. Urine samples were collected for 24-hr periods and norepinephrine, epinephrine, normetanephrine, metanephrine, 3-methoxy-4-hydroxy-mandelic acid (VMA) and 3-methoxy-4-hydroxyphenylglycol (MHPG) were determined (Anton & Sayre, 1962; Schildkraut, Gordon, & Durell, 1965; Wilk, Gitlow, Mendlowitz, Franklin, Carr, & Clarke, 1965; Dekirmenjian & Maas, 1970). Student's t test was used to determine the statistical significance of differences.

RESULTS AND DISCUSSION

Effects of a Single Electroconvulsive Shock on the
Release and Metabolism of Norepinephrine in
Rat Brain

The effects of a single electroconvulsive shock on the release and metabolism of norepinephrine-H^3 in rat brain were examined in the series of experiments summarized in Table 1. In these experiments, d,1-norepinephrine-H^3 was first

TABLE 1

Effects of ECS of Release and Metabolism of Norepinephrine-H³ in Rat Brain

Substance	Experiment I	Experiment II	Experiment III
	Percent of control mean (100%)±SEM		
NE-H³ [a]	91±3*	94±2	93±2*
NMN-H³ [b]	121±4***	113±6*	118±4***
DCM-H³ [c]	109±4	112±7	123±9**
Total DOM-H³ [d]	116±4***	111±5	107±4
Free DOM-H³ [e]	120±5***	126±8**	118±5**
(Endogenous) NE	90±2***	——	95±4

*$p<.05$ (one-tailed t test) when compared with control values.
**$p<.05$ (two-tailed t test) when compared with control values.
***$p<.01$ (two-tailed t test) when compared with control values.
[a] Norepinephrine-H³.
[b] Normetanephrine-H³.
[c] Tritiated deaminated catechol metabolites.
[d] Total tritiated deaminated 0-methylated metabolites, i.e., 3-methoxy-4-hydroxymandelic acid (VMA), 3-methoxy-4-hydroxyphenylglycol (MHPG) and the sulfate conjugate of MHPG.
[e] Tritiated deaminated 0-methylated metabolites, i.e., VMA and unconjugated MHPG.

administered by intracisternal injection and electroconvulsive shock was administered either 20 min (Experiments I and II) or 30 min (Experiment III) thereafter; animals were sacrificed 15 min after the electroconvulsive shocks. In each experiment the group of control animals was handled in a comparable manner and earclip electrodes were applied to the control animals but no current was administered. Results are expressed as the percentages of the control means (100%) ±standard errors of the means. Each group consisted of 7 to 12 animals.

The content of norepinephrine-H³ remaining in the brains of shocked animals was decreased and the levels of tritiated metabolites of norepinephrine-H³ were increased when compared with control values. Electroconvulsive shock also appeared to decrease levels of endogenous norepinephrine in the brain (Table 1). These experiments thus confirm earlier findings that electroconvulsive shock increased the rate of discharge of intracisternally administered norepinephrine-H³ within the brain and that this discharge occurred at least in part extraneuronally as reflected by an increase in levels of normetanephrine-H³ (Schildkraut et al., 1967).

In order to explore this further, the experiments summarized in Tables 2 and 3 were performed. In these experiments, desmethylimipramine, a drug that blocks the neuronal uptake of norepinephrine in the brain (Glowinski & Axelrod, 1964), was administered to a group of rats after the intracisternal injection of norepinephrine-H³ but prior to the administration of electroconvulsive shock (DMI + ECS); the other three groups used in this

TABLE 2

Effect of DMI on Re-uptake of NE–H[3] Released by ECS

Experiment number[a]	Control	ECS	DMI	DMI+ ECS
	Percent of control mean ±SEM			
I	100±3	91±2	103±7	74±5*
II	100±6	94±6	114±10	69±5*

*$p<.01$ compared to controls, ECS alone, or DMI alone.

[a]These experiments were performed in collaboration with Suzanne Roffler-Tarlov, Ph.D.

experiment were treated with either desmethylimipramine alone (DMI), electroconvulsive shock alone (ECS) or neither of these (control).

In Experiment I, d,1-norepinephrine-H[3] was initially administered by intracisternal injection. Animals were then separated into four groups (control; ECS; DMI; DMI + ECS) each containing five or six animals. The groups were then treated according to the following schedules with time designated in reference to the time (0 min) when norepinephrine-H[3] was administered. *Controls:* saline–1 ml i.p. (15 min); earclip electrodes applied for 1 min (30 min); sacrifice (45 min). *ECS:* saline–1 ml, i.p. (15 min); electroconvulsive shock administered (30 min); sacrifice (45 min). *DMI:* desmethylimipramine–25 mg per kilogram of body weight, i.p. (15 min); earclip electrodes applied for 1 min (30 min); sacrifice (45 min). *DMI + ECS:* desmethylimipramine–25 mg per kilogram of body weight, i.p. (15 min); electroconvulsive shock administered (30 min);

TABLE 3

Effects of DMI on Re-uptake of Endogenous
Norepinephrine Released by ECS

Condition	Norepinephrine		
	N	mμg/brain	Percent of control
Control	12	753±16	100±2
ECS	12	700±12*	93±2*
DMI	9	774±19	103±3
DMI + ECS	11	627±27**,***,****	83±4**,***,****

*$p<.05$ compared to controls.

**$p<.001$ compared to controls.

***$p<.05$ compared to ECS alone.

****$p<.001$ compared to DMI alone.

sacrifice (45 min). In Experiment II, a similar treatment sequence was employed for each of the four groups but there was a longer time interval after the initial administration of norepinephrine-H^3 —i.e., saline or DMI were administered after 300 min, earclip electrodes or electroconvulsive shock after 315 min, and sacrifice occurred after 330 min. Results are expressed as percentages of the control means ± standard errors of the means. The levels of norepinephrine-H^3 remaining in the brains of animals receiving desmethylimipramine plus electroconvulsive shock was compared with the levels in each of the other three groups.

Electroconvulsive shock produced a considerably greater net decrease in the levels of norepinephrine-H^3 in the brains of animals previously treated with desmethylimipramine (DMI + ECS) than in the untreated animals (ECS). In these experiments, desmethylimipramine alone did not produce a significant change in the rate of disappearance of norepinephrine-H^3 from brain[3] (Table 2).

The data presented in Table 3 were also derived from the experiments described above. Data from Experiments I and II were combined, since the exogenously introduced norepinephrine-H^3 represents only a very small fraction of the endogenous norepinephrine content of the brain and levels of endogenous norepinephrine, therefore, do not vary appreciably with time after the intracisternal injection of norepinephrine-H^3. Control, ECS, DMI, and DMI + ECS are as described above. The levels of endogenous norepinephrine are expressed in millimicrograms per brain and as percents of the control mean ± standard errors of the means. N refers to the number of animals in each group.

Prior treatment with desmethylimipramine also enhanced the net release of endogenous norepinephrine by electroconvulsive shock (Table 3), although this effect was not as pronounced as the effect on the release of tritiated norepinephrine.

These findings are compatible with the suggestion that electroconvulsive shock discharges norepinephrine extraneuronally, since desmethylimipramine would be expected to block the re-uptake of extraneuronally discharged norepinephrine and this could account for the greater net lowering of norepinephrine in the brains of animals treated with desmethylimipramine prior to electroconvulsive shock. Since desmethylimipramine, in the doses used in these experiments, produces considerably less than a 50% inhibition of the uptake of norepinephrine-H^3 in rat brain (Schildkraut, Dodge, & Logue, 1969), these findings suggest that an appreciable fraction of the total norepinephrine content of the brain may be discharged extraneuronally after a single electroconvulsion. However, other interpretations of these findings are also possible, since prior treatment with desmethylimipramine could conceivably

---

[3]It should be emphasized that in these experiments desmethylimipramine was injected only 30 min before the animals were sacrificed, since desmethylimipramine has been found to slow the disappearance of norepinephrine-H^3 from brain in experiments designed to allow the drug to act for a longer period of time (Schildkraut et al., 1967).

potentiate the action of electroconvulsive shock in releasing norepinephrine in the brain, apart from any effects on the reuptake of discharged norepinephrine. It has been suggested that the effects of electroconvulsive shock on biogenic amines in the brain may be attributed to the nonspecific stresses associated with this procedure (Hinesley, Norton, & Aprison, 1968). The experiment outlined in Figure 1 was performed to evaluate this. In this experiment the disappearance of intracisternally administered norepinephrine-H^3 was compared in three groups of animals: a group which received electroconvulsive shocks; a group of animals,

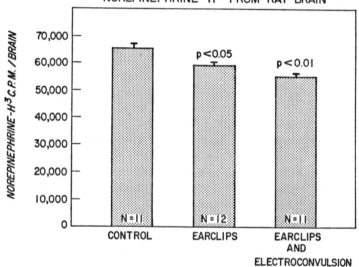

FIG. 1. Effects of electroconvulsive shock and associated stresses on the disappearance of norepinephrine-H^3 from rat brain. In this experiment, d,1-norepinephrine-H^3 was initially administered by intracisternal injection. Following this, the control animals were returned to cages where they were maintained in groups without further handling until they were sacrificed 45 min after the intracisternal injection. The group designated "earclips" was transferred to the shocking apparatus 30 min after the intracisternal injection and earclips were applied transiently but no current was passed; these animals were then sacrificed 45 min after the injection of nor-epinephrine-H^3. The group designated "earclips and electroconvulsion" was transferred to the shocking apparatus 30 min after the intracisternal injection at which time earclips were applied and an electroconvulsive shock was administered; these animals were then sacrificed 45 min after the injection of norepinephrine-H^3. Each group contained 11 or 12 animals. Results are expressed in counts per minute per brain as means and standard errors of the means. Differences are compared between the control group and the two experimental groups.

placed in the shocking apparatus to which earclips were applied without current being passed; and a control group of animals which were not handled between the time of the intracisternal injection of norepinephrine-H^3 and the time of sacrifice. Levels of norepinephrine-H^3 were lowest in the brains of animals that received electroconvulsion, but levels of norepinephrine-H^3 in brains of animals placed in the shocking apparatus and earclipped but not shocked were also significantly lower than control values. These findings suggest that part of the decrease in norepinephrine-H^3 after the administration of electroconvulsive shock may be secondary to the "stresses" of the electroshock procedure.

Effects of Cold Exposure on the Release of Norepinephrine in Rat Brain

The disappearance of norepinephrine-H^3 from rat brain may be accelerated by other stressful procedures as well as electroconvulsive shock (e.g., Thierry, Javoy, Glowinski, & Kety, 1968; Bliss, Ailon, & Zwanziger, 1968). In the experiments summarized in Figure 2, acute cold exposure was found to increase the rate of disappearance of norepinephrine-H^3 from rat brain and this is consistent with the findings of other investigators (Gordon, Spector, Sjoerdsma, & Udenfriend, 1966; Simmonds & Iversen, 1969a) although such findings have not been observed under all conditions (Simmonds & Iversen, 1969a, 1969b). It may be of some interest to note that the control and experimental curves diverged more markedly in the earlier interval from 50 to 110 min after the intracisternal injection of norepinephrine-H^3 than in the later interval from 110 to 260 min. This suggests that pools of norepinephrine with varying turnover rates may not be equally affected by cold exposure, although other interpretations of these findings are also possible.

As summarized in Figure 3, the metabolism of intracisternally administered norepinephrine-H^3 was examined during cold exposure. There were no profound alterations in the pattern of metabolites present in the brains of animals subjected to cold exposure. The decrease in norepinephrine-H^3 (relative to control values) observed in animals sacrificed 90 and 240 min after the exposure to cold (i.e., 110 and 260 min after the intracisternal injection of norepinephrine-H^3) was not accompanied by a comparable decrease in any of the metabolites.

The increased rate of disappearance of norepinephrine-H^3 during cold exposure could result from an increase in the rate of release of norepinephrine-H^3 from neurons or an inhibition in the re-uptake of norepinephrine-H^3 into neurons. In order to explore this we studied the effects of cold exposure on the uptake of intracisternally administered norepinephrine-H^3. In these experiments animals were placed in a cold room maintained at 5 to 7° C for 90 min in Experiment I and 360 min in Experiment II. Animals were then removed from the cold room, d,1-norepinephrine-H^3 was administered by intracisternal injection and animals were sacrificed 6 min thereafter. Control animals were maintained for comparable times at the

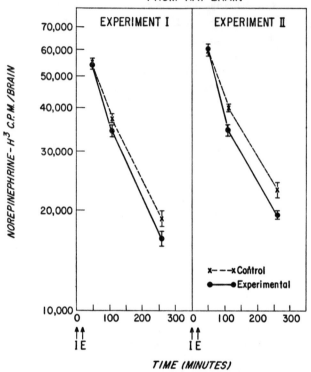

EFFECTS OF COLD EXPOSURE ON
THE DISAPPEARANCE OF NOREPINEPHRINE-H³
FROM RAT BRAIN

FIG. 2. The effects of cold exposure on the disappearance of
norepinephrine-H³ from rat brain. In these experiments, 20 min
after the intracisternal administration of d,1-norepinephrine-H³,
animals were placed in a cold room maintained at 5 to 7°C.
Animals were removed from the cold room at varying times and
sacrificed. Control animals which were maintained in the laboratory room temperature of 30°C in Experiment I and 24°C in
Experiment II were sacrificed at similar times after the intracisternal administration of norepinephrine-H³. The levels of norepinephrine-H³ remaining in the brains of control and experimental animals are expressed in counts per minute per brain
(cpm/brain) and are shown as means and standard errors of the
means. Each value represents the mean of six to nine determinations (i.e., animals). I = time of intracisternal injection of
norepinephrine-H³; E = time that experimental animals were
placed in cold room.

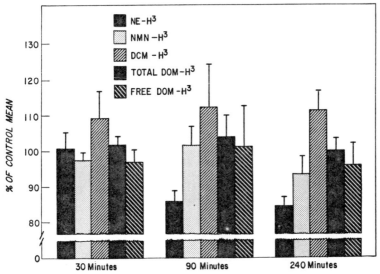

EFFECTS OF COLD EXPOSURE ON THE DISAPPEARANCE AND METABOLISM OF NOREPINEPHRINE-H^3 IN RAT BRAIN

TIME AFTER EXPOSURE TO COLD

FIG. 3. Effects of cold exposure on the disappearance and metabolism of norepinephrine-H^3 in rat brain. The data presented in this figure are derived from Experiment II described in the legend to Figure 2. The levels of norepinephrine-H^3 and its various metabolites in brains of animals subjected to cold exposure were expressed as percents of control means (100%) ± standard errors of the means. Each value represents the mean of seven to nine determinations. Abbreviations: see Table 1.

laboratory room temperature of 28° C in Experiment I and 21° C in Experiment II, prior to the intracisternal injection of norepinephrine-H^3 and were sacrificed 6 min thereafter. The levels of norepinephrine-H^3 and metabolites in the brain are expressed as percentages of the control means ± standard errors of the means. Each value represents the mean of 7 to 10 determinations.

As summarized in Table 4, levels of norepinephrine-H^3 or any of its metabolites in brain were not different from control values in animals subjected to 90 or 360 min of cold exposure prior to the intracisternal injection of norepinephrine-H^3 and sacrificed 6 min thereafter. This suggests that the increased rate of disappearance of norepinephrine-H^3 from brain during cold exposure is probably due to an increased rate of release of norepinephrine-H^3 rather than to an inhibition of re-uptake.

TABLE 4

Effects of Cold Exposure on Uptake and
Metabolism of Norepinephrine-H^3 in Rat Brain

Substance[a]	90-min Exposure		360-min Exposure	
	Control	Cold	Control	Cold
NE-H^3	100±4	99±3	100±3	105±3
NMN-H^3	100±3	100±4	100±4	98±5
DCM-H^3	100±7	99±4	100±5	92±4
Total DOM-H^3	100±3	98±4	100±5	100±5
Free DOM-H^3	100±6	90±4	100±7	103±10
Endogenous NE	100±2	103±2	100±2	101±2

[a] See Table 1 for abbreviations.

The Use of Electroconvulsive Shock as an Experimental Tool for Studying Norepinephrine Metabolism in Brain

We have also found that electroconvulsive shock may be used as an experimental tool for exploring aspects of the kinetics and metabolism of norepinephrine in rat brain (Schildkraut, Draskoczy, & Lo, 1971). The disappearance of intracisternally administered norepinephrine-H^3 from the brain exhibits a multiphasic exponential decline and the ratio of normetanephrine-H^3 to norepinephrine-H^3 in the brain is considerably higher shortly after the intracisternal injection of norepinephrine-H^3 than at later times (Figure 4). Since O-methylation of norepinephrine is thought to occur extraneuronally (Axelrod 1966), it is likely that some of the intracisternally administered norepinephrine-H^3 may be O-methylated prior to the neuronal uptake and binding of the tritiated norepinephrine. This would certainly contribute to, and could possibly fully account for, the high ratio of normetanephrine-H^3 to norepinephrine-H^3 observed shortly after the intracisternal injection of norepinephrine-H^3. However, it is also possible that there could be differences in the pathways of metabolism of norepinephrine-H^3 released in the brain at various times after its intracisternal injection which might also contribute to the changing ratio of normetanephrine-H^3 to norepinephrine-H^3.

In the experiments summarized in Table 5, we examined the conversion to normetanephrine-H^3 of norepinephrine-H^3 released by electroconvulsive shock at various times after the intracisternal administration of norepinephrine-H^3. In these experiments, d,1-norepinephrine-H^3 was administered by intracisternal injection; electroconvulsive shock was administered at varying times thereafter and animals were sacrificed 15 min after the electroconvulsive shock. Earclip electrodes were applied at appropriate times to the control animals but no current was administered. Results are expressed in counts per minute per brain (cpm/brain) as the means ± standard errors of the means. In every experiment each group contained 7 to 12 animals. The mean content of norepinephrine-H[3] in shocked animals was subtracted from the mean content of norepinephrine-H[3] in unshocked control animals to give the decrease in norepinephrine-H[3] produced by electroconvulsive shock (Δ NE-H[3]), whereas the content of normetanephrine-H[3] in control animals subtracted from the content of

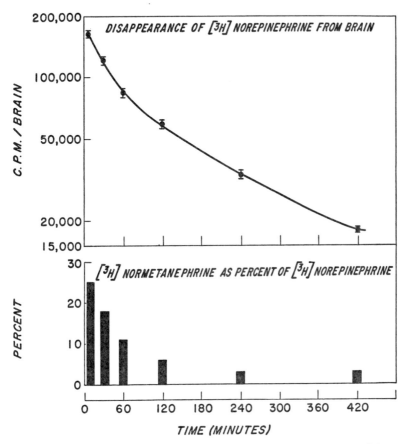

FIG. 4. The disappearance of intracisternally administered norepinephrine-H[3] from rat brain and its conversion to normetanephrine-H[3]. Animals were sacrificed at varying times after the intracisternal administration of d,1-norepinephrine-H[3]. Levels of norepinephrine-H[3] and normetanephrine-H[3] were determined in extracts of whole brain. The levels of norepinephrine-H[3] are expressed as counts per minute per brain (cpm/brain). Each point on the graph represents the mean ± standard error of the means based upon eight or nine determinations. The levels of normetanephrine-H[3] are expressed as a percentage of the level of norepinephrine-H[3] present in the brain at that time. Data from Schildkraut et al. (1971).

TABLE 5
Release of Norepinephrine-H³ by ECS and Its Conversion to Normetanephrine-H³

Experiment number	Time p̄ NE-H³ (min)	Norepinephrine-H³ (cpm/brain)			Normetanephrine-H³ (cpm/brain)			$\dfrac{\Delta\text{NMN-H}^3\,(\uparrow)}{\Delta\text{NE-H}^3\,(\downarrow)} \times 100$
		Control	ECS	ΔNE-H³ (↓)	Control	ECS	ΔNMN-H³ (↑)	
I	20	114,500 (±2,810)	107,000 (±2,650)	7,500*	21,000 (±796)	23,000 (±814)	2,000	27%
II	20	121,000 (±7,330)	113,400 (±2,790)	7,600	23,500 (±784)	26,600 (±1,310)	3,100*	41%
III	20	113,500 (±4,170)	102,800 (±3,090)	10,700*	21,300 (±741)	25,800 (±953)	4,500**	42%
IV	30	87,200 (±2,170)	81,400 (±1,950)	5,800*	15,200 (±637)	17,900 (±589)	2,700**	47%
I	300	25,100 (±890)	22,700 (±1,050)	2,400*	1,110 (±64)	1,170 (±58)	60	3%
II	420	22,500 (±1,810)	18,800 (±1,200)	3,700*	510 (±25)	650 (±34)	140**	4%

*$p < .05$ (one-tailed t test).
**$p < .01$ (one-tailed t test).

normetanephrine-H^3 in shocked animals gave the increment in normetanephrine-H^3 produced by electroconvulsive shock (Δ NMN-H^3). The increase in normetanephrine-H^3 was then expressed as a percentage of the decrease in norepinephrine-H^3—i.e., (ΔNMN-H^3 ÷ ΔNE-H^3) × 100. This provides an index of the fraction of the released norepinephrine-H^3 that was converted to normetanephrine-H^3. When electroconvulsive shock was administered 20 or 30 min after the intracisternal injection of norepinephrine-H^3, the increase in normetanephrine-H^3 accounted for 27% to 47% of the decrease in norepinephrine-H^3. In contrast, when electroconvulsive shock was administered either 300 or 420 min after the intracisternal injection of norepinephrine-H^3, the increase in normetanephrine-H^3 accounted for only 3% to 4% of the decrease in norepinephrine-H^3. The findings thus suggest that a substantial fraction of the norepinephrine-H^3 released in the brain a short time after its intracisternal injection is metabolized by catechol-O-methyl transferase with the formation of normetanephine-H^3. In contrast, only a much smaller fraction of the norepinephrine-H^3 released at later times appears to be converted to normetanephrine-H^3.

Since electroconvulsive shock could have slowed the disappearance of normetanephrine-H^3 from the brain, or caused alterations in the metabolism of normetanephrine-H^3 which might have accounted for the findings presented in Table 5, we examined the effects of electroconvulsive shock on the disappearance and metabolism of normetanephrine-H^3 (Table 6). Normetanephrine-H^3 was administered by intracisternal injection. Electroconvulsive shock was administered 20 or 300 min after the intracisternal injection of normetanephrine-H^3, and animals were sacrificed 15 min after the electroconvulsive shocks. Earclips were transiently applied to control animals at comparable times after the intracisternal injection of normetanephrine-H^3, and control animals were sacrificed 15 min after the application of earclips. Each group contained 9 to 11 animals. Control means expressed in counts per minute per brain (cpm/brain) are given in parentheses.

We found that electroconvulsive shock when administered 20 or 300 min after the intracisternal injection of the tritiated normetanephrine did not produce a significant alteration in the rate of disappearance or in the metabolism of the intracisternally administered normetanephrine-H^3. Thus, it seems unlikely that the findings presented in Table 5 could be explained by a differential effect of electroconvulsive shock on the disappearance of normetanephrine-H^3 from the brain at various times.

These findings thus suggest that pools of norepinephrine in the brain may differ not only in their rates of turnover but also in the pathways of metabolism of the released catecholamine. Moreover, these experiments demonstrate that electroconvulsive shock may provide a useful experimental tool for studying aspects of the kinetics and metabolism of norepinephrine in the brain.

TABLE 6

Disappearance and Metabolism of Normetanephrine-H^3
in Rat Brain after ECS

Substance[a]	20 min after NMN-H^3		300 min after NMN-H^3	
	Control	ECS	Control	ECS
	% of control mean ± SEM		% of control mean ± SEM	
NMN-H^3	100±3 (88,500 cpm)	103±3	100±3 (2,270 cpm)	94±3
Total DOM-H^3	100±4 (223,000 cpm)	100±4	100±1 (21,300 cpm)	99±4
Free DOM-H^3	100±6 (38,900 cpm)	101±6	100±7 (914 cpm)	113±8
Total-H^3	100±4 (319,000 cpm)	101±3	100±3 (27,800 cpm)	99±4

[a] See Table 1 for abbreviations.

Effects of Chronically Administered Electroconvulsive Shock on the Release and Metabolism of Norepinephrine in Rat Brain

The studies of Kety, Javoy, Thierry, Julou, and Glowinski (1967), indicated that after chronic administration of electroconvulsive shocks, there was an increase in the synthesis and utilization of norepinephrine in rat brain which was sustained for at least 24 hr after the last electroconvulsion. Subsequently, these investigators showed that chronically administered electroconvulsive shocks increased the activity of tyrosine hydroxylase (the rate-limiting enzyme in catecholamine biosynthesis) in rat brain (Musacchio, Julou, Kety, & Glowinski, 1969). A subsequent report (Ladisich, Steinhauff, & Matussek 1969), provided data that also appeared to suggest an increase in turnover of norepinephrine after chronic electroconvulsive shocks, but the design of this study and the presentation of the findings make definitive interpretation of these data rather difficult. In an attempt to confirm and extend these findings, we conducted a series of experiments to study the effects of chronically administered electroconvulsive shock on the disappearance and metabolism of intracisternally administered norepinephrine-H^3 in rat brain.

In the experiments summarized in Figure 5, 1-norepinephrine-H^3 was administered by intracisternal injection approximately 18 hr after the last of a series of seven daily electroconvulsive shocks, and animals were sacrificed at varying times thereafter. The levels of norepinephrine-H^3 in brains of the shocked animals when compared with control values were slightly but not

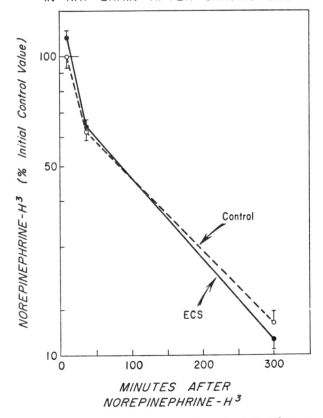

UPTAKE AND DISAPPEARANCE
OF NOREPINEPHRINE-H³
IN RAT BRAIN AFTER CHRONIC ECS

FIG. 5. Uptake and disappearance of norepinephrine-H³ in rat brain after chronic administration of electroconvulsive shocks. Electroconvulsive shocks were administered once daily for 7 days. Approximately 18 hr after the last electroconvulsive shock, 1-norepinephrine-H³ was administered by intracisternal injection and animals were sacrificed 6, 30, or 300 min after the intracisternal injection. Matched control animals, housed together with the shocked animals, were sacrificed at comparable times after the intracisternal injection of norepinephrine-H³. In this experiment, earclip electrodes were not applied to the control animals. The levels of norepinephrine-H³ remaining in the brain at various times after the intracisternal injection are expressed as a percent of the initial control value (i.e., the mean level of norepinephrine-H³ found in control animals sacrificed 6 min after the intracisternal injection). Results are shown as means and standard errors of the means. Each value represents the mean of nine determinations (i.e., one animal per determination).

significantly higher after 6 min, approximately equal after 30 min, and slightly lower after 300 min. Figure 6 indicates that a smaller percentage of the norepinephrine-H³ initially found in brain (i.e., at 6 min) remained in the brains of shocked animals at 30 and 300 min after the intracisternal injection of norepinephrine-H³; the difference between the shocked and control groups at 300 min was statistically significant.

Further experiments described in Figure 7 were performed to examine the effects of chronically administered electroconvulsive shock on the disappearance and metabolism of intracisternally administered norepinephrine-H³ in various regions of rat brain. L-norepinephrine-H³ was administered by intracisternal injection approximately 18 hr after the last of a series of seven daily electroconvulsions and the animals were sacrificed 6, 60, or 300 min after the

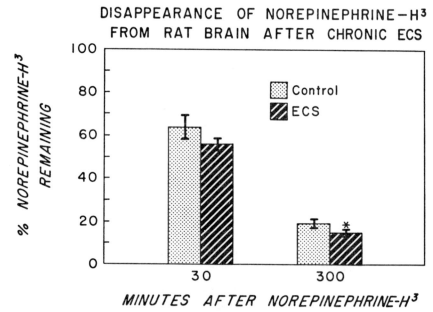

FIG. 6. Disappearance of norepinephrine-H³ from rat brain after chronic administration of electroconvulsive shock. The data shown in this figure were obtained from the experiment described in the legend to Figure 5. In that experiment there were nine separate sets of control and shocked animals, each set containing a control and a shocked animal sacrificed 6, 30, and 300 min after the intracisternal injection of norepinephrine-H³ (i.e., a total of six animals per set). Within each separate set, the levels of norepinephrine-H³ remaining in the brains (of shocked or control animals) 30 and 300 min after the intracisternal injection of norepinephrine-H³ were expressed as percentages of the norepinephrine-H³ found in the brain of the (shocked or control) animal sacrificed at 6 min for each set of animals. Results, expressed as the percentages of norepinephrine-H³ remaining in the brain, are shown as means and standard errors of the means. * $p = < 0.05$, when compared with the control value.

UPTAKE AND DISAPPEARANCE OF NOREPINEPHRINE-H³
IN RAT BRAIN REGIONS AFTER CHRONIC ECS

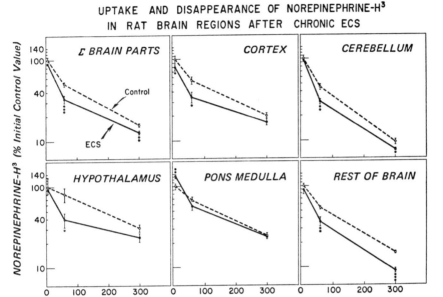

MINUTES AFTER NOREPINEPHRINE-H³

FIG. 7. Uptake and disappearance of norepinephrine-H³ in rat brain regions after the chronic administration of electroconvulsive shocks. Electroconvulsive shocks were administered once daily for 7 days; 1-norepinephrine-H³ was administered by intracisternal injection approximately 18 hr after the last electroconvulsive shock and animals were sacrificed 6, 60, or 300 min after the intracisternal injection of norepinephrine-H³. Matched control animals housed together with the shocked animals were sacrificed at comparable times after an intracisternal injection of norepinephrine-H³; earclip electrodes were not applied to the control animals in this experiment. In this experiment brains were dissected into the following parts: cortex, cerebellum, hypothalamus, pons-medulla and rest of brain (excluding the corpus striatum). Data on the sum of brain parts was obtained by adding the values from each individual part of a given brain. Results are expressed as percentages of the initial control mean values (i.e., the mean level of norepinephrine-H³ found in control animals sacrificed 6 min after the intracisternal injection of norepinephrine-H³.) Results are shown as means and standard errors of the means. Each value represents the mean of five or six determinations. In this experiment, three comparable brain parts were combined for each determination on animals sacrificed 300 min after the intracisternal injection of nor-epinephrine-H³; but individual brain parts were used for each determination at the two earlier times. * $p < 0.1$; ** $p < 0.05$; *** $p < 0.01$ for differences between ECS and control values.

intracisternal injection of norepinephrine-H³. In this experiment brains were dissected into the following parts: cortex, cerebellum, hypothalamus, pons-medulla and the rest of brain (excluding the corpus striatum). Data were obtained on each individual brain part and the values from each part of a given brain were also added to reflect the effect of the treatment on the whole brain (i.e., the sum of brain parts).

As indicated in Figure 7, the initial uptake of norepinephrine-H^3 (reflected by the levels of norepinephrine-H^3 found in brain parts of animals sacrificed 6 min after the intracisternal injection) was not significantly different from controls in any region except the pons-medulla where a statistically significant increase in norepinephrine-H^3 uptake was observed. At 60 min after the intracisternal injection of norepinephrine-H^3, the levels of norepinephrine-H^3 were lower in all brain regions of animals treated with electroconvulsive shocks when compared with control values; and these differences were statistically significant or approached statistical significance in all brain regions except pons-medulla. Thus, in animals treated with electroconvulsive shocks the disappearance of norepinephrine-H^3 from the various brain regions examined appeared to be accelerated during the interval between 6 to 60 min after the intracisternal injection of norepinephrine-H^3 (Figures 7 & 8). At 300 min after the intracisternal injection the levels of norepinephrine-H^3 were also lower in various brain regions, with the exception of pons-medulla, of animals treated with electroconvulsive shock when compared to control values (Figure 7); and a smaller fraction of the norepinephrine-H^3 initially present in the brain (at 6 min) remained in all brain regions except the cortex (Figure 8). However, during the interval from 60 to 300 min after the intracisternal injection, the rate of disappearance of norepinephrine-H^3 tended to be slower in all brain regions (except the "rest of brain") of shocked animals when compared with controls (Figure 7). This could indicate that in at least some brain regions an accelerated turnover of norepinephrine after chronic administration of electroconvulsive shocks occurs in pools of norepinephrine with rapid rates of turnover but not in more slowly turning over pools; however, the data are insufficient to permit a detailed kinetic analysis, and other possible interpretations which might account for these findings cannot be excluded.

The effects of chronically administered electroconvulsive shocks on the metabolism of norepinephrine-H^3 in the brain were also examined in these experiments. As shown in Figure 9, there were no profound changes in the metabolism of norepinephrine-H^3 in the brains of shocked animals sacrificed 6 min after the intracisternal injection of norepinephrine-H^3. However, 60 min after the intracisternal injection of norepinephrine-H^3, the levels of normetanephrine-H^3 were reduced to the same extent as norepinephrine-H^3 (60% to 70% of control values), whereas tritiated deaminated catechol metabolites and total deaminated O-methylated metabolites were not decreased to the same extent (Figure 9); comparable findings were observed in each of the brain regions examined (Figure 10). These findings would be consistent with an increased release and metabolism of norepinephrine-H^3 in the animals treated with electroconvulsive shock, since the total deaminated O-methylated metabolites (principally MHPG and its sulfate conjugate) are the major metabolites of normetanephrine and the final products of norepinephrine metabolism in the brain. It is not possible to interpret the significance of the relatively low levels of normetanephrine-H^3 observed under these conditions

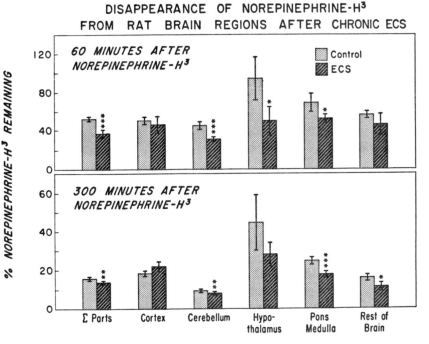

FIG. 8.   Disappearance of norepinephrine-H^3 from various regions of rat brain after the chronic administration of electroconvulsive shocks. The data presented in this figure are derived from the experiment described in Figure 7. The data were treated as described in the legend to Figure 6, i.e., the levels of norepinephrine-H^3 remaining in various brain regions 60 or 300 min after the intracisternal injection of norepinephrine-H^3 were expressed as percentages of the mean levels of norepinephrine-H^3 found in that brain region 6 min after the intracisternal injection of norepinephrine-H^3. Six separate experimental and control sets were run with each set containing a determination made at 6, 60, and 300 min after the injection of norepinephrine-H^3. The results are expressed as means and standard errors of the means of five or six individual values. * $p < 0.1$; ** $p < 0.05$; *** $p < 0.01$ for difference between ECS and control values.

since normetanephrine-H^3 has a very short half-life in the brain and is rapidly converted to MHPG, (Schanberg et al, 1968b). The levels of norepinephrine-H^3 and all of its metabolites in the brain were reduced to approximately 80% of control values in the shocked animals sacrificed 300 min after the intracisternal injection of norepinephrine-H^3 (Figure 9), and this is consistent with the suggestion that the accelerated disappearance of norepinephrine-H^3 from the brains of shocked animals which was evident initially (i.e., between 6 and 60 min after the intracisternal injection of norepinephrine-H^3) does not persist throughout the later interval (i.e., between 60 and 300 min after the intracisternal injection).

In a further experiment (Table 7), we examined the uptake and disappearance of intracisternally administered norepinephrine-H^3 in rat brain 10 days after the last of a series of chronically administered electroconvulsive shocks. Animals used in this experiment received electroconvulsive shocks once daily for 7 days together with animals used in the experiment described in the legend to Figure 7. In the present experiment 1-norepinephrine-H³ was administered by intracisternal injection 10 days after the last electroconvulsive shock and animals were sacrificed 6 and 300 min after the intracisternal injection. Control animals were sacrificed at comparable times after the injection of norepinephrine-H³. In this experiment, earclips were not applied to the control animals. The levels of norepinephrine-H³ remaining in the brain 6 or 300 min after the intracisternal injection are expressed in counts per minute per brain (cpm/brain) as means ± standard errors of the means. Each group contained nine animals.

Under these conditions, the levels of norepinephrine-H³ in the brains of shocked animals sacrificed either 6 or 300 min after the intracisternal injection, were not significantly different from control values. These findings suggest that the increased rate of disappearance of intracisternally administered norepinephrine-H³ from rat brain, which was observed to occur 18 hr after the

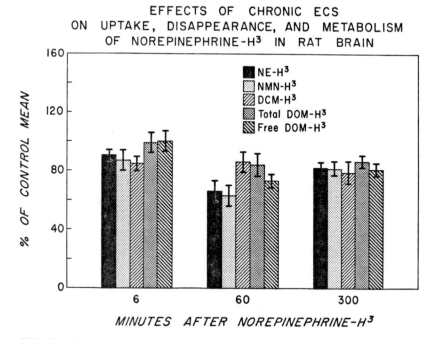

FIG. 9. Effects of chronic electroconvulsive shock on the uptake, disappearance and metabolism of norepinephrine-H³ in rat brain. The data presented in this figure are derived from the experiment described in the legend to Figure 7. The levels of nor-epinephrine-H³ and its various metabolites in the sum of the brain parts from shocked animals were expressed as percentages of the control means (100%) ± the standard errors of the means. Each value represents the mean of 4 to 6 determinations. Abbreviations: see Table 1.

EFFECTS OF CHRONIC ECS ON THE METABOLISM
OF NOREPINEPHRINE-H³ IN RAT BRAIN REGIONS

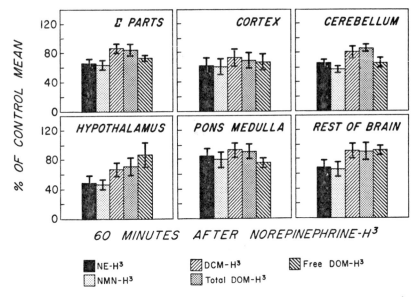

FIG. 10. The effects of chronically administered electroconvulsive shocks on the metabolism of norepinephrine-H³ in rat brain regions. The data presented in this figure were obtained in the experiment described in the legend to Figure 7. The levels of norepinephrine-H³ and its various metabolites present 60 min after the intracisternal injection of norepinephrine-H³ in various brain regions as well as in the sum of brain parts from animals treated with electroconvulsive shocks were expressed as percents of the control mean values. Results are shown as the means ± standard errors of the means of five to six determinations. Abbreviations: see Table 1.

TABLE 7

Uptake and Disappearance of Norepinephrine-H³
in Rat Brain 10 Days After Last Chronic ECS

Time after NE-H³	Norepinephrine-H³ (cpm/brain)	
	Control	ECS
6 min	186,100±6,600	178,400±9,300
300 min	31,800±2,000	33,500±1,400

last of a series of chronically administered electroconvulsive shocks, may not persist for as long as 10 days after the last electroconvulsion. However, since this experiment examined levels of norepinephrine-H³ in whole brain, it is possible that differences may have occurred in specific brain regions which went undetected.

Effects of Electroconvulsive Treatments on Norepinephrine Metabolism and Affective State in a Depressed Patient

We have recently had the opportunity to study the changes in norepinephrine metabolism as well as affective state which occurred in a depressed patient during a course of electroconvulsive treatments (ECT). As illustrated in Figure 11, the levels of MHPG excreted in urine were initially relatively low during the period of severe depression in this patient. There was a gradual decrease in depression starting after the second electroconvulsive treatment and a concomitant gradual increase in MHPG excretion, with highest levels of MHPG occurring after the course of ECT when the patient became hypomanic. These data may provide an indication of an increase in norepinephrine turnover in the brain during this course of electroconvulsive treatments, since a number of findings have recently suggested that MHPG may be the urinary metabolite which best reflects the synthesis and metabolism of norepinephrine in the brain (Maas & Landis, 1968; Schanberg, Breese, Schildkraut, Gordon, & Kopin, 1968a;

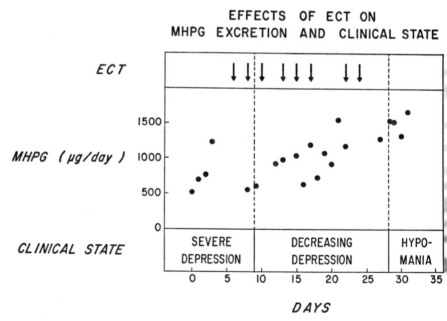

FIG. 11. Effects of electroconvulsive shock treatment (ECT) on 3-methoxy-4-hydroxy-phenylglycol (MHPG) excretion and clinical state in a depressed patient. MHPG was measured in 24-hr urine collection obtained before, during and after a course of modified electroconvulsive shock treatments (ECT).

Schanberg et al., 1968b). However, since some investigators have questioned whether MHPG is the principal metabolite of norepinephrine in the brain (Chase, Breese, Gordon, & Kopin, 1971), and it is, moreover, generally recognized that the brain cannot be regarded as the sole source of MHPG, this interpretation must be made cautiously.

Figure 12 presents data comparing levels of norepinephrine, epinephrine and several of their metabolites (including MHPG) excreted in urine before this course of electroconvulsive treatment when the patient was depressed and after the course of electroconvulsive treatments when the patient was hypomanic.

EFFECTS OF ECT ON URINARY CATECHOLAMINES AND METABOLITES IN A DEPRESSED PATIENT

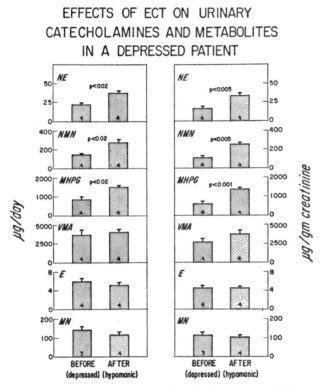

FIG. 12. Effects of electroconvulsive shock treatment (ECT) on urinary catecholamines and metabolites in a depressed patient. Norepinephrine (NE), normetanephrine (NMN), 3-methoxy-4-hydroxy-phenylglycol (MHPG), 3-methoxy-4-hydroxymandelic acid (VMA), epinephrine (E), and metanephrine (MN) were measured in 24-hr urine collections obtained before and after a course of modified electroconvulsive shock treatments. The patient was depressed before ECT and hypomanic after ECT. Data are plotted as means and standard errors of the means. The numbers within the bar graphs indicate the number of samples analyzed.

Whether the data were presented in micrograms per 24 hr or micrograms per gram of creatinine, norepinephrine, normetanephrine, and MHPG were significantly higher after the course of ECT than before. In contrast, there were no significant changes in 3-methoxy-4-hydroxymandelic acid (VMA), epinephrine or metanephrine.

It should be stressed that these data are derived from a single course of ECT in a single depressed patient and must therefore be considered preliminary observations. Further studies will clearly be required to replicate these findings as well as to determine whether the changes that we have observed during the course of ECT in this patient will occur in depressed patients who do not become hypomanic and whether similar changes will be observed after ECT in depressed patients who do not improve clinically. Recent preliminary findings from our laboratory suggest that an increase in MHPG excretion does not invariably occur during ECT in all depressed patients.

In clinical studies of the effects of electroconvulsive shock, numerous investigators have reported an increase in circulating norepinephrine and epinephrine immediately following electroconvulsions (Gravenstein, Anton, Wiener, & Tetlow, 1965; Griswold, 1958; Havens, Zileli, DiMascio, Boling, & Goldfine, 1959; Weil-Malherbe, 1955). The changes were less marked (in most studies) when barbiturates or muscle relaxants were used. Sourkes, Drujan, and Curtis (1958) found an increase in the urinary excretion of epinephrine immediately (several hours) after electroconvulsions; changes in norepinephrine were variable.

In one recent study of the effects of ECT on the urinary excretion of catecholamines and metabolites, small but significant increases on the excretion of dopamine and homovanillic acid were observed after ECT (Messiha & Turek, 1970). The excretion of norepinephrine and some of its metabolites was not significantly altered in this study. (MHPG was not determined.) The patient population in this study consisted of chronic schizophrenics with depressive features.

Rosenblatt and Chanley (1965), in their studies of the metabolism of infused tritiated norepinephrine in depressed patients, have reported that the elevated ratio of amine to oxidized metabolites ("N/O ratio") which they observed in manic-depressive depressed patients was decreased after ECT, but that patients with normal "N/O ratios" prior to ECT showed no change following ECT. The interpretation of these findings is problematic.

Recently, Nordin, Ottosson, and Roos (1971) examined the effects of ECT on levels of 5-hydroxyindoleacetic acid and homovanillic acid in the cerebrospinal fluid in a series of patients with endogenous depressions. The pretreatment levels of 5-hydroxyindoleacetic acid were found to be similar to those previously observed in a series of controls while the levels of homovanillic acid were somewhat lower. After ECT there were no significant changes in levels of 5-hydroxyindoleacetic acid and homovanillic acid despite the fact that there was considerable clinical improvement. Metabolites of norepinephrine (e.g., MHPG) were not determined in this study.

CONCLUSION

Acutely administered electroconvulsive shock appears to discharge norepinephrine in the brain with a consequent increase in normetanephrine, suggesting that this discharge occurs at least in part extraneuronally. This conclusion is further supported by the finding that prior treatment with desmethylimipramine increases the net loss of norepinephrine from brain following electroconvulsive shock, presumably as a result of the inhibition of re-uptake of extraneuronally discharged norepinephrine. Various stressful procedures lead to an increase in the rate of discharge of norepinephrine in the brain, and effects of electroconvulsive seizures, in this regard, may resemble other forms of stresses.

Electroconvulsive seizures may be used as an experimental tool to discharge norepinephrine in the brain. Utilizing this technique, we have observed that pools of norepinephrine in the brain differ in their pathways of metabolism as well as in their turnover rates. In these studies, we found that intracisternally administered tritiated norepinephrine discharged by electroconvulsive seizures 20 or 30 min after the intracisternal injection undergoes appreciable conversion to normetanephrine while conversion to normetanephrine appears to account for a very much smaller fraction of the tritiated norepinephrine discharged at later times. The pool of norepinephrine with a rapid turnover rate and an appreciable conversion to normetanephrine, identified by this technique, may correspond to a labile pool of newly synthesized norepinephrine which can be readily discharged extraneuronally by nerve stimulation (Schildkraut et al., 1971).

Confirming and extending the studies of Kety and his associates (1967), we have found that chronic administration of electroconvulsive seizures increases the rate of disappearance of intracisternally administered tritiated norepinephrine from rat brain. This increased rate of disappearance of norepinephrine was evident 18 hr after the last of a series of seven daily electroconvulsive shocks and could be observed in all five of the brain regions examined: cortex, cerebellum, hypothalamus, pons-medulla, and the rest of the brain (excluding the corpus striatum). In all brain regions the rate of disappearance of norepinephrine-H^3 was faster in the convulsed animals than in controls during the early phase of the disappearance of norepinephrine-H^3 (i.e., from 6 to 60 min) but this did not necessarily persist in the later phase (i.e., from 60 to 300 min). As noted previously, the early phase of disappearance of norepinephrine-H^3 may reflect pools of newly synthesized norepinephrine preferentially released by nerve stimulation. The specific effects of electroconvulsive seizures per se on norepinephrine turnover cannot be separated from the "nonspecific" effects of stress in these experiments (e.g., controls were not earclipped). The uptake of norepinephrine-H³ was not altered under these conditions, except in pons-medulla where there was a significant increase in the uptake of norepinephrine-H³ following the series of electroconvulsive seizures. No differences in the uptake or rate of disappearance of tritiated norepinephrine were observed to persist 10 days after the last electroconvulsion.

In our initial clinical study of the effects of ECT on norepinephrine metabolism in a depressed patient we found that there was a gradual decrease in depression and a concomitant gradual increase in MHPG excretion during the course of ECT, with the highest levels of MHPG occuring after the course of ECT when the patient became hypomanic. Norepinephrine and normetanephrine levels were also significantly higher after the course of ECT than before. There were, however, no significant changes in VMA, epinephrine, or metanephrine.

Taken together, the findings summarized in this chapter suggest that electroconvulsive seizures increase the turnover of norepinephrine in the brain, and that at least the acute electroconvulsion increases the extraneuronal discharge of norepinephrine onto receptors. Thus, by increasing norepinephrine available to receptors, the effects of electroconvulsive seizures appear to be similar to the effects of various stimulants, euphoriants, and the major antidepressant drugs (Schildkraut, 1970a). However, since electroconvulsive seizures have been shown to produce many other biochemical changes in animal brain, including alterations in the content, turnover, and metabolism of dopamine (e.g., Engel, Hanson, Roos, & Strombergsson, 1968; Cooper, Moir, & Guldberg, 1968) and serotonin (e.g., Garattini & Valzelli, 1957; Essman, 1968; Cooper et al., 1968; Engel et al., 1971) further studies will be required to determine whether the clinical effects of electroconvulsive therapy are related to its effects on norepinephrine in the brain.

REFERENCES

Anton, A. H., & Sayre, D. F. A study of the factors affecting aluminum oxidetrihydroxyindole procedure for the analysis of catecholamines. *Journal of Pharmacology and Experimental Therapeutics,* 1962, 138, 360-375.

Axelrod, J. Methylation reactions in the formation and metabolism of catecholamines and other biogenic amines. *Pharmacological Review,* 1966, 18, 95-113.

Bliss, E. L., Ailion, J., & Zwanziger, J. Metabolism of norepinephrine, serotonin and dopamine in rat brain with stress. *Journal of Pharmacology and Experimental Therapeutics,* 1968, 164, 122-134.

Breitner, C., Picchioni, A., & Chin, L. Neurohormone levels in brain after CNS stimulation including electrotherapy. *Journal of Neuropsychiatry,* 1964, 5, 153-158.

Chase, T. N., Breese, G. R., Gordon, E. K., and Kopin, I. J. Catecholamine metabolism in the dog: Comparison of intravenously and intraventricularly administered (¹⁴C) dopamine and (³H) norepinephrine. *Journal of Neurochemistry,* 1971, 18, 135-140.

Cooper, A. J., Moir, A. T. B., & Guldberg, H. C. The effect of electroconvulsive shock on the cerebral metabolism of dopamine and 5-hydroxytryptamine. *Journal of Pharmacy and Pharmacology,* 1968, 20, 729-730.

Dekirmenjian, H., & Maas, J. W. An improved procedure of 3-methoxy-4-hydroxyphenyl-ethylglycol determination by gas liquid chromatography. *Analytical Biochemistry,* 1970, 35, 113-122.

Engel, J., Hanson, L. C. F., & Roos, B. E. Effect of electroshock on 5-HT metabolism in rat brain. *Psychopharmacologia*, 1971, **20**, 197-200.

Engel, J., Hanson, L. C. F., Roos, B. E., & Strombergsson, L. E. Effect of electroshock on dopamine metabolism in rat brain. *Psychopharmacologia*, 1968, **13**, 140-144.

Essman, W. B. Changes in ECS-induced retrograde amnesia with DBMC: Behavioral and biochemical correlates of brain serotonin antagonism. *Physiology and Behavior*, 1968, **3** 527-531.

Garattini, S., & Valzelli, L. Serotonin and electroshock. In S. Garattini & V. Ghetti (Eds.), International symposium on psychotropic drugs, Milan, 1957. *Psychotropic drugs. (Proceedings)*. Amsterdam: Elsevier, 1957.

Glowinski, J., & Axelrod, J. Inhibition of uptake of tritiated noradrenaline in intact rat brain by imipramine and related compounds. *Nature*, 1964, **204**, 1318-1319.

Gordon, R., Spector, S., Sjoerdsma, A., & Udenfriend, S. Increased synthesis of norepinephrine and epinephrine in the intact rat during exercise and exposure to cold. *Journal of Pharmacology and Experimental Therapeutics*, 1966, **153**, 440-447.

Gravenstein, J. S., Anton, A. H., Wiener, S. M., & Tetlow, A. G. Catecholamine and cardiovascular response to electroconvulsion therapy in man. *British Journal of Anaesthesia*, 1965, **37**, 833-839.

Griswold, R. L. Plasma adrenaline and noradrenaline in electroshock therapy in man and in rats. *Journal of Applied Physiology*, 1958, **12**(1), 117-120.

Havens, L. L. Zileli, M. S., DiMascio, A., Boling, L., & Goldfien, A. Changes in catecholamine response to successive electric convulsive treatments. *Journal of Mental Science*, 1959, **105**, 821-829.

Hinesley, R. K., Norton, J. A., & Aprison, M. H. Serotonin, norepinephrine and 3,4-dihydroxyphenylethylamine in rat brain parts following electroconvulsive shock. *Journal of Psychiatric Research*, 1968, **6**, 143-152.

Kato, L., Gozsy, B., Roy, P. B., & Groh, V. Histamine, serotonin, epinephrine and norepinephrine in the rat brain, following convulsions. *International Journal of Neuropsychiatry*, 1967, **3**, 46-51.

Kety, S. S., Javoy, F., Thierry, A. M., Julou, L., & Glowinski, J. Sustained effect of electroconvulsive shock on turnover of norepinephrine in central nervous system of rat. *Proceedings of the National Academy of Sciences of the United States of America*, 1967, **58**, 1249-1254.

Kopin, I. J., Axelrod, J., & Gordon, E. K. The metabolic fate of H^3-epinephrine and C^{14}-metanephrine in the rat. *Journal of Biological Chemistry*, 1961, **236**, 2109-2113.

Ladisich, W., Steinhauff, N., & Matussek, N. Chronic administration of electroconvulsive shock and norepinephrine metabolism in the rat brain. *Psychopharmacologia*, 1969, **15**, 296-304.

Maas, J. W., & Landis, D. H. *In vivo* studies of metabolism of norepinephrine in central nervous system. *Journal of Pharmacology and Experimental Therapeutics*, 1968, **163**, 147-162.

Messiha, F. S., & Turek, I. Electroconvulsive therapy: Effect on catecholamine excretion by psychiatric patients. *Research Communications in Chemical Pathology and Pharmacology*, 1970, **1**, 535-546.

Musacchio, J. M., Julou, L., Kety, S. S., & Glowinski, J. Increase in rat brain tyrosine hydroxylase activity produced by electroconvulsive shock. *Proceedings of the National Academy of Sciences of the United States of America*, 1969, **63**, 1117-1119.

Nordin, G., Ottosson, J. -O., & Roos, B. E. Influence of convulsive therapy on 5-hydroxyindoleacetic acid and homovanillic acid in cerebrospinal fluid in endogenous depression. *Psychopharmacologia*, 1971, **20**, 315-320.

Rosenblatt, S. F., & Chanley, J. D. Differences in the metabolism of norepinephrine in depressions. *Archives of General Psychiatry*, 1965, **13**, 495-502.

Schanberg, S. M., Breese, G. R., Schildkraut, J. J., Gordon, E. K., & Kopin, I. J. 3-Methoxy-4-hydroxyphenylglycol sulfate in brain and cerebrospinal fluid. *Biochemical Pharmacology*, 1968, **17**, 2006-2008. (a)

Schanberg, S. M., Schildkraut, J. J., Breese, G. R., & Kopin, I. J. Metabolism of norepinephrine-H[3] in rat brain: Identification of conjugated 3-methoxy-4-hydroxyphenylglycol as the major metabolite. *Biochemical Pharmacology*, 1968, **17**, 247-254. (b)

Schanberg, S. M., Schildkraut, J. J., & Kopin, I. J. The effects of pentobarbital on the fate of intracisternally administered norepinephrine-H[3]. *Journal of Pharmacology and Experimental Therapeutics*, 1967, **157**, 311-318.

Schildkraut, J. J. *Neuropsychopharmacology and the affective disorders.* Boston: Little, Brown, 1970. (a)

Schildkraut, J. J. Tranylcypromine: Effects on norepinephrine metabolism in rat brain. *American Journal of Psychiatry*, 1970, **126**, 925-931. (b)

Schildkraut, J. J., Dodge, G. A., & Logue, M. A. Effects of tricyclic antidepressants on the uptake and metabolism of intracisternally administered norepinephrine-H[3] in rat brain. *Journal of Psychiatric Research*, 1969, **7**, 29-34.

Schildkraut, J. J., Draskoczy, P. R., & Lo, P. S. Norepinephrine pools in rat brain: Differences in turnover rates and pathways of metabolism. *Science*, 1971, **172**, 587-589.

Schildkraut, J. J., Gordon, E. K., & Durell, J. Catecholamine metabolism in affective disorders. I. Normetanephrine and VMA excretion in depressed patients treated with imipramine. *Journal of Psychiatric Research*, 1965, **3**, 213-223.

Schildkraut, J. J., Schanberg, S. M., Breese, G. R., & Kopin, I. J. Norepinephrine metabolism and drugs used in the affective disorders: A possible mechanism of action. *American Journal of Psychiatry*, 1967, **124**, 600-608.

Shatalova, A. A., & Antonov, E. K. Content of adrenaline and noradrenaline in adrenal and brain tissues and in blood of rabbits in convulsive states. *Psychopharmacology Abstracts*, 1961, **1**, 341.

Simmonds, M. A., & Iversen, L. L. Thermoregulation and norepineprhine. *Science*, 1969, **165**, 1030-1031. (a)

Simmonds, M. A., & Iversen, L. L. Thermoregulation: Effects of environmental temperature on turnover of hypothalamic norepinephrine. *Science*, 1969, **163**, 473-474. (b)

Sourkes, T. L., Drujan, B. D., & Curtis, G. C. Effects of electroshock therapy on the excretion of epinephrine, *Journal of Nervous and Mental Disease*, 1958, **127**, 191-195.

Thierry, A. M., Javoy, F., Glowinski, J., & Kety, S. S. Effects of stress on the metabolism of norepinephrine, dopamine and serotonin in the central nervous system of the rat. I. Modifications of norepinephrine turnover. *Journal of Pharmacology and Experimental Therapeutics*, 1968, **163**, 163-171.

Weil-Malherbe, H. The effect of convulsive therapy on plasma adrenaline and noradrenaline. *Journal of Mental Science*, 1955, **101**, 156-162.

Whitby, G., Axelrod, J., & Weil-Malherbe, H. The fate of H[3]-norepinephrine in animals. *Journal of Pharmacology and Experimental Therapeutics*, 1961, **132**, 193-201.

Wilk, S., Gitlow, S. E., Mendlowitz, M., Franklin, M. J., Carr, H. E., & Clarke, D. D. A quantitative assay for vanillyl-mandelic acid (VMA) by gas-liquid chromatography. *Analytical Biochemistry*, 1965, **13**, 544-551.

12
EFFECT OF REPEATED ECS ON BRAIN WEIGHT AND BRAIN ENZYMES[1]

Gordon T. Pryor, Ph.D.[2]

We have been studying the effect of repeated electroconvulsive shock (ECS) on brain and behavior in rats for the past several years (Pryor & Otis, 1969; Pryor, Otis, Scott, & Colwell, 1967; Pryor, Peache, Scott, 1972a; Pryor, Scott, & Peache, 1972). Our basic aim has been to discover brain biochemical changes associated with repeated ECS that might be associated with, or mediate, some of the persisting behavioral consequences of this treatment. Our basic design generally has been to induce grand mal convulsions daily using transcorneal ECS. We have used young male rats of several strains, beginning usually at 30 to 40 days of age. The number of such daily seizures has been varied from one to as many as five per week for 16 weeks. We have examined the effects of this treatment on growth (in terms of body weight), brain development (especially those enzymes involved in neurohumoral metabolism), and several behavioral parameters.

One of the first and most easily measured effects of repeated daily ECS in rats is a reduction in body weight (Figure 1). This effect becomes pronounced after about 10 daily convulsions and is accompanied by a noticeable change in gross cage behavior. The animals become hyperirritable, tense, and difficult to handle. It has been our experience that this behavioral syndrome persists as long as daily ECS is continued. After the initial slowing in growth, body weight

[1] The work reported here was supported by Contract Nonr-2993(00) between the United States Office of Naval Research and Stanford Research Institute, and United States Public Health Service Grant No. MH17414 from the National Institute of Mental Health. Preparation of this manuscript was partially supported by General Research Grant ISO IFR-05522 from the National Institutes of Health.
[2] The assistance of Miss Susan Peache and Mrs. M. Kaye Scott is gratefully acknowledged.

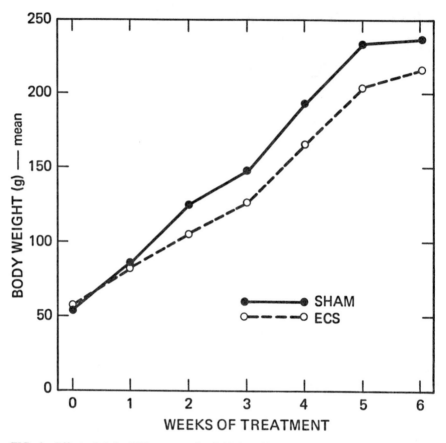

FIG. 1. Effect of daily ECS on growth of 30-day-old male Fischer rats ($N = 4$ in each group). (Pryor, unpublished data)

begins to increase almost parallel with that of controls but at a reduced absolute level. When the treatment is discontinued, body weight gradually recovers and usually, with time, surpasses that of sham-treated controls (Figure 2), a result noted in the early work with ECS by Braun, Russell, and Patton (1949) but often overlooked. The behavioral syndrome also slowly dissipates.

While body weight is adversely effected by repeated ECS, animals sacrificed after various numbers of treatments show an increase in wet brain tissue weight that is especially pronounced, and appears earliest, in cortical sections (Figure 3). The effect usually requires daily ECS for 2 to 4 weeks to reach statistical significance in groups of 8 to 10 animals (Pryor & Otis, 1969; Pryor et al., 1967). This effect also slowly dissipates after the last ECS (Figure 4). The constituents of the brain responsible for the increase in wet weight have not yet been fully explored. However, we have measured the total protein content of brain (regionally as well as in whole brain) in literally dozens of experiments and have been unable to detect any change in the concentration of protein expressed on a wet weight basis, suggesting that the effect is not due solely to edema. That is not to say, however, that the total, absolute amount of protein has not increased. Indeed, it has, but only in proportion to the increase in wet tissue weight. Recently we have determined dry weights as well as wet weights in two experiments (Figure 5). These results show significant increases in dry weight as well as increases in wet weight, again suggesting that the tissue is relatively normal with regard to gross proportions of various constituents. An increase in water content is also evident, as inferred from the difference between wet and dry weights, but again the difference is proportional to the changes in solid constituents.

Biochemically, we have concentrated on those aspects of brain metabolism that might logically participate in long-lasting changes in brain function. Moreover, we have concentrated on those biochemical systems that are closely related to synaptic transmission.

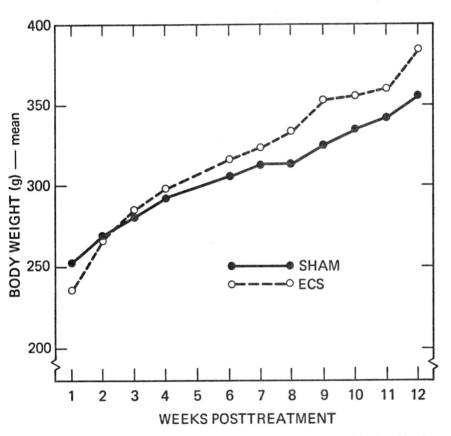

FIG. 2. Recovery in growth from the effect of daily ECS for 6 weeks of 30-day-old male Fischer rats ($N = 4$ in each group). (Pryor, unpublished data)

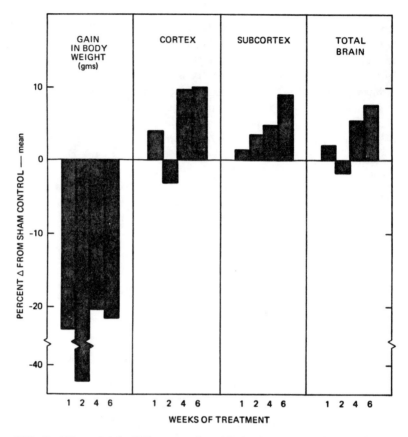

FIG. 3. Effect of daily ECS on growth and brain tissue wet weight of 30-day-old male Fischer rats as a function of the number of weeks of treatment ($N = 5$ pairs at each point). Results are expressed as the mean percentage change of ECS-treated groups from sham-treated controls. Animals were sacrificed 24 hr after the last treatment. (Pryor, unpublished data)

Initially, we chose the acetylcholine system for study and measured the activities of cholinesterase and acetylcholinesterase. In a number of experiments we were able to find no reproducible changes in cholinesterase activity and only elusive changes in acetylcholinesterase activity even after prolonged treatment schedules (Pryor & Otis, 1969; Pryor et al., 1967). Shortly thereafter we added monoamine oxidase (MAO) activity to our dependent measures since this enzyme plays a metabolic role for serotonin and norepinephrine similar in some respects to the role of the cholinergic degradative enzymes for acetylcholine. We immediately found relatively rapid and easily reproducible changes in the activity of MAO (Pryor et al., 1967), which has come to be regarded as an enzyme that helps regulate the intracellular concentrations of serotonin and norepinephrine. As a consequence of these early experiments we have

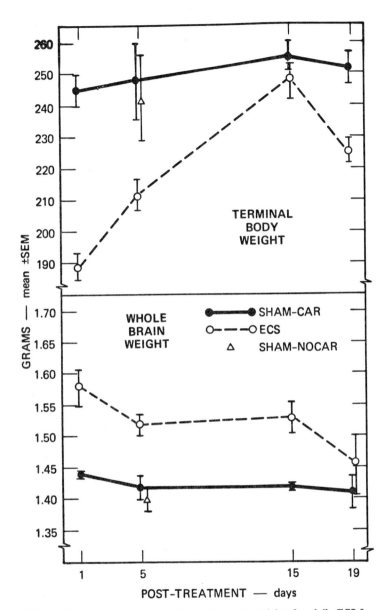

FIG. 4. Recovery in growth and brain tissue wet weight after daily ECS for 6 weeks of 30-day-old male Fischer rats (*N* = 2 to 4 pairs at each point) as a function of time after last treatment. (Pryor, Peache, & Scott, 1972)

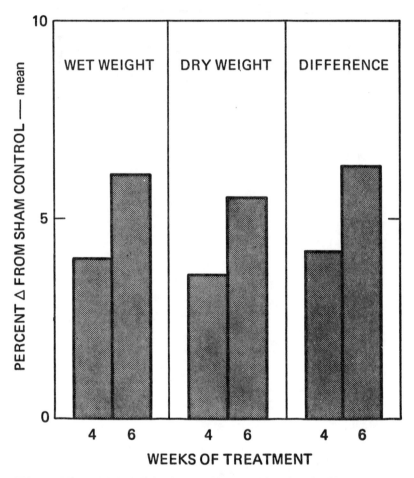

FIG. 5. Effect of daily ECS for 4 weeks (*N* = 15 pairs) or 6 weeks (*N* = 10 pairs) on whole brain wet and dry weights, and the difference (i.e., water content) of 30-day-old male Fischer rats. Results are expressed as the mean percentage change of ECS-treated groups from sham-treated controls. Animals were sacrificed 24 hr after the last treatment. (Pryor, Scott, & Peache, in preparation)

concentrated recently on the monoamine systems to the neglect of the cholinergic system.

Some of our earlier findings for MAO are shown in Figure 6, which summarizes the results of a fairly large number of experiments, expressed as the mean percentage difference between groups treated for various periods and their respective controls. Each box represents the average difference between groups of 6 to 10 ECS-treated animals compared with sham-treated controls. In these experiments we were also examining the effect of minimal threshold convulsions on brain chemistry and these results are shown as the open boxes in this figure. This figure shows that the increase in MAO activity following repeated convulsive seizures is reproducible and that cortical structures appear to be affected to a greater degree than the subcortical section which in these experiments included the cerebellum. Also, these results suggest that the intensity of ECS used is important in that minimal threshold convulsions had little or no effect on MAO activity. The average magnitude of the changes shown in Figure 6 are not large, however, since no distinction was made in this figure regarding the total number of seizures received in the various experiments.

Figure 7 shows the results of several experiments in which the number of treatments was varied from 7 to 42 and illustrates the developmental course of the effect. The lack of any clear increase in MAO activity after 7 daily treatments in these experiments is typical. We have varied several parameters thus far trying to demonstrate an earlier apperance of a detectable increase. The intensity of shock (50 to 150 mA) used to induce the convulsion and the age of the animals when first treated (25 to 50 days) were varied in this regard without any major effect (Pryor et al., 1972). It thus appears that with the measures we have used thus far, between 7 and 14 single daily ECS are required to obtain reproducible increases in the activity of this enzyme. Beyond this number of

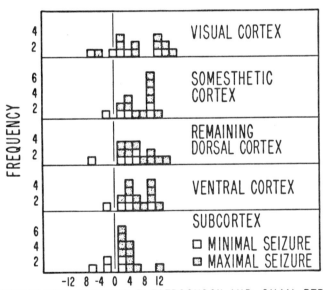

DIFFERENCE BETWEEN ELECTROSHOCK AND SHAM-PERCENT

FIG. 6. Effect of daily ECS on brain MAO activity of 30-day-old male Wistar rats. Each block represents the mean percentage change of an ECS-treated group from its respective sham-treated control (N = 6 to 10 pairs for each block). The number of treatments has been ignored in this figure. Data are extracted and summarized from Pryor and Otis (1969) and Pryor (unpublished data).

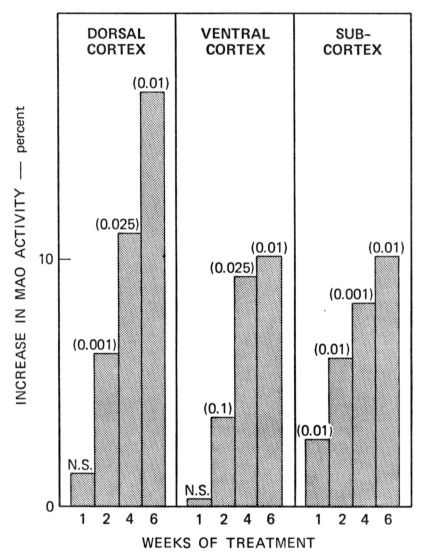

FIG. 7. Effect of daily ECS on brain MAO activity of 30-day-old male Fischer rats as a function of the number of weeks of treatment (N = 33, 8, 8, and 5 pairs at 1, 2, 4, and 6 weeks of treatment, respectively). Data are taken from Pryor, Scott, and Peache (1972).

ECS the effect is clear with little or no overlap between values for experimental and control groups.

We also considered the possibility that the total number of ECS might be the important variable. We therefore gave 7 or 14 ECS at 30-min intervals without seeing any appreciable increase in MAO activity (Pryor et al., 1972). However, in a more recent preliminary experiment we gave 1, 2, or 3 seizures per day for 7 days and the results suggest that multiple spaced daily ECS may accelerate the appearance of the effect (Figure 8), although the total number of ECS required appears to remain about the same.

The possible anatomical localization of the effect on MAO activity was examined more carefully in two experiments in which the groups received daily ECS for 4 weeks to ensure an easily measurable effect and the brain was dissected into nine more or less distinct sections. The results (Figure 9) suggest a gradient in the magnitude of effect extending from the dorsal cortex (DC) and underlying caudate nucleus (Ca) and hippocampal structures (Hipp) through the pyriform and prepyriform areas (PP), thalamus and hypothalamus (TT), and caudally back through the brain stem [colliculi and tectum (CT) and pons and medulla (PM)]. The cerebellum (Ce) and olfactory bulbs (OB) have not shown as reproducible changes as other brain sections in MAO activity in these and several other experiments. This figure also illustrates the repeatedly found absence of any change in protein concentration referred to earlier.

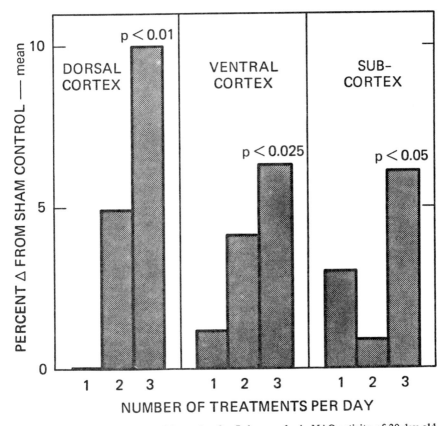

FIG. 8. Effect of 1, 2, or 3 ECS per day for 7 days on brain MAO activity of 30-day-old male Fischer rats ($N = 9$ per group). (Pryor, Scott, & Peache, in preparation)

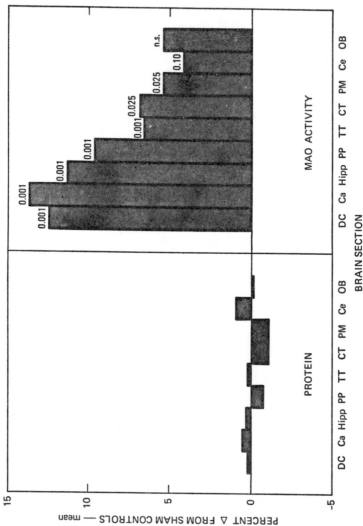

FIG. 9. Effect of daily ECS for 4 weeks on brain MAO activity of 30-day-old male Fischer rats ($N = 14$ pairs). Brain was grossly dissected into dorsal cortex (DC), caudate nuclei (Ca), hippocampus and contiguous structures (Hipp), pyriform and prepyriform areas (PP), thalamus and hypothalamus (TT), colliculi and tectum (CT), pons and medulla (PM), cerebellum (Ce), and olfactory bulbs (OB). (Pryor, Scott, & Peache, in preparation).

We have also begun to investigate the possible biochemical specificity of the MAO response. In several experiments we have measured the activities of succinate dehydrogenase and catechol O-methyl transferase (Pryor et al., 1972). Our rationale for studying succinate dehydrogenase was that it represents a nonspecific mitochondrial enzyme and since MAO is mitochondrial in location we reasoned that, perhaps, this might indicate whether a gross response of the mitochondrial system was taking place. No clear or reproducible changes in the activity of succinate dehydrogenase were found, however, suggesting a degree of specificity for the MAO response in this regard. The validity of this argument has to be tempered somewhat, however, since MAO is associated with the outer membrane, whereas succinate dehydrogenase is an inner membrane enzyme, and thus further work is required to settle this point. We chose to measure catechol O-methyl transferase because it represents an extracellular means of metabolizing norepinephrine compared with the intracellular regulatory role of monoamine oxidase. Again we were unable in several experiments to find any clear differences in the activity of this enzyme, thus providing further evidence for some biochemical specificity of the MAO response.

At the same time we were finding increased MAO activity following repeated ECS, others (Kety, Javoy, Thierry, Julou, & Glowinski, 1967) had reported increased levels of serotonin and norepinephrine, increased clearance of intracisternally injected [H³]-norepinephrine, and increased tyrosine hydroxylase activity (Musacchio, Julou, Kety, & Glowinski, 1969; Schildkraut & Draskoczy, this volume). Moreover, Ladisich, Steinhauff, and Matussek (1969) reported increases in deaminated metabolites of norepinephrine which were compatible with our findings with respect to MAO. These reports stressed the persisting nature of the changes resulting from their ECS schedule since the effects they noted were present 24 hr after the last seizure. It should be emphasized that in all of the work I have presented thus far, our animals were sacrificed at least 24 hr after the last seizure. Of greater significance, however, are the results from two sets of experiments where sacrifice was withheld for longer periods of time after the last treatment and which suggest that the persisting changes in MAO activity may be on a time scale of weeks or months. The results of one such experiment are shown in Figure 10. The animals in this experiment were treated daily for 6 weeks and sacrificed as shown in the figure. In this experiment, there was still a clear difference between sham- and ECS-treated groups throughout the brain 19 days after the last treatment when the last groups were sacrificed. In an earlier experiment (Pryor & Otis, 1970) a slight, though significant, increase in MAO activity was still present in the dorsal cortex 6 weeks after the last of a comparable series of ECS.

Our work thus far must be considered as still in a preliminary stage. We have defined some of the gross anatomical and biochemical effects of repeated ECS that may be related to the behavioral sequela and we have begun to explore some of the parameters involved. We are struck at this point by the many similarities between the conditions required to elicit these effects in rats and the

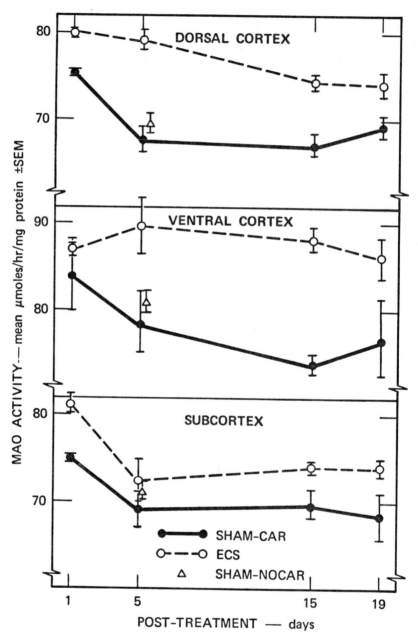

FIG. 10. Persisting increases in brain MAO activity following daily ECS for 6 weeks in 30-day-old male Fischer rats (N = 2 to 4 pairs at each point). (Pryor, Peache, & Scott, 1972b)

conditions required to have a therapeutic effect in human mental disorders (e.g., number and spacing of treatments, and the behavioral specificity). Thus, the rat may provide an adequate model for discovering some of the underlying mechanisms involved in ECS treatment. Toward this end we are currently attempting to further delimit the behavioral effects of repeated ECS as a prerequisite to relating them to the biochemical consequences, and biochemically, many questions remain to be answered regarding the MAO response, not to mention the many other aspects of amine metabolism. For example, does the increase in MAO activity represent de novo synthesis? Preliminary work in which MAO was irreversibly inhibited by pargyline suggests that recovery (increased synthesis?) is more rapid in rats given daily ECS, and fractionation experiments indicate that the increase occurs earliest in the nuclear fraction. Along the same lines the question of whether specific isoenzymes are differentially affected is in the process of being investigated.

While it seems to us very likely that a number of biochemical systems will eventually be shown to be involved in the biochemical consequences of repeated ECS, we are encouraged by our own results for MAO and the results of others for other aspects of the biogenic amine systems in brain to pursue this line of attack. The persisting nature of the MAO response we have observed has many of the required characteristics to be involved in cellular regulation that might be related to long-lasting behavioral consequences of this treatment in the laboratory and in the clinic.

SUMMARY

Repeated electroconvulsive shock (ECS) leads to a decrease in body weight but an increase in brain weight (wet and dry) in rats. These gross effects are accompanied by an increase in monoamine oxidase (MAO) activity per milligram protein throughout the brain without any detectable or marked changes in protein concentration or the relative activities of succinate dehydrogenase, catechol O-methyl transferase, and cholinesterase; acetylcholinesterase activity is sometimes, but not consistently, increased. The anatomical and biochemical changes develop slowly and differentially with daily ECS. Dissipation of these changes after the last ECS also proceeds differentially. MAO is the most responsive enzyme studied thus far and the changes appear to persist long after the last of a series of ECS. Involvement of the serotonin and/or norepinephrine system in the behavioral consequences of repeated ECS is suggested from these and other data.

REFERENCES

Braun, H. W., Russell, R. W., & Patton, R. A. Duration of decrements in learning and retention following electroshock convulsions in the white rat. *Journal of Comparative and Physiological Psychology,* 1949, **42,** 87-106.

Kety, S. S., Javoy, F., Thierry, A. M., Julou, L., & Glowinski, J. A sustained effect of electroconvulsive shock on the turnover of norepinephrine in the central nervous system of the rat. *Proceedings of the National Academy of Sciences of the United States of America*, 1967, 58, 1249-1254.

Ladisich, W., Steinhauff, N., & Matussek N. Chronic administration of electroconvulsive shock and norepinephrine metabolism in the rat brain. *Psychopharmacologia*, 1969, 15, 296-304.

Musacchio, J. M., Julou, L., Kety, S. S., & Glowinski, J. Increase in rat brain tyrosine hydroxylase activity produced by electroconvulsive shock. *Proceedings of the National Academy of Sciences of the United States of America*, 1969, 63, 1117-1119.

Pryor, G. T., & Otis, L. S. Brain biochemical and behavioral effects of 1, 2, 4 or 8 weeks' electroshock treatment. *Life Sciences*, 1969, 8, 387-399.

Pryor, G. T., & Otis, L. S. Persisting effects of chronic electroshock seizures on brain and behavior in two strains of rats. *Physiology and Behavior*, 1970, 5, 1053-1055.

Pryor, G. T., Otis, L. S., Scott, M. K., & Colwell, J. J. Duration of chronic electroshock treatment in relation to brain weight, brain chemistry and behavior. *Journal of Comparative and Physiological Psychology*, 1967, 63, 236-239.

Pryor, G. T., Peache, S., & Scott, M. K. Escape response thresholds in rats following repeated electroconvulsive shock seizures. *Physiology and Behavior*, 1972, 8, 95-99.(a)

Pryor, G. T., Peache, S., & Scott, M. K. Effect of electroconvulsive shock on avoidance conditioning and brain monoamineoxidase activity. *Physiology and Behavior*, 1972, 9, 623-628.(b)

Pryor, G. T., Scott, M. K., & Peache, S. Increased monoamine oxidase activity following repeated electroshock seizures. *Journal of Neurochemistry*, 1972, 19, 891-893.

13

THE EFFECT OF ELECTROSHOCK ON BRAIN RNA AND PROTEIN SYNTHESIS AND ITS POSSIBLE RELATIONSHIP TO BEHAVIORAL EFFECTS[1]

Adrian Dunn, Ph.D., Antonio Giuditta, M.D.,
John E. Wilson, Ph.D., and Edward Glassman, Ph.D.

It seems likely that the clinical and other behavioral effects of electroconvulsive shock (ECS) have a biochemical basis. Because of the overwhelming importance of protein in metabolism we have studied the synthesis of protein in the brains of animals after electroconvulsive shock.

Animals used were male Swiss-Webster mice 6 to 10 weeks old. The mice were given a single ECS of 17 mA and 0.1-sec duration from transcorneal electrodes delivered from a constant current apparatus. Mice normally had tonic and clonic convulsions for about 1 min and recovered without resuscitation. Only animals exhibiting this pattern were used for biochemical study. Protein synthesis was measured by following the incorporation of intraperitoneally injected L[U-^{14}C]leucine into proteins of the cerebral hemispheres over a 5-min period. Free radioactive leucine in the brain was also measured to determine uptake of the amino acid into the brain. For full details see Dunn, Giuditta, and Pagliuca (1971) and Dunn (1971a). The rate of protein synthesis is estimated from the radioactivity incorporated into protein per minute divided by the specific activity of the precursor amino acid. Since in our experiments the amount of free leucine in the brain did not change, this can be simplified to radioactivity in protein divided by radioactivity in free leucine. The results are expressed in this form which corrects for the uptake of ^{14}C leucine in the brain.

[1] During part of the research Adrian Dunn was supported by a training grant (MH-11107) of the United States Public Health Service. The work was supported by research grants from the United States Public Health Service (MH-18136 and NS 07457), the U.S. National Science Foundation (GB 18551), the CIBA-Geigy Corporation, the Dreyfus Foundation, and a Faculty Grant (VC 337) from the University of North Carolina at Chapel Hill.

The combined results of five experiments are shown in Figure 1. The incorporation of leucine into protein was decreased by about 50% when the leucine was injected immediately after the ECS ($p < 0.001$, paired sample t test (one-tailed) on the logarithms of the ratios). This reversed soon after ECS and by 15 min there was no significant difference between grouped electroshocked and sham-treated animals. However, at times greater than 15 min after electroshock there is the suggestion of a slight stimulation. Occasional animals showed low incorporation at these later times, generally correlated with poor recovery from the ECS. But, frequently high incorporations were seen between 15 and 30 min after injection (6 out of 15 animals), an effect not seen at other times nor in sham controls which received identical treatment except that no current was transmitted to the electrodes.

A decrease in the incorporation of radioactive leucine into protein immediately after ECS has also been shown recently by Cotman, Banker,

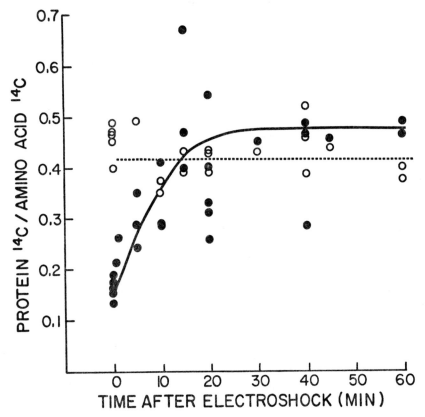

FIG. 1. The incorporation of [^{14}C]leucine into brain protein relative to the radioactivity of the free brain amino acid at various times after electroconvulsive shock (●) or sham treatment (○). Each point is the mean estimate for one mouse. The broken line is the mean of the sham controls. (From Dunn, 1971a)

TABLE 1

The Incorporation of Amino Acids into Mouse Brain after ECS

Amino acid incorporated	Sham control	ECS	Inhibition %	p (t test)
Lysine-4,5-^{3}H (100 μCi)				
Protein dpm	17,700 (6,300)	7,460 (1,030)	58	<.025
Free amino acid dpm	177,000 (56,500)	176,000 (41,000)	0	
Protein/amino acid	.097 (.012)	.047 (.01)	51	<.005
Leucine-1-^{14}C (10 μCi)				
Protein dpm	10,900 (2,900)	1,600 (370)	85	<.005
Free amino acid dpm	22,000 (5,700)	11,400 (2,330)	48	<.01
Protein/amino acid	.486 (.067)	.144 (.026)	71	<.001

Note. — Amino acids were injected intraperitoneally and animals sacrificed 5 min later. Experimental details are given in the text. Numbers in parentheses are standard deviations.

Zornetzer, and McGaugh, (1971) and Essman (1972). Other precursors show a similar effect. Earlier Geiger, Horvath, and Kawakita, (1960) and Dunn and Giuditta (1971) showed an inhibition of incorporation into protein of ^{14}C derived from glucose via principally glutamic and aspartic acids. Table 1 shows that the incorporation of L[1-^{14}C]leucine and L[4,5-^{3}H]lysine is also inhibited. The last two precursors have no nonvolatile radioactive metabolites in the brain at short times after administration, which reduces artifacts and simplifies the necessary biochemical procedures (see Banker & Cotman, 1971; Tiplady, personal communication, 1972).

Does this change in amino acid incorporation truly reflect a change in protein synthesis? In the case of leucine there is indeed a decreased uptake of the amino acid from the periphery (see Table 1), and Cotman et al. (1971) reported a small increase in the leucine content of brain immediately following the ECS. While the magnitude of both these effects does not appear to be large enough to explain the inhibited incorporation into protein, compartmentation phenomena or variations in rates of uptake could confound this. Fortunately, it is possible to estimate the rate of protein synthesis in the cell in another way. Since protein synthesis occurs principally on polyribosomes, examination of the polyribosome content or more specifically the ratio of polyribosomes to monomeric ribosomes gives an indication of the protein synthetic activity of the cell.

Figure 2 shows a sucrose gradient analysis of brain polyribosomes and that the polyribosome peaks disappear and are replaced by a single large (monoribosome) peak after brief treatment with ribonuclease, leaving no light-absorbing material in the lower part of the gradient. Figure 3 shows the brain polyribosome profiles of mice 2.5 min after subjection to ECS or sham ECS. There is a loss of the larger polyribosome species exactly balanced by an increase in the smaller

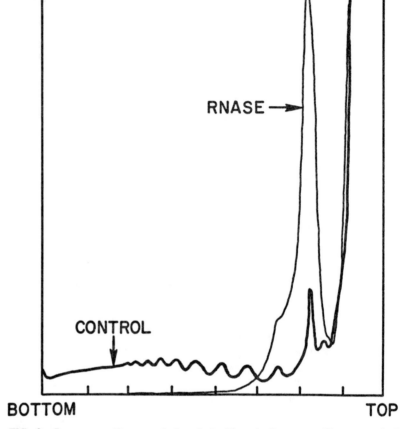

RNASE ⟶

CONTROL

BOTTOM   TOP

FIG. 2. Sucrose gradient analysis of brain polyribosomes. Mouse cerebral hemispheres were homogenized in 1 ml of 0.25 M sucrose, 0.02 M tris-HCl, 0.1 M KCl, 0.04 M NaCl, 0.005 M MgCl$_2$ and centrifuged at 1,000 x g for 10 min and 10,000 x g for 20 min. The postmitochondrial supernatants were layered over linear gradients of 20% to 40% sucrose in the same salts medium used for the homogenization tissue and centrifuged for 4 hr at 25,000 rpm (63,000 x g) in the spinco SW 25.1 rotor at 2°. Gradients were analyzed in an ISCO ultraviolet fractionator at 254 mμ. The ordinate is optical density. RNase: 100 μg pancreatic ribonuclease was added to the postmitochondrial supernatant after it was layered on the gradient ready for centrifugation (thin line).

polyribosome species and monoribosomes. The data for four pairs of animals are summarized in Table 2 which shows a mean decrease in polyribosome/monoribosome ratio of 20% which is statistically significant. This confirms the data of MacInnes, McConkey, and Schlesinger, (1970) and earlier data of Vesco and Giuditta (1968) after six successive shocks in the rabbit. It is notable that there is excellent agreement between the post-ECS time course of leucine incorporation seen in Figure 1 and the polyribosome profiles of MacInnes et al.

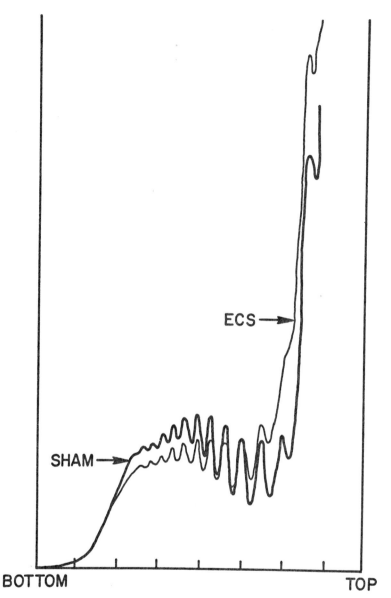

BOTTOM   **TOP**

FIG. 3   The same as Figure 2 but the postmitochondrial supernatant was isolated 2.5 min after a single ECS or sham ECS as described in the text. Centriguation time was only 3 hr and the optical density scale has been expanded from Figure 2 by a factor of approximately 2.5. The monoribosome peak is the first peak from the top of the gradient. After 3 hr this was not resolved from the lower molecular weight (soluble) absorbing material.

TABLE 2

Polyribosome/Monoribosome Ratio after ECS

Type	Polyribosomes/monoribosomes	Control %
Sham ECS	2.37 (0.34)	[100]
ECS	1.90* (0.17)	80

*$p<.05$ ($N = 4$).

Note.–Polyribosomes in the postmitochondrial supernatant of brains of mice sacrificed 2.5 min after ECS or sham–ECS were analysed on sucrose gradients as described in Figure 3. The polyribosome/monoribosome ratio is calculated from the area under the absorbance profile determined by planimetry.

(1970), including the stimulation after 20 min. Thus we may be reasonably sure that leucine incorporation into protein reflects the real rate of protein synthesis and that there is an inhibition of protein synthesis immediately following ECS, although the magnitude of the effect measured by the two techniques differs possibly for experimental reasons.

Is the effect of ECS on protein synthesis due to the electroshock per se or to the convulsions induced? Figure 4 shows the results of an experiment to determine if there was any relationship between current passed and the inhibition of leucine incorporation into protein immediately after the electroshock. It shows a clear, high correlation (correlation coefficient, $r = 0.91$, $p < 0.005$, $N = 13$), between the current passed and the leucine incorporation. Other experiments showed similar results. Convulsions occurred consistently in those animals receiving 17 mA or more, variably for those between 10 and 15 mA, and were totally absent for lower currents. The slopes of the regression lines obtained separately for the convulsed and nonconvulsed mice on all experiments did not differ significantly. It can be concluded that the decrease in incorporation is due to the passage of current itself or a direct effect of that current on the brain rather than to the bodily convulsions.

Cotman et al. (1971) have also shown that subconvulsive shock may cause an inhibition of leucine incorporation into protein. In their case they used ether to inhibit the convulsions and found incorporation was inhibited using 30-mA shock under ether or 12-mA shock without ether. Appreciable inhibition was not observed when 12-mA shock was administered under ether, under which conditions no detectable electrophysiological seizures were present. Thus an inhibition of the incorporation of leucine into brain protein was correlated with the presence of brain electrophysiological seizures.

What then is the mechanism of the inhibition of brain protein synthesis? The most obvious possibility is a fall of adenosine triphosphate (ATP) levels on which protein synthesis is very dependent and which is known to occur during and after overt convulsions induced by electroshock (King, Lowry, Passonneau, & Venson, 1967). However, the fall in ATP levels is apparently due to anoxia and is not observed during convulsions when animals are adequately oxygenated (Collins, Posner, & Plum, 1970). Since an inhibition of protein synthesis was observed in the absence of convulsions (Figure 4) another mechanism may be operative, although the ATP level undoubtedly has an effect in convulsive shock. It also seems likely that the electric shock causes an ion imbalance in the tissue due to massive depolarization. Protein synthesis by isolated brain ribosomes is unusually sensitive to the concentrations of monovalent cations compared to liver ribosomes (Zomzely, Roberts, & Rapaport, 1964; Dunn, 1968). Brain polyribosomes are also less stable than those of liver to unphysiological concentrations of monovalent cations (Zomzely, Roberts, Brown, & Provost, 1966). Thus, changes in ion concentrations caused by electroshock could account for the decrease in protein synthesis and the breakdown of polyribosomes. Supporting evidence arises from the studies that show application of KC1 to the cortex inhibits protein synthesis (Bennett & Edelman, 1969; Křivánek, 1969) and increasing the K^+ concentration or addition of

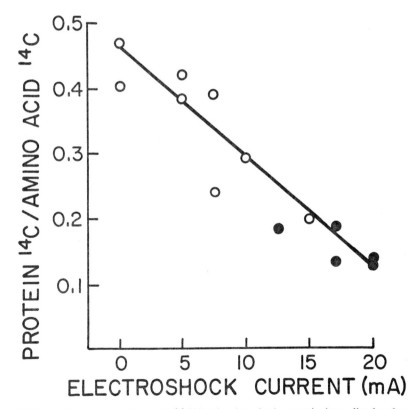

FIG. 4. The incorporation of [^{14}C]leucine into brain protein immediately after electroshocks of various intensities. Animals which showed full tonic convulsions are denoted by filled circles.

ouabain to the incubation medium decreases protein synthesis by brain slices (White, McBride, Mahler, & Moore, 1972). Recently Jones has shown that the Na+ gradient across the cell membrane is related to the ATP concentration in chopped brain cortex after electrical stimulation, and that the uptake and incorporation into protein of exogenous amino acids is also related to the Na+ gradient (Jones & Banks, 1971).

Is the effect of electroshock on brain protein synthesis related to the behavioral effects of the treatment? The work of McGaugh and others has firmly established in experimental animals the amnesic effect of ECS previously observed clinically (McGaugh, 1966). More recent work has shown that overt convulsions are not necessary for the production of amnesia since inhibition of the convulsions with ether (McGaugh & Alpern, 1966) or subconvulsive shocks (Jarvik & Kopp, 1967; Dorfmann & Jarvik, 1968; Lee-Teng, 1969; Ray & Barrett, 1969) may also cause amnesia. The graded effect of the electroshocking current on amnesia shown by Lee-Teng (1969) and others is remarkably similar to that shown here for protein synthesis (Figure 4). Further Cotman et al. (1971) showed that brain protein synthesis was only inhibited under conditions where brain seizures were observed; in the same laboratory Zornetzer and McGaugh (1971) showed that amnesia was elicited only when brain seizures occurred. There is thus a good correlation between the effects of electroshock on protein synthesis and retrograde amnesia.

The other agents most often used to elicit retrograde amnesia are the antibiotic inhibitors of protein synthesis, puromycin (Flexner, Flexner, & Stellar, 1963; Agranoff, 1967) and cycloheximide and its acetoxy derivative (Barondes & Cohen, 1967, 1968; Quartermain & McEwen, 1970). Also cortical spreading depression evoked by topical application of strong solutions of KCl to the cortex produces amnesia (Black, Suboski, & Freedman, 1967; Burešová, & Bureš, 1969; Kupfermann, 1966; Pearlman & Jarvik, 1961; Ray & Emley, 1964) and also inhibits protein synthesis (Bennett & Edelman, 1969; Křivánek, 1969). Other agents which have amnesic effects and which also inhibit protein synthesis are Metrazol (Pearlman, Sharpless, & Jarvik, 1961; Geiger et al. 1960), and hypoxia (Ransmeier & Gerard, 1954; Thompson & Pryer, 1956; Blomstrand, 1970).

There is thus evidence for a correlation between the ability of an agent to elicit amnesia and to inhibit protein synthesis indicating an interdependency or possibly a causal relationship.

There is one important discrepancy in this simple hypothesis. This is that in order to produce retrograde amnesia, puromycin or cycloheximide must be given in doses which cause high inhibitions (> 80%) of protein synthesis (Barondes, 1970; Flexner, Flexner, & Stellar, 1965). Lower doses with lower levels of protein synthesis inhibition are not effective amnesic agents. In contrast, electroshock causes a much lower inhibition of protein synthesis (24%–Cotman et al. 1971; 50%–this work) and cortical spreading depression even less (14%–Bennett & Edelman, 1969; 33%–Křivánek, 1969). Clearly if inhibition of protein synthesis is the cause of the amnesia, this discrepancy must be accounted for. A possible explanation is that there are certain sites of protein synthesis that are crucial to memory consolidation, and which are more susceptible to electroshock or KC1-induced inhibition. In addition these sites may be less susceptible to antibiotic inhibition. Indeed if the antibiotics puromycin and cycloheximide are producing amnesia through an effect on brain protein synthesis then there probably is a selective effect, especially since an 80% inhibition of the incorporation of amino acids into protein most probably represents a much greater inhibition of the production of whole functional proteins. Protein synthesis at nerve terminals could be such a site (Autilio, Appel, Pettis, & Gambetti, 1968; Austin, Morgan, & Bray, 1970). Some small molecules are known to have limited access to nerve terminals so antibiotics may not reach the nerve terminals in sufficient concentration to inhibit protein synthesis unless very high doses are injected. On the other hand, brain seizures and KC1 may have a greater effect at nerve terminals. In fact preliminary findings have shown that protein synthesis in nerve endings is more affected by electroshock than that of the whole brain (Essman, 1972). Protein synthesis in isolated nerve endings is very sensitive to monavalent cation concentration (Appel, Autilio, Festoff, & Escueta, 1969; Morgan & Austin, 1969). Also synaptosomes isolated from a rat after a series of electroshocks have a decreased ability to retain K^+ (Escueta & Appel, 1972). Inhibition of protein synthesis at the synapse, either pre- or postsynaptically, may then be sufficient to produce retrograde amnesia.

Does electroshock affect RNA synthesis? Earlier Mihailović, Janković, Petković, and Isaković, (1958) and Noach, Bunk, and Wijling, (1962) showed that following ECS there is a decrease in the total brain content of RNA, a result recently confirmed by Essman (1972). Table 3 shows that electroconvulsive shock inhibits the uptake and incorporation of $[5\text{-}^3H]$uridine into RNA in mouse brain. However, after short pulses of uridine the only species of RNA in the brain that is labeled is nuclear RNA which has a half-life of less than 10 min (Dunn, unpublished observation). This invalidates the assumptions of the labeled precursor method to measure rates of synthesis.

TABLE 3

The Incorporation of $[^3H]$ Uridine into Mouse Brain after ECS

	Total dpm	RNA dpm	RNA dpm/non RNA dpm
Sham control	75,000 (14,900)	3,230 (1,100)	0.044 (0.011)
ECS	52,100 (12,200)	1,250 (440)	0.025 (0.008)
% Inhibition	30	61	44
p (t test)	<.0001	<0.0005	<0.0005

Note.—100 μCi [5-^{3}H] uridine was injected intraperitoneally into Swiss-Webster mice (6 weeks old). Animals were sacrificed 5 min later and total brain nonvolatile radioactivity and RNA radioactivity was determined by the method of Dunn (1971b). Numbers in parentheses are standard deviations.

It is also important to note that the uptake of [^{3}H]uridine is significantly decreased after ECS (Table 3). This may be consequent to the destruction of RNA and increase in uridine nucleotides (Piccoli, Camarda, & Bonavita, 1969). It is interesting that both uridine and leucine are apparently exceptions to the general increased blood-brain permeability following ECS (Ottosson, this volume).

In summary, we have shown that electroconvulsive shock inhibits the uptake and incorporation of radioactive precursors into RNA and protein in mouse brain. Protein synthesis is probably inhibited and the effect is not dependent on the bodily convulsions. There is a good correlation between the effect of electroshock on protein synthesis and retrograde amnesia, which is consistent with many other data.

An interesting outstanding problem is to explain the fact that, in order to be effective clinically, multiple electroshocks have to be administered at intervals of a day or so and are ineffective when given in only one session. This suggests the necessity for a growth or healing process after each shock. Many data suggest that there is a small amount of tissue damage following ECS. The small increase in free leucine observed by Cotman et al. (1971), and earlier data on amino acid changes following electroshock by Okumura, Otsuki, and Nasu (1959) suggest a small amount of protein degradation which would not be, and was not, detectable by gross protein analyses. Bazán (1971) has shown an increase in free fatty acids following ECS which is not explained by the anoxia. These two results combined may indicate membrane damage. Work referred to above by Mihailović et al. (1958), Noach et al. (1962), and Essman (1972), showed that ECS causes a substantial breakdown of RNA in the brain. If the conduction of impulses across a synapse under suitable conditions may alter the probability of the passage of subsequent impulses, then a brain seizure may have a profound effect at the synapse, and may, by its intensity, disrupt these delicate mechanisms or even inactivate the snyapse. That ECS does indeed have a pronounced effect at synapses is indicated by the sudden release of many diverse neurotransmitters, of which we have heard earlier, and also by the effect on protein synthesis at the nerve endings shown by Essman (1972). It may not be protein synthesis at the synapse that is important for the behavioral effects; but the data may be interpreted to demonstrate that the metabolism at the nerve ending is disrupted following ECS. Escueta and Appel (1972) have shown that following administration to adult rats of one or two ECS per day for 6 days the ability of isolated synaptosomes to retain K$^+$ is severely impaired (ca. 40%). The effect is apparently additive, a series of eight shocks in 4 days showing approximately half the impairment, which may indicate a slow recovery. This of course fits in very well with the idea of cation imbalances at the nerve terminals being responsible for the other biochemical changes.

Thus ECS may be able to induce a new plasticity into the nervous system. Certain synapses, and possibly, therefore, certain pathways, may be rendered temporarily nonfunctional, permitting the opportunity to re-form differently. If only a small proportion of synapses are selectively affected by each shock (perhaps only those that are conducting at the time of the seizure for example), and if different synapses were selectively affected each time a shock was given, this would provide a mechanism for subtly modifying the brain. Possibly the reformation or reactivation of the nonfunctional synapses would follow the original developmental pattern and might also be affected by the psychiatric aspects of the therapy. Over a series of electroshocks it might thus be possible to alter the brain to alleviate clinical disorders without causing undue permanent damage.

POSTSCRIPT

Recently Alexandrovskaia and Kruglikov (1971) have observed histological changes in motor cortex of the rat following ECS. These changes included enlargement of neuronal perikarya, hyperplasia of oligodendrocytes, and proliferation of astroglia and microglia. If true, this would indicate structural damage or rearrangement much greater than suggested above.

REFERENCES

Agranoff, B. W. Memory and protein synthesis. *Scientific American,* 1967, **216**, 115-122.

Alexandrovskaia, M. M., & Kruglikov, R. I. Influence of electroshock on memory function and glial-neuronal relationships in rat brain. *Proceedings Academy of Sciences, of the Union of Soviet Socialist Republics,* 1971, **197**, 1216-1218.

Appel, S. H., Autilio, L., Festoff, B. W., & Escueta, A. V. Biochemical studies of synapses *in vitro*: III. Ionic activation of protein synthesis. *Journal of Biological Chemistry,* 1969, **244**, 3166-3172.

Austin, L., Morgan, I. G., & Bray, J. J. The biosynthesis of proteins within axons and synaptosomes. In A. Lajtha (Ed.), *Protein metabolism of the nervous system.* New York: Plenum Press, 1970.

Autilio, L., Appel, S. H., Pettis, P., & Gambetti, P. L. Biochemical studies of synapses *in vitro*. I. Protein synthesis. *Biochemistry, Easton,* 1968, **7**, 2615-2622.

Banker, G., & Cotman, C. W. Characteristics of different amino acids as protein precursors in mouse brain: Advantages of certain carboxyl-labeled amino acids. *Archives of Biochemistry and Biophysics,* 1971, **142**, 565-573.

Barondes, S. H. Is the amnesic effect of cycloheximide due to specific intereference with a process in memory storage? In A. Lajtha (Ed.), *Protein metabolism of the nervous system.* New York: Plenum Press, 1970.

Barondes, S. H., & Cohen, H. D. Delayed and sustained effect of acetoxycycloheximide on memory in mice. *Proceedings of the National Academy of Sciences of the United States of America,* 1967, **58**, 157-164.

Barondes, S. H., & Cohen, H. D. Memory impairment after subcutaneous injection of acetoxycycloheximide. *Science,* 1968, **160**, 556-557.

Bazán, N. G. Changes in free fatty acids of brain by drug-induced convulsions, electroshock and anaestheisa. *Journal of Neurochemistry* 1971, **18**, 1379-1385.

Bennett, G. S., & Edelman, G. M. Amino acid incorporation into rat brain proteins during spreading cortical depression. *Science,* 1969, **163**, 393-395.

Black, H., Suboski, M. D., & Freedman, N. L. Effect of cortical spreading depression and ether following one-trial discrimination avoidance learning. *Psychonomic Science*, 1967, 9, 597-598.

Blomstrand, C. Effect of hypoxia on protein metabolism in neuron- and neuroglia cell-enriched fractions from rabbit brain. *Experimental Neurology*, 1970, 29, 175-188.

Burešová, O., & Bureš, J. The effect of prolonged cortical spreading depression on learning and memory in rats. *Journal of Neurobiology*, 1969, 1, 135-146.

Collins, R. C., Posner, J. B., & Plum F. Cerebral energy metabolism during electroshock seizures in mice. *American Journal of Physiology*, 1970, 218, 943-950.

Cotman, C. W., Banker, G., Zornetzer, S. F., & McGaugh, J. L. Electroshock effects on brain protein synthesis: Relation to brain seizures and retrograde amnesia. *Science*, 1971, 173, 454-456.

Dorfman, L. F., & Jarvik, M. E. A parametric study of electroshock-induced retrograde amnesia in mice. *Neuropsychologia*, 1968, 6, 373-380.

Dunn, A. J. Protein synthesis in rat brain. Doctoral thesis, University of Cambridge, 1968.

Dunn, A. J. Brain protein synthesis after electroshock. *Brain Research*, 1971, 35, 254-259. (a)

Dunn, A. J. Use of cetyl trimethylammonium bromide for estimation of the *in vivo* incorporation of radioactive precursors into RNA. *Analytical Biochemistry*, 1971, 41, 460-465. (b)

Dunn, A. J., & Giuditta, A. A long-term effect of electroconvulsive shock on the metabolism of glucose in mouse brain. *Brain Research*, 1971, 27, 418-421.

Dunn, A. J., Giuditta, A., & Pagliuca, N. The effect of electroconvulsive shock on protein synthesis in mouse brain. *Journal of Neurochemistry*, 1971, 18, 2093-2099.

Escueta, A. V., & Appel, S. H. The effects of electroshock seizures on potassium transport within rat brain synaptosomes. *Journal of Neurochemistry*, 1972, 19, 1625-1638.

Essman, W. B. Neurochemical changes in ECS and ECT. *Seminars in Psychiatry*, 1972, 4, 67-77.

Flexner, J. B., Flexner, L. B., & Stellar, E. Memory in mice as affected by intracerebral puromycin. *Science*, 1963, 141, 57-59.

Flexner, L. B., Flexner, J. B., & Stellar, E. Memory and cerebral protein synthesis in mice as affected by graded amounts of puromycin. *Experimental Neurology*, 1965, 13, 264-272.

Geiger, A., Horvath, N., & Kawakita, Y. The incorporation of ^{14}C derived from glucose into the proteins of the brain cortex, at rest and during activity. *Journal of Neurochemistry*, 1960, 5, 311-322.

Jarvik, M. E., & Kopp, R. Transcorneal electroconvulsive shock and retrograde amnesia in mice. *Journal of Comparative and Physiological Psychology*, 1967, 64, 431-433.

Jones, C. T., & Banks, P. The influence of the intracellular concentration of sodium on the uptake of L-$[^{14}C]$ valine by chopped tissue from cerebral cortex. *Biochemical Journal*, 1971, 123, 341-345.

King, L. J., Lowry, O. H., Passonneau, J. V., & Venson, V. Effects of convulsants on energy reserves in the cerebral cortex. *Journal of Neurochemistry*, 1967, 14, 599-611.

Křivánek, J., Changes in protein, electrolyte, and water metabolism caused by prolonged spreading cortical depression in rats. *Journal of Neurobiology*, 1969, 1, 147-154.

Kupfermann, I. Is the retrograde amnesia that follows cortical spreading depression due to subcortical spread? *Journal of Comparative and Physiological Psychology*, 1966, 61, 466-467.

Lee-Teng, E. Retrograde amnesia in relation to subconvulsive and convulsive currents in the chick. *Journal of Comparative and Physiological Psychology*, 1969, 67, 135-139.

MacInnes, J. W., McConkey, E. H., & Schlesinger, K. Changes in brain polyribosomes following an electro-convulsive seizure. *Journal of Neurochemistry*, 1970, 17, 457-460.

McGaugh, J. L. Time-dependent processes in memory storage. *Science*, 1966, 153, 1351-1358.

McGaugh, J. L., & Alpern, H. P. Effects of electroshock on memory: Amnesia without convulsions. *Science,* 1966, 152, 665-666.

Mihailović, L., Janković, B. D., Petković, M., & Isaković, K. Effect of electroshock upon nucleic acid concentrations in various parts of cat brain. *Experientia,* 1958, 15, 144-145.

Morgan, I. G., & Austin, L. Ion effects and protein synthesis in synaptosomal fraction. *Journal of Neurobiology,* 1969, 1, 155-167.

Noach, E. L., Bunk, J. J., & Wijling, A. Influence of electroshock and pentobarbital on nucleic acid content of rat brain cortex. *Acta Physiologica et Pharmacologica Neerlandica,* 1962, 11, 54-69.

Okumura, N., Otsuki, S., & Nasu, H. The influences of insulin hypoglycaemic coma, repeated electroshocks, and chlorpromazine or β-phenylisopropylmethylamine administration on the free amino acids in the brain. *Journal of Biochemistry,* 1959, 46, 247-252.

Pearlman, C., & Jarvik, M. E. Retrograde amnesia produced by cortical depression. *Federation Proceedings,* 1961, 20, 340.

Pearlman, C. A., Sharpless, S. K., & Jarvik, M. E. Retrograde amnesia produced by anesthetic and convulsant agents. *Journal of Comparative and Physiological Psychology,* 1961, 54, 109-112.

Piccoli, F., Camarda, R., & Bonavita, V. Purine and pyrimidine nucleotides in the brain of normal and convulsant rats. *Journal of Neurochemistry,* 1969, 16, 159-169.

Quartermain, D., & McEwen, B. S. Temporal characteristics of amnesia induced by protein synthesis inhibitor: Determination by shock level. *Nature,* 1970, 228, 677-678.

Ransmeier, R. E., & Gerard, R. W. Effects of temperature, convulsion and metabolic factors on rodent memory and EEG. *American Journal of Physiology,* 1954, 179, 663-664.

Ray, O. S., & Barrett, R. J. Disruptive effects of electroconvulsive shock as a function of current levels and mode of delivery. *Journal of Comparative and Physiological Psychology,* 1969, 67, 110-116.

Ray, O. S., & Emley, G. Time factors in interhemispheric transfer of learning. *Science,* 1964, 144, 76-78.

Thompson, R., & Pryer, R. S. The effect of anoxia on the retention of a discrimination habit. *Journal of Comparative and Physiological Psychology,* 1956, 49, 297-300.

Vesco, C., & Giuditta, A. Disaggregation of brain polysomes induced by electroconvulsive treatment. *Journal of Neurochemistry,* 1968, 15, 81-85.

White, F. P., McBride, W. J., Mahler, H. R., & Moore, W. J. Subcellular distribution of proteins synthesized in slices of rat cerebral cortex. *Journal of Biological Chemistry,* 1972, 247, 1247-1256.

Zomzely, C. E., Roberts, S., Brown, D. M., & Provost, C. Cerebral protein synthesis. I. Physical properties of cerebral ribosomes and polyribosomes. *Journal of Molecular Biology,* 1966, 20, 455-468.

Zomzely, C. E., Roberts, S., & Rapaport, D. Characteristics of amino acid incorporation into proteins of microsomal and ribosomal preparations of rat cerebral cortex. *Journal of Neurochemistry,* 1964, 11, 567-582.

Zornetzer, S. F., & McGaugh, J. L. Retrograde amnesia and brain seizures in mice. *Physiology and Behavior,* 1971, 7, 401-408.

14
MEMORY AND ECT[1]

Rhea L. Dornbush, Ph.D. and Moyra Williams, Ph.D.

Memory impairment produced by electroconvulsive therapy (ECT) can be separated from its therapeutic action (d'Elia, this volume; Fink, this volume; Inglis, 1969). The evidence suggests that memory effects are independent and unrelated to improvement; rather they are side-effects of the treatment process. However, until the mechanism of action of ECT is understood so that either another more circumscribed technique employing that mechanism can be used, or until the spread of electricity can be controlled, a method of using ECT should be sought which eliminates memory disturbance as a source of patient complaint.

The most promising route to this end appears to be the *site* of electrode placement. The relevance of electrode placement relates directly to our knowledge of cerebral lateralization—differential hemispheric functioning. Certain behaviors are mediated by one hemisphere rather than the other (Milner, 1962, 1966; Kimura, 1967). At this stage of our research, lateralization has been most extensively explored for modality of input and task content (Dornbush, 1970; Cohn, 1971). Typically, auditory processes are more fully represented in the left hemisphere and visual processes are represented in the right hemisphere. By the same mechanism, recall of verbal material is associated with the left and nonverbal with the right hemisphere. That the verbal-nonverbal nature of the material may be the more relevant aspect is indicated by the fact that visual material with a verbal content seems to be mediated by the left rather than the right hemisphere (Milner, 1962, 1966). A number of studies, using normal

[1] Partial support for this research was provided through United States Public Health Service Grant MH-15561.

199

populations, demonstrate different EEG responses over the two hemispheres as a function of the stimuli or task (Morrell & Salamy, 1971; Cohn, 1971; McAdam & Whitaker, 1971; Wood, Goff, & Day, 1971). For example, when a subject must identify linguistic and nonlinguistic stimuli, there are no differences in EEG responses over the right hemisphere but there is a marked difference over the left hemisphere which is associated with speech (Wood et al., 1971).

Even more specifically than hemispheric localization, the temporal lobes and neural structures underlying these lobes—the hippocampal areas—have been assigned a major role in memory functioning. For example, Milner (1962) reported that patients with left temporal lobe injuries exhibited greater impairment on verbal tasks (e.g., certain subtests of the Wechsler memory scale) than those with lesions elsewhere, whereas right temporal lobe injuries resulted in impairment in nonverbal task discriminations, as in the discrimination of pitch and loudness. Similar evidence was reported by Kimura (1961). Patients with left temporal lobectomies showed greater impairment of verbal material presented to the right ear than material presented to the left. Subjects with right temporal lobectomies, however, exhibited only a small loss in recall in verbal material presented to the left ear. In comparable tests with nonverbal material, right ear recall for items (clicks) was better than left ear recall.

In addition to the general seizure effects of ECT, there are direct local effects on the structures immediately under the electrodes. In this view, all treatments—bilateral, unilateral nondominant, and unilateral dominant placements—focus currents through the temporal lobes and neural structures in the region of the temporal lobes so that functions mediated by the lobe on the treated side are affected. The unilateral placements result in less obvious deficit because only one temporal lobe is involved. To avoid both the diffuse memory loss of bilateral treatments and the more limited loss of unilateral treatments, Inglis (1969) suggested application of electrodes to the bilateral anterior frontal area. This placement would have two advantages: (*a*) it would be bilateral; and (*b*) electrodes would not be placed immediately over the temporal lobes.

Indeed, the studies most productive of changes in treatment of benefit to patients, would be those that systematically manipulate electrode placement to determine specific effects on both anterograde and retrograde amnesia.

Studies in lower animals have, in fact, related the locus of ECS stimulation to interference with specific tasks. For example, Gold, Farrell, & King, (1971) trained rats in a passive-avoidance task (footshock avoidance) and then administered brain shock through either posterior or anterior skull screws. There was significantly greater retrograde amnesia of the avoidance task when ECS was delivered through the anterior placements. Similarly, Kral (1972) employed the same skull screw placements with a taste aversion task in rats. In this instance the posterior brain shock was more disruptive to the conditioning of the taste aversion.

Although experimental studies are not as easy to perform in man as in animals, owing to the difficulty of controlling the relevant factors, certain aspects of memory can be seen in man which defy study in animals. For example, the persistence of an aroused affect despite amnesia for the event which caused it, and its "displacement" onto an irrelevant stimulus, was described in one case by Williams (1952). Similar displacements and distortions of memory have often been reported by subjects after ECT, which would not have come to light if the subjects had not been able to speak and describe them.

ECT affects the memory for events experienced before the seizure (retrograde amnesia) and for those experienced after it (anterograde amnesia). The factors affecting memory in both conditions are, however, similar, and include:

1. Time. The closer the event occurs to the induced convulsion, the more seriously is the memory of it impaired. At the same time, events experienced before the convulsion which cannot be recalled immediately after recovery of consciousness, can often be remembered later (shrinkage of retrograde amnesia). The opposite—i.e., forgetting of an event after a lapse of time which was recalled soon after recovery of consciousness, has seldom been described by human subjects but might occur (Hargreaves, Fischer, Elashoff, & Blacker, 1972).

2. Nature of Event or Stimulus. Emotionally important, easily assimilated, and "familiar" events are recalled better than rare ones (Williams, 1966, 1969).

3. Mental Set at Time of Perception. Material which the subject has consciously tried to retain is better remembered than that which he has not consciously tried to retain (Stones, 1970).

4. Mental Set at Time of Assessment. Methods of testing which involve a restructuring of the original situation (e.g., by prompting or recognition tests) can arouse memories which otherwise may seem to have been forgotten (Mayer-Gross, 1944; Zubin & Barrera, 1941; Williams, 1950).

Most studies in man have concentrated on the anterograde effects of ECT, i.e., learning and retention occurring after treatment (Abrams, 1967; Cronholm, 1969; Dornbush, Abrams, & Fink, 1971; Zinkin & Birtchnell, 1968) and these studies are broadly represented in the literature. It has been shown convincingly by many investigators, but particularly by Ottosson, Cronholm and their associates, that ECT affects retention and not learning (Cronholm & Blomquist, 1959; Cronholm & Lagergren, 1959; Cronholm & Molander, 1961; Cronholm, 1969; Ottosson, 1960, this volume), and that long term memory is more affected than short term memory (Dornbush et al., 1971; Williams, 1966, 1969). Tests which have both an immediate recall and delayed recall period are effective in demonstrating anterograde effects and in distinguishing the relative deficits of different electrode placements.

The time after treatment that the memory test is administered is an issue of relevance that has thus far been overlooked. For example, most studies acknowledge the period of postictal confusion and administer tests at least 3 hr post treatment: Mayer-Gross (1944) tested 24 hr or less after treatment; Levy (1968), 6 hr after treatment; Dornbush et al. (1971), 24 hr after treatment. Some test earlier, for example, Zinkin and Birtchnell (1968) tested 1 and 2 hr after treatment.

However, Hargreaves et al. (1972) noted the delayed onset of impairment after ECT. Performance decrement may not be evident in the hours after treatment but may first become manifest 24 hr after treatment.

We noted this phenomenon coincidentally in our own studies. In an attempt to examine the entire testing procedure, we decided to see patients 3 hr after treatment and found their performance to be better than patients tested 24 hr after treatment. Because the 3-hr post-ECT test interfered with hospital procedures we abandoned it in favor of the 24-hr test and were left with too few patients tested at 3 hr to be useful except in forming an impression.

Hargreaves et al. (1972) indicate that in those studies which assessed memory within 2 hr posttreatment there were clear and consistent differences between unilateral and bilateral treatments, the former resulting in less impairment. Those studies which assessed memory 24 hr or more after treatment demonstrated fewer differences between the different electrode placements— with unilateral generally producing less impairment than bilateral. In other words, impairment after unilateral placement increased in the interval between the more immediate testing and the delayed testing.

Despite the wealth of anterograde studies, most patient complaints are about memory impairments for events occurring prior to treatment, i.e., retrograde effects. Yet there are few adequate human studies of retrograde amnesia. It would seem the opposite is so for the animal literature, which has many detailed studies. There is little agreement in many studies as to the learning-ECS interval during which the memory trace was still subject to disruption (Chorover & Schiller, 1965; Jarvik & Geller, 1968). Many of the studies suggested that ECS-induced amnesia is limited to tasks presented within a few seconds, no more than 10, before the ECS.

Recent studies, however, employing systematic investigation of this and related parameters, indicate that the learning-ECS interval during which shock will interfere with recall is a function of the current intensity, the locus of stimulation, as well as the length of the learning-ECS interval. McGaugh and associates (Haycock & McGaugh, 1973; Gold, Macri, & McGaugh, 1973) administered ECS to mice trained on an inhibitory avoidance task. Current intensities varied between 1 mA and 15 mA at intervals after training varying between 0 sec and 240 min. The amnestic effect was present at the longest interval but required greater current intensities whereas weaker intensities were effective at shorter learning-ECS intervals.

These findings are difficult to relate to outcome in man and the relevance of these studies to the mechanism of action of ECT is difficult to judge, since few studies provide similar dosage and duration of stimulations, seizures frequency, and electrode locations to those assessed in man. Additionally, effects on language ability, so critical in studies of memory tasks in man, are essentially untestable in animals.

It should, however, be noted here, that Ottosson (1960) found in humans that both the EEG effect and therapeutic effect of ECT were directly related to the seizure activity and not to the current; memory disturbances could, however, be accounted for by the current and not the seizure.

Retrograde amnesia effects in man are most frequently attributed to interference with the consolidation process or the transition from impermanence to permanence of the memory trace—in Hebb's (1949) formulation, the trace moves from an activity to a structural trace.

If consolidation is not complete, trauma, or in this instance ECT, can result in memory loss to the degree to which the trace is still impermanent. Consolidation is a function of time—the longer the interval between learning and ECT the greater the chance of consolidation or retention of the learning after ECT. Typically the consolidation time is thought to be short and the difference between a trace which can be disrupted and one which is not susceptible is characterized by short and long term memory respectively. Consolidation or the temporal differences between long and short term memory is thought to be of the order of seconds by some and somewhat longer (minutes to hours) by others.

It is not unlikely that total consolidation can require considerably longer than seconds or minutes and may be dependent on the nature and complexity of the task (Miller, 1970), particularly if there are other ongoing activities.

It is surprising that so few studies have examined a range of learning-ECT intervals—particularly the longer intervals. The work of McGaugh and associates serves as a useful model for these studies in man. Zinkin and Birtchnell (1968) presented material 3 min prior to treatment; Mayer-Gross (1944) employed a 1-min interval; Cronholm and Lagergren (1959) varied the interval from 5 sec to 60 sec. The applicability for such short durations to actual patient complaints of memory loss and overt behavior seems limited.

On the other hand, Miller (1970) found retrograde amnesia extending to a task presented 30 min prior to the treatment, and Williams (1969) found amnesia for tasks presented 11 to 17 min pretreatment. d'Elia (this volume) also found retrograde amnesia for material presented 1 hr prior to treatment and related it to electrode placement: bilateral patients exhibited greater amnesia than unilateral nondominant patients; unilateral dominant patients fell somewhere between the two. In each of these studies only one learning-ECT interval was employed, or in cases where more than one interval was studied it was at unrealistically short durations. No study varied the ECT-testing interval to determine how long each treatment inhibits recovery. Thus whether retrograde amnesia is an invariant effect, permanent, or susceptible to gradual recovery, and how far back in time memory is susceptible to ECT, is not known. To clarify these issues the focus of amnesia studies should be on the following points: How long prior to treatment is learning subject to the interfering effects of ECT? What is the temporal course of recovery? Does the time of recall after ECT interact with the recency of learning prior to treatment? What is the effect of different electrode placements in regard to the above points?

Several studies measured neither anterograde amnesia nor the effect of specific treatments on retrograde amnesia but some very general form of memory. For example, Cannicott and Waggoner (1967) administered various tests "no less than 48 hours prior to the first treatment" (but typically 1 hr before treatment) and measured retention no more than 24 hr after the fifth treatment. Levy (1968) presented memory tests the day prior to treatment and again after the sixth treatment. Likewise Costello, Belton, Abra, and Dunn (1970) gave their patients a battery of tests 16 to 19 hr before the first treatment and tested various types of retention 28 to 31 hr after the fourth treatment. Abrams (1967) presented the Wechsler memory scale before the first treatment and again after the 20th treatment.

The various methods of retention are particularly sensitive in distinguishing ECT effects. These methods (recall, recognition, and relearning) are not equivalent but seem related to the processing of memory. Typically, performance is best on recognition tests, worst on recall, with performance in relearning between the two, but closer to recall. Patients who show retention impairment using a recall or relearning method may not evidence this impairment when retention is measured by recognition. For example, Costello et al. (1970) examined the effects of different electrode placements on the three measures of retention. On the recognition measure, unilateral dominant and nondominant groups performed equally better than the bilateral group. On the other hand, both bilateral and unilateral dominant groups were placed at a disadvantage by the use of the recall and relearning measures and made more errors than the unilateral nondominant group.

In one view, the method of measurement is only relevant when ECT affects retrieval and not storage. If there is difficulty in storing the event, i.e., if it is not transferred from the short term store to the long term store, then no method of retention will elicit that event. On the other hand, if the event has already passed to the long term store, as for events occurring well prior to treatment, then one method of retention might be more successful than another in maximizing retrieval of these events. In this view, ECT destroys the trace; if it is not completely stored or committed to long term memory, it is lost.

In another view, the method of measurement is related to the *transition* of material from impermanence to permanence, i.e., material in the process of storage. Traces are merely interrupted temporarily and one method of retention will more easily elicit more impermanent material than another method. There is yet a third view (Weiskrantz, 1966) which combines components of the first two. For very short term traces, up to 5 sec, ECT will destroy the trace; but long term traces, (beyond 5 sec) are subject to progressive consolidation. Thus ECT should cause items learned within 5 sec prior to treatment to be totally lost, and no method of retention will elicit that material. On the other hand, material learned at longer intervals prior to ECT should be increasingly susceptible to retrieval. Recognition should be more effective for shorter learning-ECT intervals with progressively less differences in the methods with the longer learning-ECT intervals.

There is some confusion about (a) how short short-term memory is (estimates range from the time it takes to utter a single word—some milliseconds—to hours or even days); (b) how memories become transferred from short term to long term storage, and (c) how they are coded in either store. If rehearsal is essential for consolidation, how is it that some experiences seem to be retained after less rehearsal than others? Do some bypass the short term store and go straight to the long term?

Even if answers to such questions are forthcoming from animal experiments, it is difficult to see how such models would account for the many gradations of memory (displacements, distortions, partial recollections, etc.) to which Bartlett (1932) drew attention many years ago in the forgetting of man, and which appear to be accentuated by ECT.

While seizures have different effects on memory functions depending on the modality (auditory or visual), content (verbal or nonverbal), and the method of testing retention (recall, recognition, or relearning), these are only ways in which to assess the memory deficit once it has already occurred. Manipulation of electrode location is the most promising line of research to prevent or reduce memory impairment.

REFERENCES

Abrams, R. Daily administration of unilateral ECT. *American Journal of Psychiatry*, 1967, 124, 384-386.

Bartlett, F. C. "Remembering". London: Cambridge University Press, 1932.

Cannicott, S. M., & Waggoner, R. W. Unilateral and bilateral electroconvulsive therapy. *Archives of General Psychiatry*, 1967, 16, 229.

Chorover, S. L., & Schiller, P. H. Short-term retrograde amnesia in rats. *Journal of Comparative and Physiological Psychology*, 1965, 59, 73.

Cohn, R. Differential cerebral processing of noise and verbal stimuli. *Science*, 1971, 172, 599.

Costello, C. G., Belton, G. P., Abra, J. C., & Dunn, B. E. The amnesic and therapeutic effects of bilateral and unilateral ECT. *British Journal of Psychiatry*, 1970, 116, 69.

Cronholm, B. Post-ECT amnesias. In G. Talland & N. Waugh (Eds.), *The pathology of memory*. New York: Academic Press, 1969.

Cronholm, B., & Blomquist, C. Memory disturbances after electroconvulsive therapy. II. Conditions one week after a series of treatments. *Acta Psychiatrica et Neurologica Scandinavica*, 1959, 34, 18.

Cronholm, B., & Lagergren, A. Memory disturbances after electroconvulsive therapy. III. An experimental study of retrograde amnesia after electroshock treatment. *Acta Psychiatrica et Neurologica Scandinavica*, 1959, 34, 283.

Cronholm, B., & Molander, L. Memory disturbances after electroconvulsive therapy. IV. Influence of an interpolated electroconvulsive shock on retention of memory material. *Acta Psychiatrica et Neurologica Scandinavica*, 1961, 36, 83-90.

Dornbush, R. L. Attention in bisensory simultaneous short-term memory. *Perception Psychophysics*, 1970, 4, 244.

Dornbush, R. L., Abrams, R., & Fink, M. Memory changes after unilateral and bilateral convulsive treatment (ECT). *British Journal of Psychiatry*, 1971, 119, 75.

Gold, P. E., Farrell, W., & King, R. A. Retrograde amnesia after localized brain shock in passive-avoidance learning. *Physiology and Behavior*, 1971, 7, 709-712.

Gold, P. E., Macri, J., & McGaugh, J. L. Retrograde amnesia gradients: Effects of direct cortical stimulation. *Science*, 1973, 180, 1199-1201.

Hargreaves, W. A., Fischer, A., Elashoff, R. M. & Blacker, K. H. Delayed onset of impairment following electrically induced convulsions. *Acta Psychiatrica Scandinavica*, 1972, 48, 69-77.

Haycock, J. W., & McGaugh, J. L. Retrograde amnesia gradients as a function of ECS - intensity. *Behavioral Biology*, 1973, 9, 123-127.

Hebb, D. O. *Organization of behavior*. New York: Wiley, 1949.

Inglis, J. Electrode placement and the effect of ECT on mood and memory in depression. *Canadian Psychiatric Association Journal*, 1969, 14, 463.

Jarvik, M. E., & Geller, A. Associative interference and consolidation. *Recent Advances in Biological Psychiatry*, 1968, 10, 316.

Kimura, D. Cerebral dominance and the perception of verbal stimuli. *Canadian Journal of Psychology*, 1961, 15, 166.

Kimura, D. Functional asymmetry of the brain in dichotic listening. *Cortex*, 1967, 3, 163.

Kral, P. Localized ECS impedes taste aversion learning. *Behavioral Biology*, 1972, 7, 761-765.

Levy, R. The clinical evaluation of unilateral electroconvulsive therapy. *British Journal of Psychiatry*, 1968, 114, 459.

Mayer-Gross, W. Retrograde amnesia: Some experiments. *Lancet*, 1944, 2, 603.

McAdam, D. W., & Whitaker, H. A. Language production: Electroencephalographic localization in the normal human brain. *Science*, 1971, 172, 499.

Millar, E. The effect of ECT on memory and learning. *British Journal of Medical Psychology*, 1970, 43, 57.

Milner, B. Laterality effects in audition. In V. B. Mountcastle (Ed.), *Interhemispheric relations and cerebral dominance*. Baltimore: Johns Hopkins Press, 1962.

Milner, B. Amnesia following operation on the temporal lobes. In C. Whitty & O. L. Zangwell (Eds.), *Amnesia*. London: Butterworths, 1966.

Morrell, L. K., & Salamy, J. Hemispheric asymmetry of electrocortical responses to speech stimuli. *Science*, 1971, 174, 164-166.

Ottosson, J. -O. Experimental studies of the mode of action of electroconvulsive therapy. *Acta Psychiatrica Scandinavica*, 35 (Suppl. 145), 1960.

Stones, M. The effect of priming on recall and recognition after ECT. Bachelor's dissertation, Brunel University, London, 1970.

Williams, M. Memory studies in ECT. *Journal of Neurology, Neurosurgery and Psychiatry*, 1950, 13, 30, 314.

Williams, M. A case of displaced affect following ECT. *British Journal of Medical Psychology* 1952, 25, 156.

Williams, M. Memory disorders associated with electroconvulsive therapy. In C. Whitty & O. L. Zangwill (Eds.), *Amnesia*. London: Butterworths, 1966.

Williams, M. Traumatic retrograde amnesia and normal forgetting. In G. Talland & N. Waugh (Eds.), *The pathology of memory*. New York: Academic Press, 1969.

Weiskrantz, L. Experimental studies in amnesia. In C. Whitty & O. L. Zangwill (Eds.), *Amnesia*. London: Butterworths, 1966.

Wood, C., Goff, W., & Day, R. Auditory evoked potentials during speech perception. *Science*, 1971, 173, 1248-1252.

Zinkin, S., & Birtchnell, J. Unilateral electroconvulsive therapy: Its effects on memory and its therapeutic efficacy. *British Journal of Psychiatry,* 1968, 114, 973.

Zubin, J., & Barrera, S. E. Effect of ECT on memory. *Royal Society of Experimental Biology and Medicine,* 1941, 48, 596.

15
SYSTEMIC BIOCHEMICAL EFFECTS OF ECT

Jan-Otto Ottosson, M.D.

ECT has a multitude of effects on the organism—in fact it is hardly possible to imagine a variable not influenced by the treatment. It is likely that the central neurochemical effects which are covered in other chapters of this book give more promise than the systemic effects of elucidating factors which are relevant for the therapeutic process. The systemic effects were reviewed by Holmberg in 1963 and a renewed survey of this area is warranted only to take into account recent findings and to scrutinize them along with the older observations against what is known today about the mechanism of action of ECT.

As pointed out elsewhere (Ottosson, 1968) ECT has several clinical effects, e.g., antidepressive, antimanic, antipsychotic, anticonfusional, which are regarded as therapeutic, and "organic" effects, above all memory disturbance, which are regarded as side-effects. There is reason to believe that these effects occur via different mechanisms of action. We know so far that the antidepressive effect and the memory disturbance have different mechanisms of action, viz., that the antidepressive effect is bound to the cerebral seizure activity and that the memory disturbance is partly an effect of the seizure activity, partly a direct effect of the electrical current, and related to the amount of electrical energy supplied to the brain (Ottosson, 1960). The antimanic, antipsychotic, and anticonfusional effects are less well studied but it has been suggested that at least the two first are part of an organic shock syndrome. We further know that narcosis, elimination of the muscular activity, and improved oxygenation has not diminished the therapeutic efficacy. Investigations which describe an influence on a variable but do not make an analysis of whether it is an effect related to seizure activity *or* a direct effect of the electrical stimulation *or* whether it disappears after relaxation or narcosis do not have much interest. It is now possible to vary the electrical stimulation from subliminal, liminal to superliminal and to vary the seizure discharge with analeptic and anticonvulsant drugs. Every interesting effect should further be studied both with ECT and pharmacologic seizures. It is true that both electricity and convulsant drugs may have similar effects in their own right but a similar effect argues for a seizure-related influence. Finally, a similar effect from convulsive treatment and antidepressive drugs may be an important clue.

A few examples may be given to illustrate the principles of the analysis.

ADRENAL MEDULLARY ACTIVITY

The sympathetic-adrenal response is fairly well analyzed. It has been shown that convulsions cause a rise in the levels of adrenaline and noradrenaline in blood (Weil-Malherbe, 1955; Gravenstein, Anton, Wiener, & Tetlow, 1965) as well as in urine (Sourkes, Sloane, & Drujan, 1957; Sourkes, Drujan, & Curtis, 1958). The rise is greater after cardiazol-induced seizures than after ECT. Since the former are often longer, the difference indicates that the. rise is a consequence of seizure activity. However, subconvulsive electrical stimulation applied bilaterally also induces a rise in the level of adrenaline which rapidly subsides when the stimulation stops. This shows that the adrenaline response may also be a direct effect of the current. After unilateral subconvulsive stimulation, on the other hand, there is no change, suggesting that the adrenaline response was not caused by stimulation of cutaneous receptors but by central stimulation and that in unilateral ECT the sympathetic-adrenal activation is a consequence of the seizure activity only (Weil-Malherbe & Bone, 1952; Montagu, 1955). These findings suggest that the catecholamine responses should be considered in relation to the antidepressive effect of ECT. However, the rise in the level of noradrenaline decreases when the muscular activity of the seizure is blocked with succinylcholine (Havens, Zileli, Di Mascio, & Boling, 1959) and the adrenaline and noradrenaline response can be blocked by narcosis (Weil-Malherbe, 1955; Griswold, 1958; Havens et al., 1959). Since muscle relaxation and narcosis do not influence the antidepressive efficacy, the rise of catecholamines in itself can have nothing to do with the therapeutic process. What may be more significant is that Havens et al. (1959) found an increased response of adrenaline and Gravenstein et al. (1965) a decreased response of noradrenaline the longer the ECT series progressed. These represent types of long term cumulative changes that might be expected to be related to the therapeutic response. One may speculate whether an increased level of adrenaline in the blood may influence transmission in central synapses, e.g., by sensitization to some transmitters. However, it is also possible, and perhaps more likely, that the increased reactivity of the adrenals and the lower level of noradrenaline are secondary effects of basic neurochemical changes related to the improved clinical condition or mere coincidental phenomena.

ADRENAL CORTICAL ACTIVITY

ECT causes a rapid and short-lasting activation of the pituitary-adrenocortical system with an elevation of glucocorticoids corresponding to an effect of ACTH. It has been shown that nonconvulsive electrical stimulation may give a similar activation which, however, is less when a seizure is not evoked (Taylor, Gross, & Ruby, 1951; Kallio & Tala, 1959). If the seizure activity is reduced with diphenylhydantoin, the adrenocortical response is also reduced (Bliss, Migeon, Nelson, Samuels, & Branch, 1954). We may thus conclude that both the current itself and the seizure contribute to the adrenocortical response and it seems natural to look upon it as part of an unspecific stress reaction which is of no importance for the antidepressive effect of ECT. The reasons are (a) that infusion of ACTH has no antidepressive effect and (b) in depressive conditions of various kinds there are increased serum levels of corticoids which are gradually lowered coincident with improvement in the depression (Board, Wadeson, & Persky, 1957). Since ECT tends to increase the corticoid level, the decrease in the level of corticoids is a consequence of the clinical improvement and not a cause of it.

Curzon (1969) has presented the hypothesis that corticoids stimulate tryptophan pyrrolase and thereby decreases the breakdown of tryptophan to 5-HT. If the indolamine hypothesis for affective disorders is correct, a high corticoid level should then maintain a depressive state. ECT may, therefore, by further increasing the corticoid level, counteract other central effects of the therapy that promote a decrease.

CAUSE, EFFECT, OR COINCIDENCE

The examples mentioned illustrate that if a variable is influenced in ECT and this influence seems to be bound to the seizure (and may, therefore, be related to the antidepressive effect) there are three possible explanations: (a) The change is cause of or a link in the antidepressive effect. (b) The change is a consequence of the antidepressive effect. (c) The two phenomena are coincidental, i.e., parallel and independent effects of the seizure. The only way to elucidate whether the first possibility is correct would be to establish the change in another way and find it to have an antidepressive effect. A few examples may be mentioned.

CEREBROVASCULAR PERMEABILITY

An increased cerebrovascular permeability lasting for several days has been described after ECT as measured with trypan blue (Bjerner, Broman, & Swensson, 1944) and cocaine (Aird, 1958). This may be of causal importance for the antidepressive or organic effects of ECT or it may be quite coincidental. It is, therefore, interesting to note that the same degree of increased cerebrovascular permeability can be caused by antidepressant drugs (imipramine, amitriptyline, and nortriptyline) but not by chlorpromazine (Angel & Roberts, 1966). There are similarities in the solubility properties of cocaine and the biogenic amines (noradrenaline and serotonin) and the changes in permeability to cocaine may therefore also concern these amines. In fact, evidence has been presented that ECT increases the permeability of the barrier system to noradrenaline (Rosenblatt, Chanley, Sobotka, & Kaufman, 1960).

The reason why ECT increases the permeability may be related to systemic biochemical effects. During the epileptic seizure with its increased metabolism the production of carbon dioxide and other acid substances in the brain is enhanced. In experiments with carbon-dioxide inhalation the same increased cerebrovascular permeability to trypan blue is obtained as after ECT (Clemedson, Hartelius, & Holmberg, 1958).

There is thus evidence that permeability changes are relevant for the antidepressive effect of ECT and antidepressive drugs. It seems more doubtful that CO_2 accumulation is a therapeutic agent in ECT. Therapeutic trials with CO_2 inhalation according to Meduna (1958) have hardly given the impression of an antidepressive efficacy comparable to ECT or antidepressive drugs. Possibly CO_2 inhalation therapy produces too brief an effect or creates only one of several necessary conditions for a therapeutic effect. In an analogous way, we cannot maintain that antidepressive drugs exert their effect only via permeability changes. This effect may at most be relevant in addition to blockade of the uptake in presynaptic neurons.

Increased cerebrovascular permeability may also be of relevance for the memory disturbance after ECT, and CO_2 accumulation may then be seen as an undesirable side-effect. It is possible that the effects of CO_2 and ECT on the one hand and antidepressive drugs on the other are of different type and consequence although they appeared equal in Angel and Roberts' experiments (1966). It would be interesting to know whether the increased cerebrovascular permeability caused by CO_2 predominates in certain areas, e.g., the mamillary-hippocampal system which would argue in favor of its relevance for the memory disturbance.

CEREBRAL HYPOXIA

The blood gas changes in ECT are not often discussed since the introduction of anesthesiological principles; and the theory that the treatment works via hypoxia has been discarded because of the absence of antidepressive effect with nitrogen inhalation. However, even with modern technique with abundant oxygen supply and relaxation, local cerebral hypoxia probably arises due to the excessive oxygen demands. As a whole, the oxygen consumption of the brain is markedly increased during a seizure (Plum, Posner, & Troy, 1968). As long as muscular convulsions are eliminated and oxygen is supplied throughout the seizures, there was no hypoxia in animal experiments by Plum et al. However, ECT in clinical practice is not always given under such ideal circumstances. Besides, some parts of the brain, e.g., the hippocampus, have a higher oxygen consumption than other parts (Berlyne & Strachan, 1968), which may give rise to local cerebral hypoxia. As indicated in animal experiments, the epileptogenic threshold is lower in the hippocampus than in other parts of the brain, the after-discharges are often complex and it is suggested that the hippocampus may be involved with a higher metabolic rate in the epileptic activity than other parts (Liberson & Cadilhac, 1953).

The importance of the hippocampal-mamillary system in memory function is well known (Barbizet, 1963; Turner, 1969). In chronic alcoholics with Korsakoff's syndrome, lesions in the mamillary bodies have been described. After carbon monoxide poisoning or attempted hanging there may arise a Korsakoff syndrome with gross defects of retention due to bilateral damage of the hippocampus (Whitty & Lishman, 1966). As shown by Cronholm and Molander (1957), the anterograde amnesia after ECT may be characterized as a mild and reversible Korsakoff syndrome.

There are reasons, therefore, that cerebral hypoxia caused by the seizure may be relevant for the organic memory disturbing effects of convulsive therapy. This conclusion gains further support from a comparison between ECT and flurothyl therapy (ICT, Indoklon convulsive therapy) (Laurell, 1970). After a single treatment there is less retrograde amnesia after ICT which is explained by the elimination of the electrical current (Ottosson, 1960; Cronholm & Ottosson, 1961, 1963). After a series of treatments, ECT and ICT cause about the same memory disturbance. In ICT the total seizure time is much longer, which probably causes a more pronounced cerebral hypoxia. A gain from the elimination of electricity is thus outweighed by the forced prolongation of seizure activity in ICT. ICT has a definite drawback in that respect compared to unilateral ECT.

MINERAL METABOLISM

After balance techniques were supplanted by isotope dilution techniques it was possible to show that there is a changed distribution of water and electrolytes in affective disorders. Although the picture is not entirely clear, there appears to be increased intracellular sodium and water and decreased intracellular potassium, both in depressive and especially in manic states (Coppen, 1965, 1967). These conditions return to normal after recovery. There is also a slow transfer of sodium from blood to CSF which may be explained by the greater amount of intracellular sodium space (Coppen, 1960). The transfer rate is also normalized after recovery. Most of the recovered patients were treated with ECT and the question then arises whether ECT exerts a direct effect on water and mineral metabolism and, if so, whether this effect is relevant to the therapeutic process. Early studies indicated that the intensive muscular convulsion caused changes in water distribution, with hemoconcentration and delayed diuresis among other changes (Altschule & Tillotson, 1949). In a study of the influence of ECT on mineral metabolism with balance technique (Russel, 1960) a transient retention of sodium and water on the day of ECT was observed. However, these changes occurred also in patients who were only subjected to the procedures preliminary to ECT (atropine, intravenous barbiturate) without electrical stimulation and seizure. It is probable, therefore that sodium and water retention were related to the emotional reaction to ECT and not to the treatment itself.

There is another observation which argues against the hypothesis that ECT exerts its antidepressive effect via changes in mineral metabolism. In the transfer studies referred to above, patients who were treated with ECT but did not recover had the same low values as initially, while the recovered patient reached values observed in healthy controls. It would seem, therefore, that changes in mineral metabolism are secondary to the recovery and not a direct effect of ECT. Additional evidence from manipulating body water and electrolytes by dietary or pharmacological methods is still lacking. There are, however, observations indicating that administration of water and vasopressin has a depressogenic effect (Coppen, 1967).

DIENCEPHALIC INFLUENCES

It is a common clinical experience that variables which are regulated by diencephalic nuclei such as body weight, appetite, sleep, digestion, circulation, libido, and menstruation often change early in the course of therapy. The mechanism is not known, but since these variables also show early disturbance, sometimes before other clinical manifestations, they seem to reflect a basic disorder in affective disease. Accordingly, the mechanism of action of ECT has been described as stimulation of, or release from, inhibiting influences on diencephalic centers controlling autonomic and visceral functions (Jung, 1949). Behavior is thus changed by activating energy-determining or drive-determining mechanisms rather than by interfering with integrating functions by disrupting the neuronal connections underlying recent organized patterns of behavior (Elithorn, 1962). Departing from this hypothesis some experiments will be reviewed which are aimed at delimiting convulsive activity to the brain stem (Ottosson, 1962). When ECT is given under the influence of lidocaine, the pattern changes in a characteristic way (Figures 1 & 2). First, there is a shortening of the duration to about one-third which represents a lidocaine-resistant part of the seizure. Secondly, the pattern changes and assumes a regular bilaterally synchronous wave-and-spike appearance. Thirdly, there is no electrical silence but a regular alpha activity is seen immediately after the seizure. As in petit mal epilepsy and myoclonus petit mal, these circumstances are given the interpretation that the lidocaine-modified seizure signals seizure activity mainly in the brain stem and that cortical areas are driven from a centrencephalic pacemaker and do not actively participate in the seizure. It is then interesting to observe that the amount of this brain stem seizure activity is related to the antidepressive efficacy of the therapy. This relationship does not apply to the unmodified grand mal seizure where there is an active involvement of the cortex and alternating pacemakers.

The suggestion that the antidepressive efficacy of ECT is dependent upon the amount of epileptic activity in the brain stem is in agreement with Cannon's

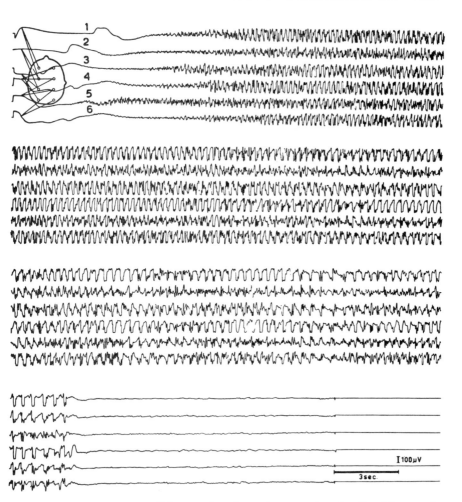

FIG. 1.   Seizure discharge in light narcosis and complete muscular relaxation. The record was obtained at the second treatment of a woman of 60. Electrode positions according to the 10/20 system. Leads: 1 - F3-C3, 2 - C3-P3, 3 - P3-01, 4 - F4-C4, 5 - C4-P4, and 6 - P4-02.

theory which implies that in emotions a subcortical structure, the hypothalamus, has a central role in coordinating autonomic-endocrine and somatic discharges and modifying cortical processes. This theory has gained support from animal experiments where emotional behavior has been evoked by electrical stimulation of diencephalon (Masserman, 1943; Hess, 1954) and where the phenomenon of "sham rage" may arise in decorticate animals. In man, manialike states have been described after lesion in the orbital brain, interpreted as "hypothalamic release." Diencephalic lesions as well as electrical stimulations in the hypothalamus and the midbrain in the course of brain operations have evoked manic as well as depressive symptoms. The EEG following ECT with its bilaterally synchronous

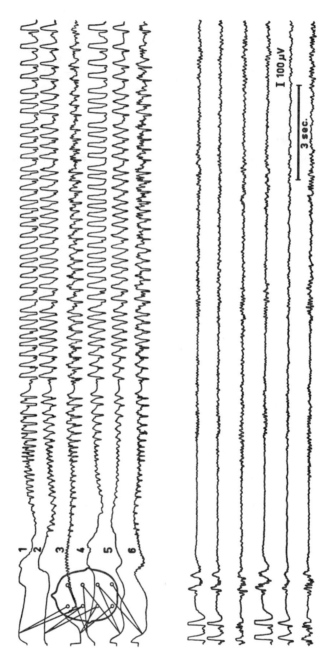

FIG. 2. Seizure discharge modified by 3 mg/kg lidocaine but otherwise identical conditions as in Figure 1. The record was obtained from the fourth treatment to the same patient.

slow waves which are probably of diencephalic origin, seems to be related to the stability of a remission from a depressive disorder (Roth, Kay, Shaw, & Green, 1957). Finally, a lidocaine-modified seizure takes place in the region which has the highest concentration of biogenic amines, substances of greatest interest for the etiology of affective disorders. Thus, there are several circumstances indicating that seizure activity in the brain stem is essential for the antidepressive activity of ECT. The electroencephalographic changes after ECT and the systemic vegetative effects may then be seen as effects on the same or adjacent structures as those determining the antidepressive effect.

SUMMARY

The main question to be answered after a survey of systemic effects of ECT is whether such effects are links in the therapeutic process or links in the process leading to side-effects (Type 1); whether they represent more or less direct consequences of basic neurochemical changes underlying the therapeutic effect (Type 2); or whether they are coincidental, parallel phenomena, arising via different and for the therapeutic process uninteresting mechanisms (Type 3). In these terms the following conclusions can be drawn with regard to the *antidepressive* effect of ECT:

1. The adrenal medullary and the noradrenaline responses are of Type 3 in respect of the rise in the levels of adrenaline and noradrenaline after each treatment and probably of Type 2 in respect of the increased reactivity of the adrenals and the decreased resting noradrenaline levels as the ECT series progresses.

2. The adrenal cortical response is of Type 3. The increased corticoid levels after ECT may even counteract therapeutic processes.

3. The increased cerebrovascular permeability may be of Type 1. The main reason is that similar changes are evoked by antidepressive drugs. CO_2 inhalation increases cerebrovascular permeability but CO_2 accumulation during the seizure more likely contributes to memory disturbance than to antidepressive effects.

4. Cerebral hypoxia is of Type 1 but has only relevance for the memory disturbance.

5. Changes in mineral and water metabolism are probably of Type 2.

6. The effects indicating diencephalic influence (weight, appetite, sleep, digestion, circulation, libido, and menstruation) are of Type 2. The relationship between the amount of brain stem seizure activity and antidepressive efficacy indicates that these effects have a very close relationship to the changes underlying the antidepressive effect. Available evidence indicates that closely adjacent and related or even the same diencephalic nuclei regulate mood, affect and vegetative changes and possibly also mineral and water metabolism.

For a closer understanding of the antidepressive effect of ECT there are good reasons to divert interest from systemic effects to the neurochemical events in the brain stem region. Evidence is accumulating that influences on synthesis and turnover of 5-HT and noradrenaline are Type 1 effects.

REFERENCES

Aird, R. B. Clinical correlates of electroshock therapy. *Archives of Neurology and Psychiatry*, 1958, 79, 633-639.

Altschule, M. D., & Tillotson, J. Effect of electroconvulsive therapy on water metabolism in psychotic patients. *American Journal of Psychiatry*, 1949, 105, 829-833.

Angel, C., & Roberts, A. J. Effect of electroshock and antidepressant drugs on cerebrovascular permeability to cocaine in the rat. *Journal of Nervous and Mental Disease*, 1966, 142, 376-380.

✓ Barbizet, J. Defect of memorizing of hippocampal-mamillary origin: A review. *Journal of Neurology, Neurosurgery and Psychiatry*, 1963, 26, 127-135.

✓ Berlyne, N., & Strachan, M. Neuropsychiatric sequelae of attempted hanging. *British Journal of Psychiatry*, 1968, 114, 411-422.

Bjerner, B., Broman, T., & Swensson, A. Tierexperimentelle Untersuchungen über Schädigungen der Gefässe mit Permeabilitätsstörungen und Blutungen im Gehirn bei Insulin, Cardiazol- und Elektroshockbehandlung. *Acta Psychiatrica et Neurologica Scandinavica*, 1944, 19, 431-452.

Bliss, E. L., Migeon, C. J., Nelson, D. H., Samuels, L. T., & Branch, C. H. H. Influence of ECT and insulin coma on level of adrenocortical steroids in peripheral circulation. *Archives of Neurology and Psychiatry*, 1954, 72, 352-361.

Board, F., Wadeson, R., & Persky, H. Depressive affect and endocrine functions. *Archives of Neurology and Psychiatry*, 1957, 78, 612-620.

Clemedson, C. -J., Hartelius, H., & Holmberg, G. The influence of carbon dioxide inhalation on the cerebral vascular permeability to trypan blue ("the blood-brain barrier"). *Acta Pathologica et Microbiologica Scandinavica*, 1958, 42, 137-150.

Coppen, A. Abnormality of the blood-cerebrospinal-fluid barrier of patients suffering from a depressive illness. *Journal of Neurology, Neurosurgery and Psychiatry*, 1960, 23, 156-161.

Coppen, A. Mineral metabolism in affective disorders. *British Journal of Psychiatry*, 1965, 111, 1133-1142.

Coppen, A. The biochemistry of affective disorders. *British Journal of Psychiatry*, 1967, 113, 1237-1264.

✓ Cronholm, B., & Molander, L. Memory disturbances after electroconvulsive therapy. I. Conditions 6 hours after electroshock treatment. *Acta Psychiatrica Scandinavica*, 1957, 32, 280-306.

Cronholm, B., & Ottosson, J. -O. "Countershock" in electroconvulsive therapy. Influence on retrograde amnesia. *Archives of General Psychiatry*, 1961, 4, 254-258.

Cronholm, B., & Ottosson, J. -O. Ultrabrief stimulus technique in electroconvulsive therapy. I. Influence on retrograde amnesia of treatments with the Elther ES electroshock apparatus, Siemens Konvulsator III and lidocaine-modified treatment. *Journal of Nervous and Mental Disease*, 1963, 137, 117-123.

Curzon, G. Tryptophan pyrrolase—a biochemical factor in depressive illness? *British Journal of Psychiatry*, 1969, 115, 1367-1374.

Elithorn, A. The treatment of depression. In D. Richter, J. M. Tanner, L. Taylor, & O. L. Zangwill (Eds.), *Aspects of psychiatric research*. London: Oxford University Press, 1962.

Gravenstein, J. S., Anton, A. H., Wiener, S. M., & Tetlow, A. G. Catecholamine and cardiovascular response to electro-convulsion therapy in man. *British Journal of Anaesthesia*, 1965, 37, 833-839.

Griswold, R. L. Plasma adrenaline and noradrenaline in electroshock therapy in man and in rats. *Journal of Applied Physiology*, 1958, 12, 117-120.

Havens, L. L., Zileli, M. S., DiMascio, A., & Boling, L. Changes in catecholamine response to successive electric convulsive treatments. *Journal of Mental Science*, 1959, **105**, 821-829.

Hess, W. R. *Das Zwischenhirn: Syndrome, Lokalisationen, Funktionen*. (2nd ed.) Basel: Schwabe, 1954.

Holmberg, G. Biological aspects of electroconvulsive therapy. *International Review of Neurobiology*, 1963, **5**, 389-412.

Jung, R. Hirnelektrische Untersuchungen uber den Elektrokrampf: Die Erregungsablaufe in corticalen und subcorticalen Hirnregionen bei Katze und Hund. *Archiv fur Psychiatrie und Nervenkrankheiten vereinigt mit Zeitschrift fur die Gesamte Neurologie und Psychiatrie*, 1949, **183**, 206-244.

Kallio, I. V. I., & Tala, E. O. J. Changes in the free 17-hydroxycorticosteroid levels in plasma after electroshock therapy. *Acta Endocrinologica*, 1959, **30**, 99-108.

Laurell, B. Flurothyl convulsive therapy. *Acta Psychiatrica Scandinavica*, 1970, **46** (Supplement 213).

Liberson, W. T., & Cadilhac, J. G. Electroshock and rhinencephalic seizure states. *Confinia Neurologica*, 1953, **13**, 278-286.

Masserman, J. H. *Behavior and neurosis*. Chicago: University of Chicago Press, 1943.

Meduna, L. J. *Carbon dioxide therapy*. Springfield, Ill.: Charles C.Thomas, 1958.

Montagu, J. D. Differential cerebral electrostimulation. *Journal of Mental Science*, 1955, **101**, 110-122.

Ottosson, J. -O. Experimental studies of the mode of action of electroconvulsive therapy. *Acta Psychiatrica Scandinavica*, 1960, **35** (Supplement 145).

Ottosson, J. -O. Seizure characteristics and therapeutic efficiency in electroconvulsive therapy. An analysis of the anti-depressive efficiency of grand mal and lidocaine-modified seizures. *Journal of Nervous and Mental Disease*, 1962, **135**, 239-251.

Ottosson, J. -O. Psychological or physiological theories of ECT. *International Journal of Psychiatry*, 1968, **5**, 170-174.

Plum, F., Posner, J. B., & Troy, B. Cerebral metabolic and circulatory responses to induced convulsions in animals. *Archives of Neurology*, 1968, **18**, 1-13.

Rosenblatt, S., Chanley, J. D., Sobotka, H., & Kaufman, M. R. Interrelationships between electroshock, the blood-brain barrier, and catecholamines. *Journal of Neurochemistry*, 1960, **5**, 172-176.

Roth, M., Kay, D. W. K., Shaw, J., & Green, J. Prognosis and pentothal induced electroencephalographic changes in electroconvulsive treatment. An approach to the problem of regulation of convulsive therapy. *Electroencephalography and Clinical Neurophysiology*, 1957, **9**, 225-237.

Russel, G. F. M. Body weight and balance of water, sodium and potassium in depressed patients given electroconvulsive therapy. *Clinical Science*, 1960, **19**, 327-336.

Sourkes, T. L., Drujan, B. D., & Curtis, G. C. Effects of electroshock therapy on the excretion of epinephrine. *Journal of Nervous and Mental Disease*, 1958, **127**, 191-195.

Sourkes, T. L., Sloane, R. B., & Drujan, B. D. Pyrocatecholamine (catecholamine) metabolism and effects of electroconvulsive therapy. *Archives of Neurology and Psychiatry*, 1957, **78**, 204-206.

Taylor, R. H., Gross, M., & Ruby, I. J. Nonconvulsive electrostimulation and the pituitary-adrenocortical system. *Journal of Nervous and Mental Disease*, 1951, **114**, 377-383.

Turner, E. Hippocampus and memory. *Lancet*, 1969, **2**, 1123-1126.

Weil-Malherbe, H. The effect of convulsive therapy on plasma adrenaline and noradrenaline. *Journal of Mental Science*, 1955, **101**, 156-162.

Weil-Malherbe, H., & Bone, A. D. The concentration of adrenaline-like substances in blood during insulin hypoglycaemia. *Journal of Mental Science*, 1952, **98**, 565-578.

Whitty, C. W. M., & Lishman, W. A. Amnesia in cerebral disease. In C. W. M. Whitty & O. L. Zangwill (Eds.), *Amnesia*. London: Butterworths, 1966.

16
EFFECT OF ELECTROSHOCK ON INDOLEAMINE METABOLISM AND AGGRESSIVE BEHAVIOR

Luigi Valzelli, M.D. and Silvio Garattini, M.D.

For the past many years, considerable attention has been paid to biogenic amines present in the brain, which are now generally considered as neurochemical transmitters at the synapse. Based upon the role that these substances are believed to play in normal as well as in altered behavior, many studies have been devoted to elicit possible relationships between brain neurochemical variations and behavioral modifications induced by pharmacological or physical interventions.

In this latter context, cerebral electric shock is known to induce changes in peripheral and central biochemical processes as well as modifications of affective disturbances of behavior. Moreover, the therapeutic value of electroshock (ES) was shown to be practically the same when the muscular convulsions are reduced or prevented by muscle relaxants (Holmberg, 1955) so that it seems likely that the site of action of ES is central rather than peripheral and, in the central nervous system, the indoleamine which appears to be consistently modified by ES is 5-hydroxytryptamine (5HT).

Previous work (Garattini & Valzelli, 1957; Garattini, Kato, & Valzelli, 1960; Bertaccini, 1959; Breitner, Picchioni, Chin, & Burton, 1961; Breitner, Picchioni, & Chin, 1964; Essman, 1967; Kato, Gozsy, Roy, & Groh, 1967) have reported an increased level of brain 5HT in rodents after ES, with a decreased amount of noradrenaline in cat and rat brain (Breitner et al., 1961, 1964). Also in rats, however, abolition of the ES convulsions by barbiturates, succinylcholine or diphenylhydantoin did not prevent the observed ES-induced increase in brain 5HT level (Bisiani, Garattini, Kato, & Valzelli, 1958; Garattini, et al. 1960), and these findings, like those reported by Holmberg (1955) in man further support the view that the ES effects are essentially central. Moreover, in vitro experiments show also that in incubated brain tissue, when stimulation at 15 pulses per second is performed, there is a significant increase of 5HT output (McIlwain, 1971).

However, the main obstacle in comparing the ES effects in experimental animals with the central events induced by such treatment in human beings, is perhaps represented by the fact that ES therapy is clinically applied to correct behavioral affective disorders, while, in laboratory experiments, ES is performed in normal animals. Based upon the fact that prolonged isolation is able to induce stable behavioral alterations both in mice (Yen, Stanger, & Millman, 1959; Valzelli, 1967b, 1969a; Essman, 1971a) and in rats (Goldberg & Salama, 1969; Valzelli, 1971a; Valzelli & Garattini, 1972) as well as several brain neurochemical variations (Valzelli, 1967a,b; 1971a; Garattini, Giacalone & Valzelli, 1969; Valzelli & Garattini, 1972; Essman, 1971a,b; Essman, Heldman, Barker, & Valzelli, 1972) and that, moreover, the behaviorally disturbed animals respond to psychoactive drugs differently from the normal ones (Valzelli, 1969b, 1971b; Valzelli & Bernasconi, 1971; Valzelli, Ghezzi, & Bernasconi, 1971), the present experiments deal with the ES effect on brain 5HT level and turnover as well as on behavior of normal and isolated mice and rats.

MATERIALS AND METHODS

Male Swiss Albino mice, weighing 20±2 g were isolated in single Makrolon cages for 4 weeks at a constant room temperature of 22°C and 60% relative humidity and fed ad libitum. At the end of the period of isolation all the animals were constantly and repetitively aggressive while no similar behavioral alteration was present in normal control mice living together, eight per cage.

Wistar male rats, weighing 200±10 g were isolated in single Makrolon cages for a period of 6 weeks at a constant room temperature of 22°C and 60% relative humidity and fed ad libitum. The development of the different behavioral alterations was followed over the period of isolation, by putting a naive normal mouse in contact with isolated rats and evaluating the muricidal, friendly, or indifferent behavior, according to the parameters listed in Table 1.

Electroshock was delivered through pinnal electrodes with the following parameters: 100 cycles per second, 20 mA, 0.2 sec.

Brain 5HT and 5-hydroxyindolacetic acid (5HIAA) were simultaneously extracted from the same tissue sample and spectrofluorometrically measured according to Giacalone and Valzelli (1969). Calculation of brain 5HT turnover was made according to Tozer, Neff, and Brodie, (1966).

RESULTS AND DISCUSSION

The effect of a single ES application on brain 5HT and 5HIAA levels in normal and aggressive mice is reported in Table 2 in which it is possible to observe that brain 5HT level is elevated both in normal and aggressive animals,

TABLE 1

Types of Behavior of Rats Subjected to 6 Weeks
Isolation toward a Mouse Put into Their Cage

Behavioral patterns[a]	Types of rats			
	Normal	Muri-cidal	Friendly	Indif-ferent
	Percent			
Approaching	100	100	100	4
Sniffing	100	20	100	4
Licking	56	0	100	0
Grooming	15	0	64	0
Nest preparing	0	0	22	0
Picking up	0	0	91	0
Carrying around	0	0	87	0
Joking	18	0	65	0
Jumping	0	10	12	0
Incoordinated hyperactivity	0	0	34	0
Tremor	0	0	12	0
Piloerection	2	100	0	0
Digging	0	85	0	0
Compulsive eating and drinking	0	16	2	67
Attacking	0	100	0	0
Killing	0	100	0	0

[a]Observations of 800 rats made by two observers.

while 5HIAA is not substantially changed in normal mice but is significantly increased in aggressive ones.

These findings lead one to suppose that brain 5HT turnover can be differently changed by ES in these two types of animals. In fact, calculation of brain 5HT turnover in normal mice shows a decrease of this parameter which instead is increased in aggressive animals. These metabolic differences, clearly evident immediately after ES application, are less but still significantly present 30 min later (Tables 3 and 4).

As in normal mice, ES treatment in normal rats induces a significant increase in brain 5HT content but is unable to induce any appreciable changes of the 5HIAA levels (Table 5), so that the calculation of brain 5HT turnover shows only a minor and not significant decrease of the turnover of this indoleamine (Table 6).

Subchronic ES treatment, consisting of one ES delivered to animals once a day for 7 days is, however, able significantly to reduce the brain 5HT turnover of the rats (Table 7).

TABLE 2

Single Electroshock Effects on Brain 5-Hydroxytryptamine
(5HT) and 5-Hydroxyindolacetic Acid (5HIAA) Levels
of Normal and Aggressive Mice

Treatment	Time after treatment (min)	Brain contents µg/g			
		Normal mice		Aggressive mice	
		5HT	5HIAA	5HT	5HIAA
Untreated controls	–	0.58±0.01	0.32±0.01	0.60±0.01	0.25±0.01
Electroshock	1	0.67±0.01*	0.32±0.01	0.65±0.02	0.28±0.01
	30	0.69±0.01*	0.33±0.01	0.69±0.01*	0.35±0.02*
	60	0.68±0.01*	0.36±0.02	0.72±0.02*	0.39±0.02*

$* = p < 0.01$.

However, it has been demonstrated that ES leaves the brain
monoamineoxidase activity unchanged (Essman 1968a, 1969), insofar as the
variations in level and metabolism of brain 5HT induced by such a treatment are
concerned, the results can vary depending on the electrical characteristics of ES
delivered (Pecile & Valsecchi, 1959; Breitner et al., 1961, 1964), acute or
chronic ES treatment (Kato et al., 1967) and the time interval between the ES
application and the biochemical determinations.

The relationship between brain 5HT metabolism and ES treatment is further
suggested by the variations of the 5HIAA concentrations which take place in
cerebrospinal fluid (CSF) of dogs (Cooper, Moir, & Guldberg, 1968), monkeys,
and severely depressed patients (Essman, 1972). Such changes become most

TABLE 3

Single Electroshock (ES) Effects on Brain
5-Hydroxytryptamine (5HT) Turnover of
Normal and Aggressive Mice (Measured
Immediately after ES Application)

Treatment	Brain 5HT turnover					
	Normal mice			Aggressive mice		
	$K(h^{-1})$	Rate (µg/g/h)	Time (min)	$K(h^{-1})$	Rate (µg/g/h)	Time (min)
Untreated controls	1.64	0.50	65	1.20	0.35	90
ES	1.17*	0.38	94	1.51*	0.46	70

$* = p < 0.01$.

TABLE 4

Single Electroshock (ES) Effects on Brain
5-Hydroxytryptamine (5HT) Turnover of
Normal and Aggressive Mice (Determined
30 min after ES Application)

Treatment	Brain 5HT turnover					
	Normal mice			Aggressive mice		
	$K(h^{-1})$	Rate (μg/g/h)	Time (min)	$K(h^{-1})$	Rate (μg/g/h)	Time (min)
Untreated controls	1.60	0.47	67	1.15	0.33	110
ES	1.27*	0.40	89	1.38**	0.41	92

* = $p < 0.05$.
** = $p < 0.01$.

TABLE 5

Single Electroshock (ES) Effects on Brain
5-Hydroxytryptamine (5HT) and
5-Hydroxyindolacetic Acid (5HIAA)
Content of Normal Rats

Treatment	Time after treatment (min)	Brain contents μg/g	
		5HT	5HIAA
Untreated controls	–	0.32±0.02	0.25±0.01
ES	15	0.38±0.01*	0.26±0.01
	30	0.40±0.01*	0.29±0.02
	60	0.42±0.01*	0.25±0.01

* = $p < 0.01$.

TABLE 6

Single Electroshock (ES) Effects on Brain
5-Hydroxytryptamine (5HT) Turnover of
Normal Rat (Measured Immediately
after ES Application)

Treatment	Brain 5HT turnover		
	$K(h^{-1})$	Rate (μg/g/h)	Time (min)
Untreated controls	1.28	0.35	80
ES	1.12	0.29	96

TABLE 7

Subchronic Electroshock (ES) Effects
on Brain 5-Hydroxytryptamine (5HT)
Turnover in Normal Rats

Treatment	Brain 5HT turnover		
	$K(h^{-1})$	Rate (μg/g/hr)	Time (min)
Untreated controls	1.23	0.36	72
ES[a]	0.60*	0.20	112

[a]One ES daily for 7 days.
* = $p < 0.001$.

evident after repeated ES applications, probably as a consequence of increased permeability of the brain-CSF barrier to acidic metabolites of biogenic amines.

From the behavioral point of view, it is well known that experimental animals subjected to ES, after recovery from the convulsive manifestations induced by such treatment, do not show any particular change in spontaneous behavior, except for some specialized nervous functions, such as memory processes that exhibit a retrograde amnesia (Essman, 1968b). By contrast, in some types of psychiatric patients ES intensively changes mood and behavior and it is

TABLE 8

Effect of Single Electroshock (ES) on Behavioral Alterations
Induced by Isolation in Mice and Rats, in Comparison with
Activity of Some Antianxiety and Antidepressant Drugs

Treatment	mg/kg i.p.	Change in activity (% of 10 animals)			
		Mice	Rats		
		Aggressive	Muricidal	Friendly	Indifferent
Saline	—	0	0	0	0
Chlordiazepoxide	10	100(3)	0	0	0
Oxazepam	10	100(3)	0	0	0
Medazepam	10	100(5)	0	0	0
Imipramine	10	0	100(15)	0	0
Desipramine	10	0	100(36)	0	0
Nortriptyline	10	0	100(26)	0	0
ES		0	100(10)	(24)[a]	0

Note.—In parentheses: duration of the observed effect in hours.
[a] Friendly rats become indifferent.

interesting to observe that ES acts differentially on the alterations of the behavioral patterns induced in mice and rats by prolonged isolation.

In fact, as shown in Table 8 in which the effect of ES is compared with that of some psychoactive drugs, a single ES is unable to block aggressive behavior in mice but is effective in changing friendly rats to indifferent ones and in blocking, for several hours, rat muricidal behavior. This last effect is quite similar to that of tricyclic antidepressant drugs.

This observation further supports the hypothesis, elsewhere put forward (Valzelli, 1971a; Valzelli & Bernasconi, 1971), that the effects of prolonged isolation are differently modulated by mice and rats in such a way as to represent a sort of bimodal system on which drugs and treatments may have different activity according to the model of altered behavior on which they act. When it is considered that the diverse behavioral alterations in mice and rats are accompanied by several changes in brain neurochemistry, such a consideration seems compatible with some of the current biochemical interpretations of several psychiatric disturbances (Ax, 1953; Brune, 1967; Schildkraut & Kety, 1967) and in their different responses to therapeutic management. Thus, isolation in mice and rats appears to be a useful laboratory tool by which to study some aspects of mental disease.

SUMMARY

Electroshock was shown to alter certain monoamine levels in brain. Previous data showed that brain 5-hydroxytryptamine is increased after electroshock in rodents.

The present studies deal with the effect of electroshock on concentration and turnover of brain 5-hydroxytryptamine in normal mice, in mice made aggressive by isolation, and in rats.

A single electroshock significantly increases the level of brain 5-hydroxytryptamine in normal and aggressive mice as well as in rats, but it is able to increase significantly the brain 5-hydroxyindolacetic acid content only in aggressive mice. From the behavioral point of view, electroshock is unable to modify the aggressive behavior produced in mice by isolation, but is very effective in blocking the muricidal reaction produced in rats by isolation.

REFERENCES

Ax, A. F. The physiological differentiation of fear and anger in humans. *Psychosomatic Medicine*, 1953, 15, 433-442.

Bertaccini, G. Effect of convulsant treatment on the 5-hydroxytryptamine content of brain and other tissues of the rat. *Journal of Neurochemistry*, 1959, 4, 217-222.

Bisiani, M., Garattini, S., Kato, R., & Valzelli, L. L'aumento di serotonina cerebrale dopo elettroshock non é in rapporto con lo stato convulsivo. *Atti della Societa Lombarda di Scienze Medico-Biologiche*, 1958, 13, 345-348.

Breitner, C., Picchioni, A., & Chin, L. Neurohormone levels in brain after CNS stimulation including electrotherapy. *Journal of Neuropsychiatry*, 1964, 5, 153-158.

Breitner, C., Picchioni, A., Chin, L., & Burton, L. E. Effect of electrostimulation on brain 5-hydroxytryptamine concentration. *Diseases of the Nervous System,* 1961, 22: 93-96. (Supplement)

Brune, G. G. Tryptophan metabolism in psychoses. In H. E. Himwich, S. S. Kety, & J. R. Smythies (Eds.), *Amines and schizophrenia.* Oxford: Pergamon Press, 1967.

Cooper, A. J., Moir, A. T. B., & Guldberg, H. C. The effect of electroconvulsive shock on the cerebral metabolism of dopamine. *Journal of Pharmacy and Pharmacology,* 1968, 20, 729-730.

Essman, W. B. Changes in memory consolidation with alterations in neural RNA. In H. Brill (Ed.), *Neuropsychopharmacology,* Proceedings of the 5th CINP Congress, Washington, D.C. 1966. Amsterdam: Excerpta Medica Foundation, 1967.

Essman, W. B. Changes in ECS-induced retrograde amnesia with DBMC: Behavioral and biochemical correlates of brain serotonin antagonism. *Physiology and Behavior,* 1968, 3, 527-531. (a)

Essman, W. B. Electroshock-induced retrograde amnesia and brain serotonin metabolism: Effects of several antidepressant compounds. *Psychopharmacologia,* 1968, 13, 258-266. (b)

Essman, W. B. Alterations in brain serotonin metabolism mediating enhanced memory consolidation. In A. Cerletti & F. J. Bové (Eds.), *The present status of psychotropic drugs.* Amsterdam: Excerpta Medica Foundation, 1969.

Essman, W. B. Isolation-induced behavioral modification: Some neurochemical correlates. In M. G. Sturman, D. J. McGinty, A. M. Adinolfi (Eds.), *Brain development and behavior.* New York: Academic Press, 1971. (a)

Essman, W. B. Neurochemical changes associated with isolation and environmental stimulation. *Biological Psychiatry,* 1971, 3, 141-147. (b)

Essman, W. B. Neurochemical changes associated with electroconvulsive shock. *Seminars in psychiatry,* 1972, 4, 67-79.

Essman, W. B., Heldman, E., Barker, L. A., & Valzelli, L. Development of microsomal changes in liver and brain of differentially housed mice. *Federation Proceedings,* 1972, 31, 121.

Garattini, S., Giacalone, E., & Valzelli, L. Biochemical changes during isolation-induced aggressiveness in mice, In S. Garattini & E. B. Sigg (Eds.), *Aggressive behaviour.* Amsterdam: Excerpta Medica Foundation, 1969.

Garattini, S., Kato, R., & Valzelli, L. Biochemical and pharmacological effects induced by electroshock. *Psychiatria et Neurologia (Basel),* 1960, 140, 190-206.

Garattini, S., & Valzelli, L. Serotonin and electroshock. In S. Garattini & V. Ghetti (Eds.), *Psychotropic drugs.* Amsterdam: Elsevier, 1957.

Giacalone, E., & Valzelli, L. A spectrofluorometric method for the simultaneous determination of 2-(5-hydroxyindol-3yl) ethylamine (serotonin) and 5-hydroxyindol-3yl-acetic acid in the brain. *Pharmacology,* 1969, 2, 171-175.

Goldberg, M. E., & Salama, A. I. Norepinephrine turnover and brain monoamine levels in aggressive mouse-killing rats. *Biochemical Pharmacology,* 1969, 18, 532-534.

Holmberg, G. The effect of certain factors on the convulsions in electric shock treatment. *Acta Psychiatrica et Neurologica Scandinavica* (Suppl. 98) 1955, pp 1-19.

Kato, L., Gozsy, B., Roy, P. B., & Groh, V. Histamine, serotonin, epinephrine and norepinephrine in the rat brain, following convulsions. *International Journal of Neuropsychiatry,* 1967, 3, 46-51.

McIlwain, H. Metabolic and neurohumoural studies with superfused tissues from the brain. *Proceedings of the Int. Union of Physiological Sciences, XXV International Congress,* 1971, 9, 382. (Abstracts)

Pecile, A., & Valsecchi, A. Variazioni di serotonina a livello mesencefalico in rapporto a stimolazioni di intensità e durata variabili. *Bollettino della Societa Italiana di Biologia Sperimentale,* 1959, 35, 726-728.

Schildkraut, J. J., & Kety, S. S. Biogenic amines and emotion. *Science,* 1967, **156,** 21-37.

Tozer, T. N., Neff, N. H., & Brodie, B. B. Application of steady state kinetics to the synthesis rate and turnover time of serotonin in the brain of normal and reserpine-treated rats. *Journal of Pharmacology and Experimental Therapeutics,* 1966, **153,** 177-182.

Valzelli, L. Biological and pharmacological aspects of aggressiveness in mice. In H. Brill (Ed.) *Neuropsychopharmacology,* Proceedings of the 5th CINP Congress, Washington D. C. 1966. Amsterdam: Excerpta Medica Foundation, 1967. (a)

Valzelli, L. Drugs and aggressiveness. *Advances in Pharmacology,* 1967, **5,** 79-108. (b)

Valzelli, L. Aggressive behaviour induced by isolation. In S. Garattini & E. B. Sigg (Eds.), *Aggressive behaviour.* Amsterdam: Excerpta Medica Foundation, 1969. (a)

Valzelli, L. The exploratory behaviour in normal and aggressive mice. *Psychopharmacologia* 1969, **15,** 232-235. (b)

Valzelli, L. Agressivité chez le rat et la souris: Aspects comportementaux et biochimiques. *Actualités Pharmacologiques,* 1971, **24,** 133-152. (a)

Valzelli, L. Further aspects of the exploratory behavior in aggressive mice. *Psychopharmacologia,* 1971, **19,** 91-94. (b)

Valzelli, L., & Bernasconi, S. Differential activity of some psychotropic drugs as a function of emotional level in animals. *Psychopharmacologia* 1971, **20,** 91-96.

Valzelli, L., & Garattini, S. Biochemical and behavioral changes induced by isolation in rats. *Neuropharmacology,* 1972, **11,** 17-22.

Valzelli, L., Ghezzi, D., & Bernasconi, S. Benzodiazepine activity on some aspects of behavior. *Totus Homo,* 1971, **3,** 73-79.

Yen, C. Y., Stanger, R. L., & Millman, N. Ataractic suppression of isolation-induced aggressive behavior. *Archives Internationales de Pharmacodynamie et de Therapie,* 1959, **123,** 179-185.

17
EFFECTS OF REPEATED ELECTROCONVULSIVE SHOCK ON BRAIN CATECHOLAMINES

Seymour S. Kety, M.D.

Not long after the discovery of the biogenic amines, serotonin, dopamine, and norepinephrine, in the brain, their involvement in certain behavioral and mental states was suggested by a number of provocative interactions between them and the newly developed psychoactive drugs. Some of these observations have suggested a special, although probably not an exclusive relationship between central catecholamines and mood. Reserpine, a hypotensive and tranquilizing agent that produces a state closely resembling endogenous depression (in some patients receiving it), was found characteristically to deplete the brain of biogenic amines (Shore, 1962). On the other hand, a number of drugs that elevate mood and have been found to be of value in the treatment of depression exert an action on central norepinephrine which could increase its synaptic efficacy either by inhibiting its presynaptic inactivation, by favoring its release, or by inhibiting its transport from the synapse (Glowinski & Axelrod, 1966; Schildkraut, Schanberg, Breese, & Kopin, 1967).

Although there is general agreement on the therapeutic efficacy of electroconvulsive shock in the treatment of clinical depression, there has been little basis on which to formulate hypotheses regarding its mechanism of action. Many of the biochemical effects that have been observed appear to be attributable to the acute functional disturbances which attend the shock itself (Holmberg, 1963; Ottosson, this volume).

If a decrease in the central synaptic activity of norepinephrine were a crucial factor in depressive illness, and if the beneficial effects of the antidepressant drugs were attributable to their counteracting this deficiency, one would expect some change to be induced by electroconvulsive shock in the availability of this amine in the brain. In studies that were carried out at the College de France, it was observed that rats subjected to intermittent electric shock to their feet showed an increased rate of disappearance of exogenous tritiated norepinephrine from the brain during the shock period, while the daily administration of such shock resulted after 3 days in an increase in the levels of endogenous norepinephrine (Thierry, Javoy, Glowinski, & Kety, 1968). This was compatible with the hypothesis that such stress caused a synaptic release of norepinephrine acutely, resulting in an increased synthesis and turnover. The elevated endogenous levels after repeated administration suggested the possibility of an adaptive change in the processes for norepinephrine synthesis and turnover in the brain. It seemed possible that a similar process might occur with electroconvulsive shock in which each shock episode would cause the release of norepinephrine at central synapses and repeated administration would eventually result in more permanent changes favoring the increased synthesis and release of the amine at central synapses. That hypothesis was tested by examining the turnover rate of norepinephrine in three regions of the central nervous system, 24 hr after the last of a series of electroconvulsive shock (Kety, Javoy, Thierry, Jolou, & Glowinski, 1967).

Albino rats were subjected to electroconvulsive shock induced twice daily at 8:00 A.M. and 4:00 P.M. for 7 days by transocular application of a single 150 mA shock for 0.2 sec (Swinyard, Brown, & Goodman, 1952). This induced a generalized tonic, then a series of clonic convulsions, followed by postconvulsive coma and stupor from which the animals apparently recovered within 15 min. Control animals were treated in exactly the same way, even to the application of the transocular electrodes, except that the switch which applied the current was kept open.

On the day following the last of the shocks, the norepinephrine studies were carried out on the control and experimental animals. In the intervening 19 to 24 hr, all animals had been in their cages, provided with food and water ad libitum. Estimation of norepinephrine turnover rate was made from the rate of disappearance of tritium-labeled norepinephrine from the brain (Glowinski, Kopin, & Axelrod, 1965) over a period of 5 hr following its injection into the cisterna magna (Schanberg, Schildkraut, & Kopin, 1967). This was performed under brief ether anesthesia from which the animals recovered within 10 min of induction. The experimental and control animals appeared to behave normally on the morning of the measurements, with no gross differences in behavior between them, except that the animals which had been exposed to electroconvulsive shock resisted the induction of anesthesia for a longer time. After injection, the rats were returned to their respective cages and left undisturbed until sacrificed, half of each group at 30 min, the remainder at 5 hr. Norepinephrine in three regions (brainstem and mesencephalon, telencephalon and diencephalon, and spinal cord) was separated from its metabolites and assayed spectrofluorometrically and by liquid scintillation counting. The tritium-labeled norepinephrine disappeared at a significantly greater rate from the regions examined in the experimental animals than in the controls, from which an increased turnover, i.e., enhanced synthesis and utilization, was inferred. The increase in endogenous norepinephrine which was often seen in the brain regions of the shocked animals may also reflect an effect of the shock regimen on the synthetic processes. (See Figure 1.)

DISCUSSION

Although the effects of a single electroconvulsive shock on levels of endogenous norepinephrine in brain have been inconsistent (Shatalova & Antonov, 1961; Breitner, Picchioni, & Chin, 1964; Kato, Gozsy, Roy, & Groh, 1967), Schildkraut and coworkers (1967), using a more sensitive indicator,

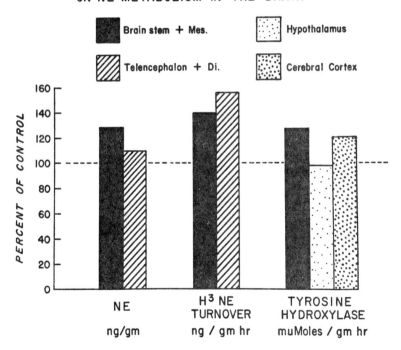

FIG. 1. Effect of a series of electroconvulsive shocks (twice daily for 7 days) on norepinephrine levels and estimated turnover [from Kety et al. (1967)] and of tyrosine hydroxylase [from Musacchio et al. (1969)] in regions of the rat brain. Analyses were made 19-24 hr after the last shock.

demonstrated an increased rate of disappearance of tritiated norepinephrine from the brain and a transient increase in levels of normetanephrine-H^3, following a single shock. It is not unreasonable that repetition of this process over a period of a week could lead to adaptive changes in the synthesis of norepinephrine which would persist for some time. The limiting enzyme in norepinephrine synthesis appears to be tyrosine hydroxylase which was found to be slightly but significantly increased in activity in the same brain regions 24 hr after the end of a similar regimen of twice daily electroconvulsive shocks (Musacchio, Julou, Kety, & Glowinski, 1969).

The changes in norepinephrine turnover, like those in the activity of tyrosine hydroxylase, following a regimen of electroconvulsive shock have not been great and subsequent studies have not unequivocally confirmed them (Hinesley, Norton, & Aprison, 1968; Ladisich, Steinhauff, & Matussek, 1969; Schildkraut & Draskoczy, this volume). Only one of these studies employed transocular shock and there is reason to believe that the biological effects of electroconvulsive shock on the brain can vary considerably depending upon electrode placements and parameters of shock. Two of the studies found evidence that the neurochemical changes induced by the shock regimen were to some extent accounted for by the stresses associated with the procedure. It is unlikely that this factor could have operated in our experiments, since the control and experimental animals were treated in exactly the same way except for the passage of the current through the electrodes and the resultant convulsion. Schildkraut and Draskoczy (this volume) found the effects of chronic electroconvulsive shock on norepinephrine-H^3 disappearance from the brain to be confined to the early part of the disappearance curve which may reflect disappearance from a smaller and more labile pool. Although studies of turnover are more sensitive than those of endogenous levels, they may still fall short of reflecting the magnitude of changes in transmitter release at specific synapses in the brain. Although the results to date are compatible with some persistent effect of repeated electroconvulsive shock on brain norepinephrine, the precise nature of this change, its magnitude and duration, and its possible relevance to the therapeutic effects of the procedure in depression remain to be explored.

REFERENCES

Breitner, C., Picchioni, A., & Chin, L. Neurohormone levels in brain after CNS stimulation including electrotherapy. *Journal of Neuropsychiatry,* 1964, 5, 153-158.
Glowinski, J., & Axelrod, J. Effects of drugs on the disposition of H^3-norepinephrine in the rat brain. *Pharmacological Reviews,* 1966, 18, 775-785.
Glowinski, J., Kopin, I. J., & Axelrod, J. Metabolism of H^3-norepinephrine in the rat brain. *Journal of Neurochemistry,* 1965, 12, 25-30.
Hinesley, R. K., Norton, J. A., & Aprison, M. H. Serotonin, norepinephrine and 3,4-dihydroxyphenylethylamine in rat brain parts following electroconvulsive shock. *Journal of Psychiatric Research,* 1968, 6, 143-152.

Holmberg, G. Biological aspects of electroconvulsive therapy. *International Review of Neurobiology*, 1963, **5**, 389-412.

Kato, L., Gozsy, B., Roy, P. B., & Groh, V. Histamine, serotonin, epinephrine and norepinephrine in the rat brain, following convulsions. *International Journal of Neuropsychiatry*, 1967, **3**, 46-51.

Kety, S. S., Javoy, F., Thierry, A. M., Julou, L., & Glowinski, J. A sustained effect of electroconvulsive shock on the turnover of norepinephrine in the central nervous system of the rat. *Proceedings of the National Academy of Sciences of the United States of America*, 1967, **58**, 1249-1254.

Ladisich, W., Steinhauff, N., & Matussek, N. Chronic administration of electroconvulsive shock and norepinephrine metabolism in the rat brain. *Psychopharmacologia*, 1969, **15**, 296-304.

Musacchio, J. M., Julou, L., Kety, S. S., & Glowinski, J. Increase in rat brain tyrosine hydroxylase activity produced by electroconvulsive shock. *Proceedings of the National Academy of Sciences of the United States of America*, 1969, **63**, 1117-1119.

Ottosson, J. -O. Systemic biochemical effects of ECT. This volume.

Schanberg, S. M., Schildkraut, J. J., & Kopin, I. J. The effects of pentobarbital on the fate of intracisternally administered norepinephrine-H^3. *Journal of Pharmacology and Experimental Therapeutics*, 1967, **157**, 311-318.

Schildkraut, J. J., & Draskoczy, P. R. Effects of electroconvulsive shock on norepinephrine turnover and metabolism: Basic and clinical studies. This volume.

Schildkraut, J. J., Schanberg, S. M., Breese, G. R., & Kopin, I. J. Norepinephrine metabolism and drugs used in the affective disorders: A possible mechanism of action. *American Journal of Psychiatry*, 1967, **124**, 600-608.

Shatalova, A. A., & Antonov, E. K. Content of adrenaline and noradrenaline in adrenal and brain tissues and in blood of rabbits in convulsive states. *Psychopharmacological Abstracts*, 1961, **1**, 341.

Shore, P. A. Release of serotonin and catecholamines by drugs. *Pharmacological Reviews*, 1962, **14**, 531-550.

Swinyard, E. A., Brown, W. C., & Goodman, L. S. Comparative assays of antiepileptic drugs in mice and rats. *Journal of Pharmacology*, 1952, **106**, 319-330.

Thierry, A. M., Javoy, F. Glowinski, J., & Kety, S. S. Effects of stress on the metabolism of norepinephrine, dopamine and serotonin in the central nervous system of the rat. I. Modifications of norepinephrine turnover. *Journal of Pharmacology and Experimental Therapeutics*, 1968, **163**, 163-177.

18
EFFECTS OF ELECTROCONVULSIVE SHOCK ON CEREBRAL PROTEIN SYNTHESIS[1]

Walter B. Essman, Ph.D., M.D.[2]

In previous studies I have examined the relationship between electroconvulsive shock as a vehicle through which retrograde amnesia may be provided in experimental animals and several biochemical alterations that have been observed as a consequence of such treatment. Utilizing a single transcorneal ECS, rather consistent biochemical changes in mouse forebrain have been observed; these included: (a), a decrease in the regional concentration of ribonucleic acid (RNA), with such a reduction dependent upon the age at which ECS treatment has been given (Essman, 1966, 1972); (b), a reduction in the incorporation of precursors into brain RNA, which has also been shown to be age-dependent (Essman, 1971); (c), an increase in forebrain and regional levels of 5-hydroxytryptamine (5-HT) observed shortly following a single ECS (Essman, 1967, 1968, 1970b); (d), an increase in ECS-induced brain 5-HT turnover time (Essman, 1968, 1970a); and (e), a relationship between RNA, free nucleotides, and 5-HT in brain that is altered as a consequence of cerebral electroshock (Essman, Bittman, & Heldman, 1971; Essman, 1971); e.g., electroshock has also been shown to produce changes in those cerebral nucleotides which are related to excitability functions (Bonavita & Piccoli, 1971).

In view of several of the previous relationships demonstrated between ECS and several endogenous constituents in brain probably relevant to regulatory mechanisms operative during cerebral protein synthesis, it has been my purpose to consider some of those parameters by which the effects of ECS on protein

[1] The research reported in this paper was supported in part by grants from the Council for Tobacco Research-U.S.A.

[2] The author wishes to acknowledge the technical assistance rendered by Mr. E. Heldman for some of the reported experiments.

synthesis may represent a relevant consideration in functional processes. One such functional process is the fixation of the memory trace and its disruption through several possible agents, one of which is ECS. Some support for the implication of protein synthesis in these events has been drawn from studies in which anti-metabolite-induced inhibition of protein synthesis has also caused amnesic-like behavior in experimental animals (Agranoff, 1967; Barondes, 1970; Flexner, Flexner, & Roberts, 1967). In the light of these investigations it is rather surprising to contrast the profound degree to which protein synthesis must be inhibited by antibiotics in brain tissue to bring about an amnesic effect, with the lesser degree of inhibition that has been shown in other approaches utilizing ECS (Cotman, Banker, Zornetzer, & McGaugh, 1971; Dunn, 1971, Essman et al., 1971; Heldman & Essman, 1971). These differences suggest either a high degree of resistance to antibiotic-induced inhibition of those proteins and/or the likelihood that the subcellular localization of protein synthetic processes altered by ECS differs from those sites showing greater susceptibility to the effects of antibiotics. This question provides additional interest for the issue of cell body versus nerve ending synthetic events, and relates to the question of whether those cerebral changes attending ECS are capable of independently modifying synthetic events in the presynaptic nerve ending.

One cerebral change predictably resulting from a single ECS is the elevation of forebrain 5-HT, and that exogenous 5-HT can reduce the rate at which amino acids are incorporated into nerve ending proteins (Essman, 1970b). The question of protein synthesis as an independent event in synaptosomes is a theoretical issue that will not be considered in detail in the present context, but will rather be used to illustrate the in vitro effects of 5-HT upon protein synthesis.

An isolated synaptosome preparation was incubated with either 5-HT $(3x10^{-7}M)$ or 0.9% NaCl; the concentration of 5-HT used was the amount which, when injected intracranially in vivo led to tissue concentrations of 5-HT approximating those observed at 10 min after a sigle ECS. The synaptosome preparations obtained in these experiments were derived from either mouse cerebral cortex, or mouse limbic system structures; the latter was constituted of tissue from amygdala, hippocampus, fornix, and septal region. Tissues from 10 mice each were pooled to provide the fractions utilized under experimental or control conditions.

The rate of incorporation of ^{14}C-leucine ($\mu\mu M$ leucine/mg protein/hr) in the cerebral cortex and limbic system synaptosomes was 34.29 and 36.60, respectively, under control conditions. The rate of incorporation following incubation with 5-HT was reduced in the synaptosomes derived from cerebral cortex and limbic system to 26.06 and 24.89, respectively. These findings, indicating 24% and 36% inhibition, respectively in presynaptic nerve endings isolated from cerebral cortex and limbic system structures, appears to constitute a first step toward which the aminergic effects of ECS may be related to changes in protein synthesis.

I have previously indicated that the age at which a single ECS is given to mice is a critically important determinant of the neurochemical sequelae of such treatment (Essman, 1970b). Specifically, the 17-day-old CF-ls strain male mouse shows a number of neural metabolic differences from either younger or older mice of the same strain. These differences in the 17-day-old mouse brain include (*a*), reduced brain 5-HT concentration; (*b*), increased forebrain 5-HT turnover rate and decreased turnover time; (*c*), a decrease in monoamine oxidase activity which remains lower after 17 days of age; and (*d*) no change in forebrain norepinephrine (NE) concentration. The unique characteristic of these metabolic changes which appear to spontaneously emerge at 17 days of age, is that their direction is completely opposite to that produced in the same tissue of young adult animals by a single ECS. Therefore, if one were to assume that some of the changes produced in cerebral indoleamine metabolism by ECS are related to metabolic events critical to memory formation or amnesia production, then one may further infer that behaviorally the 17-day-old mouse should show a reduced incidence of ECS-induced retrograde amnesia. When this hypothesis was tested utilizing male CF-ls strain mice of 15, 17, and 20 days of age, given a single transcorneal ECS (10 mA, 200 msec, 400 V) either immediately, 10 min, or 60 min after a single passive avoidance training trial, retention of the conditioned avoidance response, tested 24 hr latter, emerged as summarized in Table 1.

Both 15- and 20-day-old mice showed a characteristic temporal gradient for ECS-induced retrograde amnesia; i.e., as the interval between the training trial and ECS was increased, the incidence of conditioned response retention, measured 24 hr after training, was also increased. This observation, however, was not made in 17-day-old mice, wherein, even ECS given immediately following the training trial, produced retrograde amnesia in any of the animals tested. It would therefore appear as though male CF-ls strain mice at 17 days of age showed a critical period within which a resistance to ECS-induced amnesia and a reversal of indoleamine changes produced by ECS occurred. One factor to which both the behavioral characteristics of ECS-induced amnesia and the biochemical

TABLE 1

Percent Incidence of Conditioned
Response Retention in Mice Given
ECS at Several Posttraining Intervals

Age (days)	Time between training and ECS (sec)		
	10	600	3,600
15	40	80	100
17	80**	100*	100
20	10	50	100

*$p < .05$.
**$p < .01$.

effects of ECS relate is cerebral protein synthesis. Indeed, if those behavioral and biochemical observations already made are indirectly correlated, then one might expect an age-dependent relationship between ECS and the inhibition of protein synthesis.

Laboratory bred male mice of the CF-ls strain were treated with either a single transcorneal ECS (15 mA 200 msec, 400 V) or sham ECS (ECS–Application of only electrode-paste-dipped transcorneal electrodes without any passage of current) coincident with the intracranial injection of ^{14}C-leucine. Such treatment was given to groups of mice at either 15, 17, or 20 days of age. A 5-min labeling pulse was utilized, after which the mouse was killed, and the forebrain tissue was prepared so that proteins extracted and precipitated could be counter for the incorporated labeled amino acid. Measures of protein concentration were also made in order to utilize these as a baseline for specific radioactivity, and free leucine was also compared in brain tissue under both treatment conditions to insure that the free leucine pool had not been altered as a function of treatment.

The results of these experiments have been summarized in Table 2, wherein age-related differences in amino acid incorporation into protein have been summarized for ECS and sham ECS treatment conditions. It is apparent from these data that 17-day-old CF-ls strain mice, even under sham treatment conditions, showed a significantly higher rate of ^{14}C-leucine incorporation into forebrain proteins, than did 15- or 20-day-old animals of the same strain; this suggests that a higher rate of cerebral protein synthesis is in effect in the 17-day-old animal. When the three age groups selected for this experiment were treated with ECS and the labeled amino acid incorporated into forebrain proteins was measured 5 min later, it is apparent that the 17-day-old animals showed the least effect from such treatment; the 8.7% inhibition of protein synthesis in this age group is less than the more appreciable inhibition by ECS in 15- or 20-day-old mice.

TABLE 2

Incorporation of ^{14}C–Leucine into
Mouse Forebrain Protein (cpm/mg
Protein) in Mice of Different Ages
Given ECS or Sham Treatment

Age (days)	Treatment condition		Inhibition %
	Sham ECS	ECS	
15	357	220	38.3
17	569*	519*	8.7*
20	376	246	34.5

*$p < .01$.

These experiments exhibit several consistencies for the relationship between cerebral electroshock and its effect on cerebral protein synthesis in terms of changes in indoleamine metabolism. A question does arise as to the specificity of inhibition of 5-HT in preference to 5-HT derivatives or analogs, and this issue has been approached from several directions that suggest specificity of the phenomenon for 5-HT. Such specificity has been considered in terms of 5-HT binding by nucleic acids (Essman et al., 1971) and the affinity relationships between t-RNA and 5-HT (Essman, 1971). Within these considerations, the affinity of 5-HT for t-RNA is greater ($NK = 7.7 \times 10^{-4}$, where N = the number of binding sites on the macromolecule and K = the intrinsic association constant), than that for 5-methoxy-1-methyltryptamine ($NK = 1.2 \times 10^{-4}$), or N-acetyl-5-hydroxytryptamine ($NK = 5.9 \times 10^{-3}$). The intracerebral administration of equimolar quantities of these indoleamines resulted in 34%, 12%, and 6% inhibition of protein synthesis measured from a synaptosomal fraction isolated from the cerebral cortex of mice treated 5 min earlier. Inhibition of cerebral protein synthesis can thus be brought about with an agent that can be linked rather specifically to the direct effects of 5-HT. Such specificity for 5-HT has also been indicated for the amnesic effects of intracerebral administration of this amine.

Intracerebral administration of 5-HT is capable of bringing about a retrograde amnesic effect in mice and the nature of the amnesic effect closely approximates that observed for electroconvulsive shock (Essman, 1970b). When male CF-1s strain mice were trained for acquisition of a passive avoidance response and the training trial was followed, within 20 sec by either: (a), the intracranial administration of 5-HT (2γ in 5λ of 0.9% NaCl), or (b) an equivalent volume of 0.9% NaCl, or (c), a single transcorneal ECS (20 mA), or (d), sham ECS, (ECS), the results summarized in Figure 1, were obtained when a testing trial for the retention of an avoidance response was given 24 hr following training. Both ECS and intracranial 5-HT lead to a significant reduction in the retention of a passive avoidance response.

The specificity of the amnesic effect of 5-HT was again considered with the immediate postconditioning treatment consisting of the injection of either 0.9% NaCl, norepinephrine (NE), N-acetyl-5-hydroxytryptamine or 5-methoxy-1-methyltryptamine (N-A-S-HT) (5-MT) into the medial hippocampus. When the retention of the passive avoidance response was evaluated 24 hr following training, 80% to 100% of all animals treated with either NaCl, NE, N-A-5-HT, or 5-MT showed retention of the passive avoidance response, whereas only 20% of the mice treated with intrahippocampal 5-HT showed retention. The same type of specificity obtained behaviorally for 5-HT has also been observed biochemically. While we make no direct comparison between the behavioral and/or biochemical effects of 5-HT with those of ECS, we do indicate that the behavioral change is linked with the latter event and the effects of both are strikingly similar in several respects.

We have previously considered that the effect of a single ECS mediates an age-dependent inhibition of protein synthesis in the mouse forebrain. In several

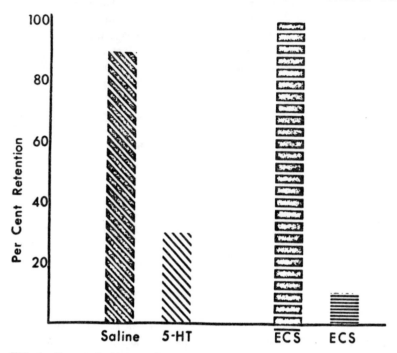

The Effect of 5-HT or ECS on Passive Avoidance Behavior

FIG. 1. Percent incidence of conditioned response retention in mice given either transcorneal ECS or intracranial 5-HT immediately following a training trial.

experiments, consideration was given to the temporal relationship between ECS and an effect on protein synthesis. The incorporation of ^{14}C-leucine into forebrain proteins of mice was measured utilizing a 5-min labeling pulse, so that incorporation differences between groups of ECS-treated and sham ECS-treated mice could be measured over intervals ranging from immediately after ECS treatment to 240 min posttreatment. The results of these experiments are summarized in Figure 2. Whereas inhibition of protein synthesis produced in vivo was in evidence for at least 15 min following ECS, and to a lesser degree by both 30 and 60 min following ECS, the maximum inhibition was found within the first 5 min following treatment.

A similar study was carried out in mice given either ECS or sham ECS with ^{14}C-leucine incorporation into protein measured immediately, 5, and 30 min following ECS. The brain tissue was separated into several discrete regions consisting of cerebral cortex, basal ganglia and diencephalon, midbrain, and cerebellum. The results of these experiments are summarized in Figure 3. The maximal extent to which regional inhibition by ECS occurred was in the basal ganglia and diencephalon, although there was appreciable inhibition observed in the cerebral cortex. Also, there was a small peak inhibition at 5-min

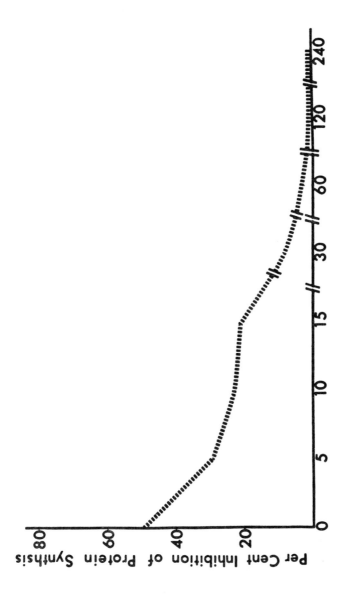

FIG. 2. Percent inhibition of cerebral protein synthesis as a function of time following ECS.

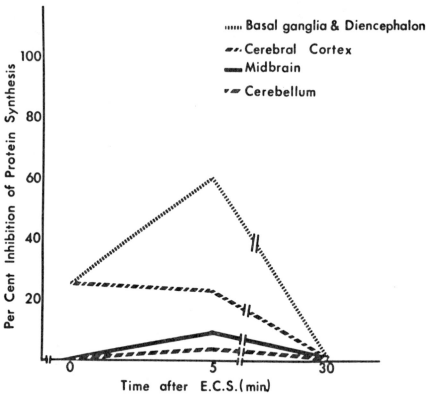

FIG. 3. Percent inhibition of protein synthesis for several regions of the mouse brain as a function of time following ECS.

posttreatment measured in the midbrain, this change appears to be less significant than that observed for the other regions. It would again appear that changes occurring within the first 5 min following ECS administration are significant for cerebral protein synthesis.

A more detailed consideration of the subcellular sites at which protein synthesis was inhibited by a single ECS have been previously considered (Essman, 1972). ^{14}C-leucine incorporation was measured in several subcellular fractions obtained from several regions of the mouse brain. Fifteen minutes following ECS, maximal inhibition measured in a synaptosome fraction (isolated presynaptic nerve endings) was observed when this fraction was derived from cerebral cortex (72%), with less inhibition in basal ganglia and diencephalon (41%), and brain stem (35%). When the cerebral cortex was obtained from mice 5 min following ECS, and fractionated, the greatest inhibition in protein synthesis was measured in the synaptosomal fraction (38%), in contrast to an ECS-related reduction of ^{14}C-leucine labeling of proteins in myelin (19%) and mitochondria (20%).

Many experiments in which the effects of ECS on protein synthesis have been summarized in previous publications (Essman, 1970b, 1971, 1972) and these data will not be reported again here. One consideration that deserves further attention is the specific sites and proteins which are altered by ECS. A significant portion of the protein synthesis inhibited by ECS may be accounted for by the synaptosome fraction, at least as derived from mouse cerebral cortex. As I have previously shown that the greatest magnitude of protein synthesis and its inhibition by ECS is accounted for by the synaptosome fraction, as derived from a crude mitochondrial fraction, it was my purpose to deal more specifically with two classes of protein derived from this fraction. This was done on the assumption that alterations in protein synthesis produced by ECS could represent effects on the soluble proteins active in intrasynaptosomal functions, and the insoluble proteins which contribute to synaptosomal membrane structure.

A crude mitochondrial fraction was obtained from pooled cerebral cortex of mice that had been given a single ECS (20 mA, 200 msec, 400 V) and immediately injected with ^{14}C-leucine; these animals were killed 5 min after the injection of the labeling pulse, and the tissue was then fractionated. Soluble proteins extracted from the crude mitochondrial pellet were precipitated and 200 γ of samples of this material were run on a disc electrophoresis utilizing polyacrylamide gels. Qualitative differences in the pattern of the 11 distinct bands observed in these gels following staining with amidoblack were not apparent when ECS-derived and control-derived samples were compared (Figure 4). A representation of the total radioactivity contributed by ^{14}C-leucine incorporated into the soluble proteins is summarized in Figure 5. Several portions of the total distribution of these proteins show markedly reduced rates of amino acid incorporation as a consequence of ECS. The inhibition of synthesis for one or more proteins of approximately similar molecular weight is summarized in Figure 6 for each of the 11 visable bands into which the soluble proteins were dispersed by electrophoresis. More than 50% of the synthesis of

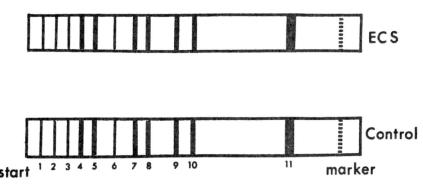

FIG. 4. Disc-gel electrophoretic pattern of soluble proteins derived from a crude mitochondrial fraction of mouse cerebral cortex following either ECS or sham ECS.

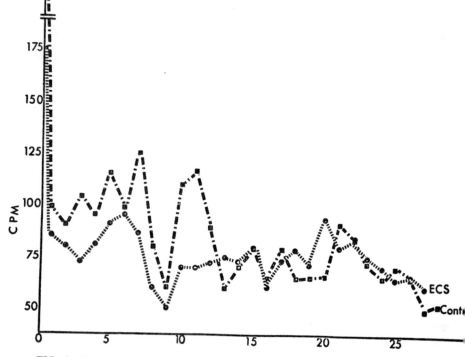

FIG. 5. Total radioactivity of soluble proteins from a crude mitochondrial fraction of mouse cerebral cortex after disc-gel electorphoresis. In vivo treatments consisted of either ECS or sham ECS.

the proteins (probably those having the highest molecular weights) were inhibited by ECS, and although several other distinct protein bands showed up to 25% inhibition of synthesis by 5 min after treatment, the lower molecular weight soluble proteins did not show an alteration in synthesis after ECS.

When the insoluble proteins were derived from the crude mitochondrial fraction and, following solubilization, were run on polyacrylamide gels each with 200 γ of protein, a representative electrophoretic pattern was obtained (Figure 7). Qualitative differences in the migration pattern of these constituent proteins are not apparent. When the total radioactivity incorporated into proteins during the 5 min of posttreatment labeling was assessed across all segments of the polyacrylamide gels the mean ($\pm\sigma$) radioactivity counts for each segment summarized in Figure 8 were obtained. As compared with the control series (sham ECS) the greatest inhibition as a consequence of treatment appears to be in the lower molecular weight insoluble proteins in this series.

These experiments, although preliminary in nature, suggest that ECS mediates the inhibition of at least two classes of proteins, probably having both functional and structural significance synaptically, and also specific polypeptides or proteins which may be differentiated on the basis of differences in molecular weight, that reside in each such protein class. It remains to be demonstrated whether the site specificity and molecular specificity indicated for ECS is also indicated for other agents and/or events which elicit similar behavioral and biochemical changes as ECS.

These experiments indicate several areas where the effects of ECS on cerebral protein synthesis may be approximated by the biological active amine, 5-hydroxytryptamine. This approximation holds biochemically and behaviorally, insofar as the amnesic effect of both postexperiential treatments are concerned.

Specific endogenous factors reduce the susceptibility of mice to the amnesic effects of both treatments, and also render the animals less susceptible to the inhibition of protein synthesis effected by both treatments. There are regional differences in the effect of ECS on protein synthesis and perhaps those areas wherein differences and the magnitude of inhibition can be compared represent differences in either (*a*) cellular involvement following current passage through the brain, (*b*) differences in the current pathway, or (*c*) differences in circulation and/or diffusion during and after current delivery. The site-specific differences in the magnitude of protein synthesis inhibition can be identified following ECS. One site with functional bearing on this issue is the synaptic region. It is probable that synthetic events related to structural changes in the synaptic

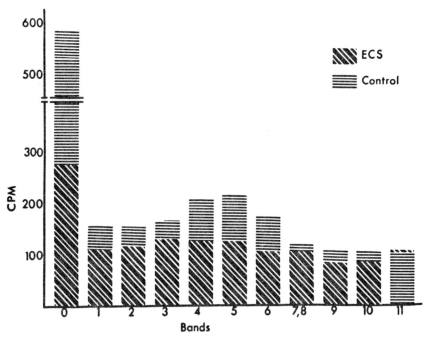

FIG. 6. Total radioactivity of soluble protein fractions separated from a crude mitochondrial fraction of mouse cerebral cortex. Mice were treated in vivo with ECS or sham ECS.

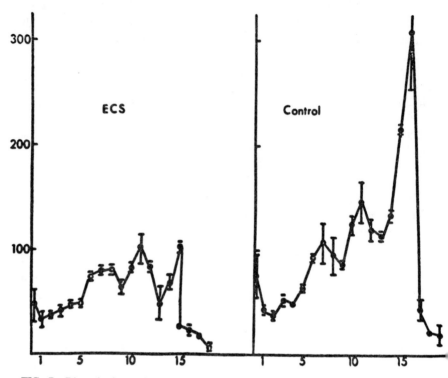

FIG. 7. Disc-gel electrophoretic patterns of insoluble proteins derived from a crude mitochondrial fraction of mouse cerebral cortex following ECS or sham ECS.

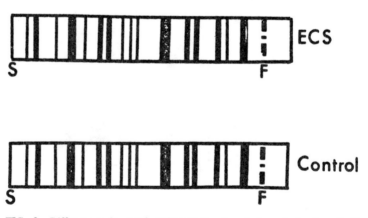

FIG. 8. Differences in total radioactivity (cpm) for electrophoretically separated insoluble proteins derived from a crude mitochondrial fraction of mouse cerebral cortex. Treatment in vivo was with ECS or sham ECS.

membrane are important both for the functional integrity of the synaptic area, and to the important functional events operative in memory and amnesic processes. The inhibition of protein synthesis, as brought about by antimetabolites, differs from the inhibition effected through ECS; the latter is more site specific as well as more effective as a tool for studying the relationship between amnesic processes and cerebral protein synthesis. It also has an empirical foundation upon which better understanding of the nature of cerebral changes important for the therapeutic applications of ECT may be built.

REFERENCES

Agranoff, B. W. Memory and protein synthesis. *Scientific American*, 1967, 216, 115-122.

Barondes, S. H. Is the amnesic effect of cyclohexamide due to specific interference with a process in memory storage? In A. Lajtha (Ed.), *Protein metabolism of the nervous system.* New York: Plenum Press, 1970.

Bonavita, V., & Piccoli, F. Brain nucleotides and excitatory processes. In R. Paolett & A. N. Davison (Eds.), *Chemistry and brain development.* New York: Plenum Press, 1971.

Cotman, C. W., Banker, G., Zornetzer, S. F., & McGaugh, J. L. Electroshock effects on brain synthesis: Relation to brain seizures and retrograde amnesia. *Science,* 1971, 173, 454-456.

Dunn, A. J. Brain protein synthesis after electroshock. *Abstracts of the First Annual Meeting of the Society for Neuroscience,* 1971.

Essman, W. B. Gastric ulceration in differentially housed mice. *Psychological Reports,* 1966, 19, 173-174.

Essman, W. B. Changes in memory consolidation with alterations in neural RNA. In H. Brill, J. O. Cole, P. Deniker, H. Hippuis, & P. Bradley (Eds.), *Neuropsychopharmacology.* Amsterdam: Excerpta Medical Foundation, 1967.

Essman, W. B. Changes in ECS-induced retrograde amnesia with DBMC: Behavioral and biochemical correlates of brain serotonin antagonism. *Physiology and Behavior,* 1968, 3, 527-532.

Essman, W. B. The role of biogenic amines in memory consolidation. In G. Adam (Ed.), *The biology of memory.* Budapest: Akademinai Kiado, 1970.(a)

Essman, W. B. Some neurochemical correlates of altered memory consolidation. *Transactions of the New York Academy of Sciences,* 1970a, 32, 948-973. (b)

Essman, W. B. Drug effects and learning and memory processes. In S. Garattini & P. Shore (Eds.), *Advances in pharmacology and chemotherapy.* New York: Academic Press, 1971.

Essman, W. B. Neurochemical changes in ECS and ECT. *Seminars in Psychiatry,* 1972, 4, 67-69.

Essman, W. B., Bittman, R., & Heldman, E. Molecular and synaptic modulation of ribonucleic acid–5-hydroxytryptamine interactions. *Abstracts of the Fourth Annual Winter Conference on Brain Research,* 1971.

Flexner, L. B., Flexner, J. B., & Roberts, R. B. Memory and mice analyzed with antibiotics. *Science,* 1967, 155, 1377-1383.

Heldman, E., & Essman, W. B. 5-Hydroxytryptamine-related changes in cerebral protein syntheses. *Abstracts of the First Annual Meeting of the Society for Neuroscience,* 1971, 52, 5.3.

19
BRAIN ACETYLCHOLINE AND SEIZURES[1]

Alexander G. Karczmar, Ph.D., M.D.[2,3]

The central cholinergic system is pertinent to the convulsive activity of the central nervous system. Drugs acting on the cholinergic system both induce seizures and influence the parameters of electroconvulsive shock (ECS); the brain levels of acetylcholine (ACh) are affected by seizures whether induced chemically or electrically. Furthermore, cholinergic drugs and the central cholinergic system exert pronounced effects on the EEG phenomena of synchrony and desynchrony which are related to cerebral susceptibility to and endogenous protective mechanisms against seizures. Following a summary of the status of central cholinergic mechanisms, some evidence dealing with the relation of the cholinergic system to seizures will be described. It should be candidly stated that this description is biased in favor of my own research and of the evidence supporting my own speculations as to the organizational and functional role of ACh in the central nervous system.

CURRENT STATUS OF THE ROLE OF ACh
IN THE CENTRAL NERVOUS SYSTEM

The wide central distribution of cholinergic synapses is suggested by the almost ubiquitous presence of the components of the cholinergic system—ACh,

[1] The published and unpublished results from laboratories described in this paper were supported in part by the NIH Research Grant NS 06645, the NIH Training Grant GM 77, and by the Research Grant 17-176 from the Illinois Mental Health Service.

[2] I am indebted to Drs. V. G. Longo and S. Nishi for their criticism and help in the preparation of this paper.

[3] I dedicate this paper to the memory of my friend J. E. P. Toman, a pioneer in the field of pharmacology of ECS, a great scientist, and a great liberal.

acetylcholinesterase (AChE) and butyrylcholinesterase (BuChE), and choline acetylase—in the spinal cord and in the brain (Koelle, 1963; Lewis & Shute, 1966; Olivier, Parent, Simard, & Poirier, 1970; Karczmar, 1967, 1970). Moreover, a significant percentage of brain neurons are cholinoceptive (Curtis & Crawford, 1960; Krnjević, 1969). Finally, certain areas—such as caudate nucleus, the thalamus, cerebellar cortex, and the mesencephalic reticular formation—contain particularly high concentrations of ACh and AChE, and the neurons in these and other areas (such as the Betz cells) show a very high percentage of cholinoceptivity. Notwithstanding, certain areas—some of the cortical layers, dorsal (sensory) columns of the spinal cord and pyramidal tracts—lack AChE and/or ACh, and contain few cholinoceptive neurons.

Yet, proven central cholinergic synapses may be few in number. The spinal interneuron (the Renshaw cell) exhibits such a synapse (Eccles, 1969; and Willis, 1969), and certain nuclei of the thalamus, the Betz and the Purkinje cells are claimed to contain such synapses (Curtis & Crawford, 1969; Karczmar, 1970). The synapses of the medial geniculate nucleus are also a strong candidate on the basis of their cholinoceptivity and its pharmacological analysis, the parallelism between their physiological and ACh-induced responses, and their ACh and AChE content (Tebēcis, 1970a. 1970b).

The additional problem is that the fast and powerful cholinoceptive response, nicotinic in nature and thus sensitive to nicotine and to curaremimetics, characterizes relatively few neurons, such as the Renshaw cell and certain thalamic neurons. The Renshaw cell shows only a secondary, delayed muscarinic response, which is sensitive to atropine rather than to d-tubocurarine or dihydro-β-erythroidine; some ventrobasal thalamic neurons are also predominantly nicotinic (Curtis & Crawford, 1969). The medial geniculate neurons show a mixed response, sensitive to curarimimetics but more so to atropine (Tebēcis, 1970a, 1970b), while most other cholinoceptive brain neurons react muscarinically (Curtis & Crawford, 1969; Karczmar, 1970). Furthermore, the central nervous system effects due to systemic administration of anti-ChE's or to intracarotid and intracerebral administration of ACh are muscarinic in character, as they are readily blocked by even small doses of atropine or scopolamine (Longo, 1966; Wills, 1970). Some investigators (Krnjević, 1969a; Krnjević, Pumain, & Renaud, 1971) consider only the nicotinic response as synaptic, and the muscarinic response as modulatory and facilitatory in nature, similar to the weak muscarinic response of the sympathetic ganglia (Koketsu, 1969; Nishi, 1970; Karczmar, Nishi, & Blaber, 1972). For these reasons, rather than referring to the central cholinergic nervous system, this chapter refers to "the central ACh system."

Two points of relevance should be raised in this context. First, the nicotinic responses frequently characterize the synapses involved in inhibitory circuitry of either recurrent or feed-forward type (Eccles, 1967, 1969). This is, however, not always true; the Betz and hippocampal neurons, also involved in such circuitry, respond muscarinically. In all cases however, certain "patterning" of the responses of the neuronal populations may result from the inhibitory circuitry (Morrell, 1967; Karczmar, 1971; Karczmar et al., 1972). Second, the facilitatory muscarinic response may be also instrumental in such "patterning"; this was proposed with regard to the effect of the ascending cholinergic pathway upon the cortical neuronal populations (Krnjević et al., 1971). These points are relevant with regard to desynchronizing actions of ACh and/or anti-ChE's, which as proposed in this paper are of significance in the control and prevention of seizure activity.

Central ACh system is coupled with synapses and systems operated by other transmitters (Feldberg, 1957). It is not surprising, therefore, that the activation of the ACh system activates other systems and also causes multiple neurochemical changes, particularly with regard to catecholamines and serotonin (Glisson, Karczmar, & Barnes, 1972; Karczmar et al., 1972). A relevant hypothesis was proposed by Koelle (1969a, 1969b) according to which ACh can release inhibitory transmitters centrally—a phenomenon which may be related to the "patterning" role of the activation of inhibitory circuitry by central ACh. All these interactions concern the seizures, and the effect of the cholinergic and anticholinergic drugs on the latter is therefore very complex.

SEIZURES INDUCED BY CHOLINERGIC DRUGS

Anticholinesterases (anti-ChE's) of both organophosphorus and carbamate or related type ("reversible" and "irreversible" cholinesterase inhibitors; cf. Usdin, 1970), as well as cholinergic stimulants, induce seizures and/or lower threshold of strychnine or pentylenetetrazol convulsions (Finger, 1947; Holmstedt, 1959; Karczmar, 1967; Esplin & Zablocka-Esplin, 1969). As the resulting convulsions are frequently of mixed clonic and tonic type, the cortical, subcortical, and spinal mechanisms are involved. Both anti-ChE agents and cholinergic agonists induce seizures and convulsions via their central rather than peripheral (including neuromuscular) actions (Karczmar, 1967).

CHOLINOMIMETIC ACTION ON REFLEXES, PARTICULARLY ON THE SPINAL CORD LEVEL

Considerable controversy exists with regard to the spinal actions of cholinergic agonists and antagonists. Cholinergic agonists and anti-ChE's exhibit both facilitatory and blocking actions on spinal reflexes, whether mono- or polysynaptic; the actual result depended on the dose, the route of administration, and the reflex in question, etc. (Holmstedt & Skoglund, 1953). This inconsistency may depend on the presence of both facilitatory and inhibitory influences of the cholinergic synapses or of cholinoceptive neurons. Indeed, various investigators (Kidokoro, Kubota, Shuto, & Sumino, 1968; Kubota, Kidokoro, & Suzuki, 1968; Iwata, Sakai, & Deguchi, 1971) proposed that the cholinergic system reduces a monosynaptic supraspinal reflex by increasing the inhibitory postsynaptic potential (IPSP) resulting from cutaneous stimulation, while Martin and Eades (1967) postulated that facilitatory cholinergic (and independent adrenergic) neurons enhance the spinal flexor reflex.

These possibilities do not explain the spinal tetanic actions of high doses of anti-ChE's. Part of the answer may be related to the Renshaw cell function. This spinal cholinergic synapse may be involved in a number of reflexes (Eccles, Fatt, & Koketsu, 1954). While the Renshaw cell system is generally understood to induce recurrent inhibition of the very motoneuron activating the Renshaw interneuron during the stretch reflex, this system may be also effective in the course of other reflex phenomena and induce a widespread inhibition of motoneurons.

Altogether, we suggest that the tetanic effect and the abolition of spinal reflexes occurs with large doses of anti-ChE's (Karczmar & Koppanyi, 1953; Wills, 1963) because the resulting accumulation of ACh may block the synapses which "modulate" the reflexes, as postulated by Japanese investigators, and because the negative feedback due to the Renshaw interneuron may be obliterated under the circumstances; indeed, the spinal action of strychnine, which resembles that of large doses of anti-ChE's may be due to the block of the Renshaw cell system (Eccles, 1969).

A difficulty with this speculation is that cholinergic blockers should produce an effect similar to that of high doses of anti-ChE's; while this indeed obtains with some anticholinergic drugs (Esplin & Zablocka-Esplin, 1969), it does not occur with atropine or scopolamine. However, these drugs synergize, to an extent, with the ECS, as will be described in another context below. The inhibitory mechanisms, examplified by the Renshaw cell system, may play a relatively small role at the spinal compared to the *supraspinal* level (Eccles, 1964, 1969) and perhaps additional, excitatory mechanisms which may be activated by the cholinergic drugs or anti-ChE's are needed for the cholinergically induced *spinal* convulsions.

BRAIN

Focal spiking arises from topical cortical application of ACh and anti-ChE's (Sjöstrand, 1937; Longo, 1962; Machne & Unna, 1963). Some of the earlier results were obtained with undue doses or concentrations, such as 10% to 20% concentrations of ACh (Arduini & Machne, 1948). Cholinergic agonists produced spiking, too, when injected intracerebrally to other areas, including hippocampus (MacLean, 1957), or into the carotid artery. Frequently, local "seizure" or spiking was preceded by low amplitude, fast frequency, EEG activity. On the contrary, applied to certain locations within the limbic system such as the hypothalamus, ACh produced spindles and slow waves (Marczynski, 1967; Langlois & Poussart, 1969), although long-acting cholinergic agonists and anti-ChE's produced fast waves, and, sometimes, spiking.

These effects agree with the characteristic EEG and behavioral action of certain cholinergic agonists and, particularly, of anti-ChE's when given systemically. As is well known, these agents produce first a typical EEG arousal and then a grand-mal-like seizure (Figure 1; also Longo, 1962; Machne & Unna, 1963; Karczmar, 1967, 1969). In the case of anti-ChE's, these effects coincide with total inhibition of all cholinesterases. By means of histochemical techniques, it is possible to show that not even a trace of either BuChE or AChE remains present at doses approximating convulsive and LD_{50} levels (Van Meter & Karczmar, 1967; Karczmar, 1969; Van Meter, 1970). Furthermore, a marked accumulation of ACh consisting actually of six- to eightfold accumulations of free ACh and a lesser accumulation of bound ACh occurs under these circumstances (Karczmar, Scudder, & Richardson, 1973; Holmstedt, Härkönen,

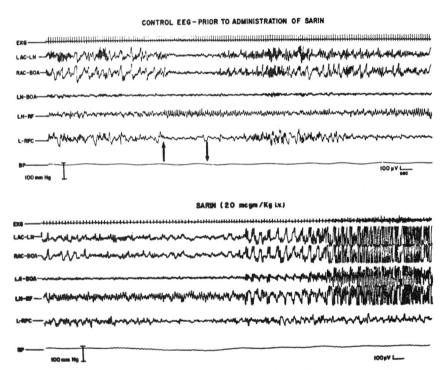

FIG. 1. Rabbit EEG following the administration of an organophosphorus anticholinesterase, Sarin. Top: *Control EEG Pattern.* Resting EEG pattern with slow wave EEG sleep interrupted by a sound (arrows) with resulting EEG alert pattern. Bottom: *Initial Sarin Seizure.* Grand mal type convulsive pattern induced by the i.v. administration of 20 μg/kg of Sarin. Note the initial EEG arousal and the onset of the seizure which quickly develops into a diffuse pattern of convulsive EEG activity. Sarin was injected approximately 2 min prior to recording. Bipolar electrodes. BOA—basal olfactory area; LAC—left anterior cortex; L-RPC—left-right posterior motor cortex; LH—left hippocampus; LN—lenticular nucleus; RAC—right anterior cortex; RF—reticular formation. EKG and BP: electrocardiogram and blood pressure records. (From Van Meter, 1970)

Lundgren, & Sundvall, 1966; Fonnum & Guttormsen, 1969). The accumulation progressed in parallel with the change of EEG from slow to fast rhythms, and, finally to seizure (Figure 2). The latter coincided with no less than a fourfold accumulation of free ACh. This suggested that the seizure coincided with the accumulation of excessive concentrations of ACh, perhaps capable of blocking cholinergic synapses and/or cholinoceptive neurons. The block of the respiratory center which occurs characteristically with large doses of anti-ChE's (Wills, 1970) and the resulting apnea or anoxia could be excluded as the causative mechanism of seizures; in fact, gill-breathing vertebrates convulsed with anti-ChE's no less than did the land forms (Figure 3; Karczmar & Koppanyi, 1947, 1953; Blum, Koppanyi, & Karczmar, 1958).

The anti-ChE-induced seizures and the depression of the respiratory center can be antagonized by small doses of atropine (Wills, 1963, 1970). The latter is understood to be due to accumulation of ACh. Altogether, the antagonism of atropine for seizures and for apnea is compatible with the notion that both these

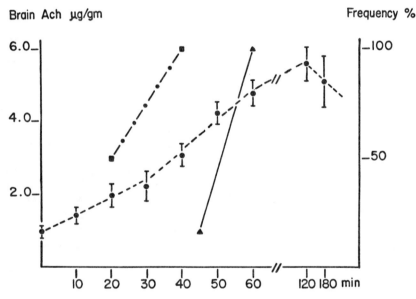

FIG. 2. ACh levels and changes in the EEG following i.p. administration of DFP to SCI mice. Abscissae: brain ACh in μg/gm ($\bullet - \bullet$) and incidence in percent of the population of the occurence of fast EEG ($\blacksquare - . - \blacksquare$) and of seizures ($\blacktriangle - \blacktriangle$). Ordinate: time in minutes following i.p. injection of diisopropyl phosphofluoridate (DFP), 5 mg/kg. Total ACh levels evaluated by the method of Blaber and Cuthbert (1961), 6 mice per point (the brackets refer to standard error). Cortical screw electrodes were employed for the EEG evaluation; fast EEG refers to continuous (epochs of 5 sec or more) beta and related rhythms. The four incidence points are based on data obtained with 6 mice per point. (After Karczmar et al., 1973, and Karczmar and Kindel, unpublished data)

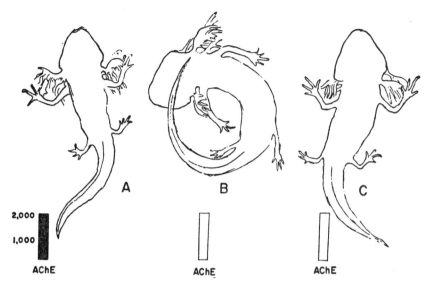

FIG. 3. Effect of DFP on larval "overt behavior" and acetylcholinesterase (AChE) activity. Top row: *A. Punctatum* larvae, State 60 (Glucksohn): A, control larva; B, larva kept for 5 days in 10^{-7}M DFP solution; C, same larva 4 days following transfer into spring water. All drawings schematized. Bottom row: AChE activity in mm^3 of CO_2 per 100 mg of larval tissue, per 30 min. The AChE activities represent averages, each obtained with six larvae or more (Karczmar & Koppanyi, 1953). Histochemically, traces of AChE were shown to be present (2-3 hr incubation time) 1 day upon transfer to spring water, and significant amounts (45 min incubation time)—3 days later.

phenomena are due to synaptolytic effect of large central accumulation of ACh and that the atropinic agents may afford protection against this effect at the postsynaptic sites. It should be noted that the EEG resulting from the administration of atropine following the anti-ChE-induced seizure differs somewhat from that resulting from the atropine given alone, the frequencies being faster in the former than in the latter case (Van Meter, 1970).

The concept of excessive levels of ACh being instrumental in anti-ChE-induced seizures is consistent with the fact that spontaneous recovery from seizures and convulsions in both mammals and fish or urodeles, as well as from respiratory paralysis in the case of the mammals, occurs within a few hours (Karczmar & Koppanyi, 1953; Karczmar, 1967), as this recovery coincides with diffusion of ACh away from synaptic sites and with the increase of the bound form of ACh (Table 1), as well as with some regeneration of the enzyme (Figure 3).

This evidence suggests that spinal, cortical, or subcortical seizures induced by anti-ChE's are due to the presence of high, possibly synaptolytic concentrations of ACh.

TABLE 1
ACh Levels of Brain Tissue $(\mu g/g)^a$

ACh form	Time in minutes following DFP			
	0	30	120	180
Free	–	1.14 ± 0.04	4.10 ± 0.52	3.08
Bound	0.95 ± 0.03	1.21 ± 0.05	1.45 ± 0.50	2.02 ± 0.50
Total	1.02 ± 0.03	2.35 ± 0.26	5.55 ± 0.45	5.10 ± 0.52

[a] Bioassay methods (Blaber & Cuthbert, 1961; Gaddum, 1965) were used for the measurement of free and bound ACh.

CHOLINERGIC EFFECTS ON BRAIN RHYTHMICITY

ACh, cholinomimetics, and anti-ChE's are powerful desynchronizing agents which, given via a number of routes, induce fast, low-amplitude EEG. Anti-ChE's presumably induce this action via accumulation of ACh. In 1955, Rinaldi & Himwich suggested the presence of a diffuse cholinergic reticulo-thalamico-cortical system concerned with desynchrony (Rinaldi & Himwich, 1955; Himwich, 1962, 1963). That this system cannot consist only of cholinergic synapses became obvious later (Karczmar, 1969).

Other systems must be concerned as well in the desynchronizing action of anti-ChE's. For instance, Domino and others suggested that two mechanisms, nicotinic and muscarinic, are involved in ACh desynchrony (Domino, 1968; Domino, Yamamoto, & Dren, 1968; Kawamura & Domino, 1969). Our studies, indicating an even greater complexity of the pertinent system, departed from the classical finding of Longo and Silvestrini (1957) that at moderate doses, anti-ChE's are specific blockers of recruitment induced by the repetitive stimulation of nonspecific thalamic nuclei. In this context, recruitment is related to the synchronizing mechanisms as well as to slow, synchronous EEG activities such as spindles or alpha waves (Andersen & Andersson, 1968). Desynchrony induced by behavioral alerting or by drugs other than anti-ChE's such as amphetamine raises the recruitment threshold although, compared to anti-ChE's, they do so incompletely (Longo, 1962). The antirecruitment effect of moderate doses of anti-ChE's, i.e., of moderate increase of brain ACh levels, depends on the presence of catecholamines, most likely of norepinephrine (NE), and on activation of central alpha sympathetic receptors (Van Meter, 1970; Van Meter & Karczmar, 1971). Accordingly, antirecruitment action of ACh can be prevented by NE depletors (Van Meter, 1970). However, even when NE depletion renders the recruitment block due to ACh accumulation impossible, anti-ChE's or ACh still produce desynchronization. In fact, anti-ChE's convert the slow-wave EEG pattern that follows the depletors such as α-methyl-p-tyrosine or reserpine into an EEG arousal. In other words, ACh accumulation produces desynchrony via more than one mechanism and more than one system (Karczmar, 1969, 1971; Karczmar et al., 1972).

With increasing doses of anti-ChE's and consequently in the presence of higher and higher brain levels of ACh, the antirecruitment action of anti-ChE's diminishes. While this may be explained as a phenomenon of the occlusion of recruitment by the seizure EEG, it may be hypothesized that we deal here with a specific antagonism of the antirecruitment effect; this antagonism would result from excessive ACh accumulation and concomitant synaptic blockade.

Atropinics present a picture which is opposite to that produced by anti-ChE's, moderate accumulation of ACh, or by cholinomimetics. Atropinics produce synchronization and induce slow waves of high voltage (Longo, 1966). In fact, almost seizurelike patterns occur with high doses of these drugs, and their action may resemble that of higher doses of anti-ChE's.

The actions of anti-ChE's and atropinics on recruitment and brain rhythms are consistent with the speculation that low levels of brain ACh are related, via several mechanisms, to desynchronization, while their high levels as well as the atropinic block lead to phenomena of synchronization. It is expedient to note that an EEG seizure is described as a phenomenon of "hypersynchrony" (Gastaut & Fischer-Williams, 1959). Thus, desynchronization mechanisms—such as described here with regard to anti-ChE's—may be considered as antagonistic to EEG seizures and decreasing the susceptibility to the latter. This speculation is marred, however, by the fact that, ACh applied to certain locations produces spindling and synchrony rather than desynchrony. However, this effect may be rationalized away as resulting from localized application of high ACh concentrations and from concomitant synaptic block.

ENDOGENOUS LEVELS OF ACh AND CONVULSIVE SUSCEPTIBILITY

While the above line of reasoning relates moderate levels of brain ACh to *anticonvulsive* tendencies, in the past brain ACh was frequently related to *convulsive* phenomena. Obviously, the induction of seizures by anti-ChE's was described in this sense. Furthermore, data dealing with the endogenous levels of brain ChE's and of ACh led to the concept that the high tonus of the components of the cholinergic system predisposes the animals to seizures. For instance, Kurokawa, Machiyama, & Kato (1963), Naruse, Kato, Kurokawa, Haba, & Yabe (1960), Takahashi, Nasu, Tamura, & Kariya (1961) and Pryor (1968) came to this conclusion on the basis of comparative data dealing with genetically convulsive mice strains. Similarly, it was stressed that young animals from the convulsive strains are less prone to seizures and have lower ACh levels than the older mice (Naruse et al., 1960; Schlesinger, Boggan, & Freedman, 1965; Fink, 1966; Reeves, 1966; and Sobotka, 1969). Additionally, Naruse et al. (1960) attributed the onset of spontaneous seizures to conversion of bound (stable) to free (labile) form of ACh (Sobotka, 1969).

Yet, the evidence for the parallelism between high ACh and/or AChE levels and seizures is not always consistent (Wooley, Timiras, Rosenzweig, Krech, & Bennett, 1963). Furthermore, the audiogenic seizure threshold was found to be either independent of ACh levels or even inversely related to the latter (Takahashi et al., 1961). Altogether, the genetically controlled audiogenic seizure may, however, constitute a special case. In a comparative study of nonconvulsive mice strains and genera, we have found that an inverse proportionality exists between brain ACh and AChE levels, and susceptibility to ECS (Hanigan, Scudder, & Karczman, 1970; Karczmar, 1970; Karczmar et al., 1972): ECS latency was longer, ECS duration shorter and, in some cases, the threshold higher in mouse types characterized by higher ACh and/or AChE levels (Figure 4).

ACh and ChE's cannot be regarded alone in the present context. Toman (1963) demonstrated a marked effect of sympathomimetics on ECS parameters,

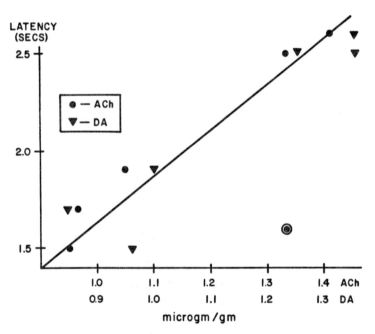

FIG. 4. The relationship between the levels of brain ACh and of dopamine, and the ECS latency in seven mice types. Abscissa: ECS latency in seconds. Ordinate: ACh and dopamine levels in μg/g (Cf. Blaber & Cuthbert [1961] and Glisson, Karczmar & Barnes [1972] for the methods used for ACh bioassay and fluorospectrophotometric measurement of dopamine.) The solid circles and triangles refer to brain levels of ACh and dopamine, respectively, in six related strains and genera of mice, from 6 to 10 mice brains per point; the double circle refers to the level of ACh in the mouse strain which did not fit the general relationship. The correlation coefficient was found to be 0.735 (the calculation included the aberrant point). (From Karczmar et al., 1973)

and the effect of depletors of catecholamines and/or serotonin on ECS parameters was reported by Schlesinger, Boggan, & Freedman, (1968) and Schlesinger and Griek (1970). We have also suggested that the depletion of NE and of dopamine increases seizure proneness, while amphetamine has the opposite action (Hanigan et al., 1970). Maneuvers leading to changes in serotonin levels have a more complex effect on ECS (De la Torre, Kawanaga, & Mullan, 1970). Similar conclusions could be reached on the basis of comparative studies (Scudder, Karczmar, Everett, Gibson, & Rifkin, 1966; Scudder, Richardson, & Karczmar, 1969; Karczmar & Scudder, 1967, 1969; Karczmar, 1971). As indicated in Figure 4, ECS proneness as exemplified by the brevity of latency, is inversely proportional to brain levels of both ACh and of dopamine (as well as of AChE) (Karczmar, Sobotka, & Scudder, 1968; Karczmar et al., 1972).

SEIZURES AND ACh

Additional evidence for the significance of the ACh system in seizures deals with the effect of seizures on ACh and AChE of the brain and of the cerebrospinal fluid. Postictally, bound and free ACh decreases, the latter more drastically (by some 70% to 80%, 10 to 20 min after ECS; Richter & Crossland, 1949; Fink, 1966; Essman, 1972). Our data also indicate that the turnover of ACh increases postictally; furthermore, the levels of both types of ACh increase significantly during the seizure itself (Figure 5). The cerebrospinal fluid seems also to reflect increased activity of the ACh system, as its choline and ACh levels increase (Fink, 1966; Essman, 1972). Older data (Tower & McEachern, 1949) dealing with cerebrospinal levels of BuChE and AChE do not seem reliable. Furthermore, the occurrence of free ACh in the cerebrospinal fluid is a general concomitant of convulsions, whether induced by head trauma, epilepsy, ECS or pentylenetetrazol (Fink, 1966). This evidence is compatible with the concept of mobilization of the ACh system by the seizure; it may be speculated that this mobilization is initiated by an attempt by the central cholinergic system to prevent the seizure.

CHOLINERGIC DRUGS AND SEIZURES

In view of the above it can be expected that cholinergic drugs should affect ECS parameters. Drugs which cause ACh accumulation by different mechanisms, such as anti-ChE's and methionine sulfoximine (MSI), are at present available. Both types of agents generate seizures, the anti-ChE's drugs relatively rapidly and MSI after a several-hours latency (Tower & Elliott, 1953; Tower, 1955). In fact, Tower suggested that MSI-induced convulsions mimic human epilepsy more closely than those induced by any other drug.

The effects of these drugs on latency and duration of mice ECS show, in spite of certain inconsistency, a definite trend. At most doses and at 15 min to 4 hr

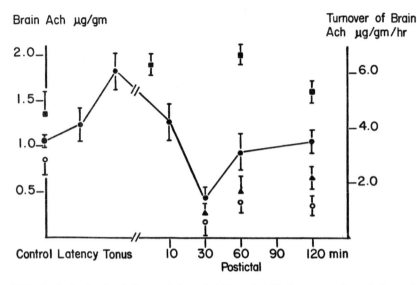

FIG. 5. Brain levels of free and bound ACh and ACh turnover values during and following ECS. SCI mice. Abscissa: control values and values obtained during ECS latency and tonus, and postictally (in minutes following the clonus). Ordinate: brain levels in μg/g of total, free and bound ACh (●, ○ and ▲, respectively) and turnover values of ACh in μg/g/hr (■). The brackets indicate the standard error. The three forms of ACh were evaluated by the methods of Blaber and Cuthbert (1961) and Gaddum (1965). Turnover values of ACh were evaluated in terms of accumulation of total ACh following an LD_{50} dose of DFP, given 1 hr prior to the assay (the turnover values 10 and 30 min postictally could be, therefore, affected by the change in ECS caused by administration of DFP prior to ECS). (Karczmar and Kindel, unpublished data)

after administration, MSI decreases the duration and increases the latency of ECS. Diisopropyl phosphofluoridate (DFP) and physostigmine, employed at subconvulsive doses, always decrease the duration of ECS, and occasionally, but not always, increase the latency (Figure 6; Sobotoka, 1969; Hanigan et al., 1970; Hanigan, 1972; cf. also Karczmar, 1971 and Karczmar et al., 1973). Furthermore, slight increase in the ECS threshold is noticed with small (0.05 to 0.1 mg/kg) doses of DFP.

These data must be discussed in the light of the neurochemical analysis. The anti-ChE-induced accumulation of ACh was already described; after a 1 to 4 hr latency, MSI increased brain ACh, particularly in the case of mouse telencephalon. Other important neurochemicals are also involved. Both MSI and anti-ChE's induce changes in catecholamines and serotonin; MSI, additionally, has profound effects on protein synthesis and on glutamic acid-glutamine-gamma-aminobutyric acid cycle (DeRobertis, Sellinger, Arnaiz, Alberici, & Zieher, 1967; Lamar, 1968; Sellinger, Azcurra, Ohlsson, Kohl, & Zand, 1972). In fact, judging by the kinetics of the changes in ACh levels and by their relationship to the parameters of ECS, factors other than ACh accumulation should be involved in the causation of the MSI seizures.

In mice, MSI caused a slight increase in DA and NE levels (Hanigan et al., 1970; Karczmar et al., 1973), while anti-ChE's lowered DA and NE levels (Figure 6) accompanied the accumulation of ACh. [However, the effect of anti-ChE's on catecholamines may depend on their original brain level and on species (Glisson et al., 1972).] Catecholamine depletion is related to increased susceptibility to ECS, more rapid onset (latency *decrease*) and *increased* duration of seizures. Thus, MSI-induced increase in catecholamines on the one hand and the anti-ChE-induced decrease in catecholamines on the other will constitute opposite contributions to the net ECS effect of the two drugs.

In view, particularly, of the effects of anti-ChE's on ECS, atropinics should decrease the latency and increase the duration of the ECS. No such clearcut effect was, however, obtained (Heilbrunn, 1943). Again, this may be due to the multiple neurochemical actions of the atropinic compounds. Giarman and Pepeu (1964) and my associates and I (Karczmar, 1971; Karczmar et al., 1973) demonstrated that these drugs markedly lowered ACh levels, which would have an effect opposite from that predicted. Furthermore, these drugs also induce changes in serotonin and catecholamines (Karczmar, 1971; Karczmar et al.,

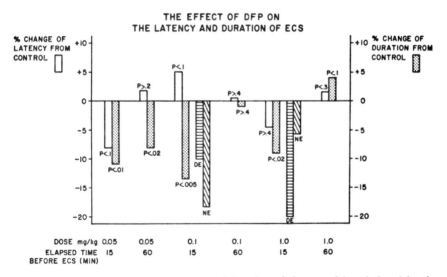

FIG. 6. The effect of DFP on latency and duration of the convulsions induced by the electroshock (ECS). SCI mice. The doses of DFP and time elapsed (minutes) between the administration of the drug and the ECS shown along the abscissa. The measurement of dopamine (DE) and norepinephrine (NE) after two doses of DFP shown also (cross-hatched and shaded bar graphs, respectively); ECS was not applied to these mice. The changes in the latencies and durations are indicated by blank and dotted bar graphs, respectively, and expressed on the ordinates in percentages of the controls. (From Hanigan et al., 1970, and Karczmar et al., 1973)

1973). In this context, when scopolamine is given shortly before ECS treatment, it increases the lethality of ECS.

These data illustrate the complexity of the subject. This could be expected, as anti-ChE's and other cholinergics have neurochemical effects that embrace, beside ACh, several neurotransmitters and related substances that affect the parameters of ECS (De La Torre, Kawanaga and Mullan, 1970; Lovell, 1971). Yet, the tendency of anti-ChE's to increase the latency and decrease the duration of the ECS, i.e., to act as seizure antagonists seems clear. It should be added that small and large doses of physostigmine decreased and increased, respectively, the audiogenic seizure susceptibility of rats (Humphrey, 1942); thus, the effects of small doses of this anti-ChE on the susceptibility to the audiogenic seizure and on ECS were similiar.

SUMMARY AND COMMENT

The preceding sections provide evidence showing that ECS markedly affects the levels and turnover of the components of ACh system, and that cholinergic drugs induce changes in the ECS parameters as well as (in the case of cholinergic agonists like anti-ChE's) induce generalized convulsions.

These facts should be discussed in the context of the effects of the cholinergic drugs on brain rhythmicity, and the relationship of a seizure to brain rhythms. Cholinergic agonists are specific dysrhythmic agents, several independent mechanisms being involved. But, seizures constitute a "hypersynchronous" phenomenon (Gastaut & Fischer-Williams, 1959; Ward, Jasper, & Pope, 1969). Desynchronizing agents should act, therefore, as anticonvulsants, and a tendency for such action was described above and related to the prolongation of the latency and decrease of duration of the seizure. In fact, classical anticonvulsants such as various aliphatic depressants, including barbiturates, exhibit these particular effects, as well as increase the ECS threshold (Workman, Swinyard, Rigbly, & Swinyard, 1958); effects similar to these three were obtained in our hands with certain doses of DFP.

It may appear that this concept is incompatible with the fact that anti-ChE's (and several other cholinergic agonists) induce seizures. This occurs only with large doses of these drugs and, in the case of anti-ChE's, against the background of extensive ACh accumulation: the seizures cease when the ACh levels decrease even so slightly with time. It may then be hypothesized that anti-ChE seizures reflect a blocking, synaptolytic effect of ACh, synchronous in nature contrary to the effect of a less marked elevation of ACh levels.

Which is the mechanism that is involved in this desynchronizing action of the cholinergic system? The participation of the central cholinergic system in inhibitory circuitry was alluded to above; this point and the location of such circuitry both in the brain and spinal cord (Koketsu, Karczmar, & Kitamura, 1969) were described in detail (Karczmar, 1967, 1969, 1971; Karczmar & Nishi, 1971; Karczmar, Nishi, & Blaber, 1970, 1972). Additional physiologic (Kubota et al., 1968) and pharmacologic evidence (Vazquez, Krip, & Pinsky, 1969) supports this contention. It was further speculated how the inhibitory circuitry, activated by ACh, may divide the synchronously functioning neuronal population and throw out of phase the resulting subpopulations (Karczmar, 1969, 1971).

Altogether, it is proposed that the inhibitory mechanisms, in which ACh is involved, act desynchronously and, consequently, as antagonists of seizures. The anti-inhibitory action of several convulsant agents (Krnjević, 1969b; Eccles, 1969) should be quoted in this context. Perhaps what is new in this speculation is only the proposed *role of ACh* in the control of seizures via desynchronization; as early as 1931 Hunt suggested: "There is much in the convulsive and other paroxysmal phenomena of epilepsy to suggest a loss of inhibitory function." Commenting on Hunt's work, Ward et al. (1969) stated that the hypersynchrony of the EEG seizure indicates "massive discharge of many neurons in unison, abolishing . . . the normal integrative activity of the brain" which depends on the inhibitory mechanisms (Eccles, 1964, 1969; Spencer & Kandel, 1969).

Fink (1966 and this volume) stressed that, in man, atropinics produced EEG desynchronization following ECS. As atropinics are drugs that otherwise induce, in most species including man, slow waves and synchrony (Longo, 1966), the postictal effect of these drugs is paradoxical. Yet, it may be explained in the framework of the present speculation. If excess of ACh leads to seizure and hypersynchrony that extend into immediate postictal period, the antagonism of the effect of ACh accumulation by the atropinic agents may lead under these circumstances to faster waves and to desynchrony, or, to put it differently, may induce a shift toward normal EEG, as suggested by Lechner (1956) with regard to the action of anticholinergic drugs on the EEG slowing due to brain injury. As already described, this effect may be analogous to the antagonism by atropine of anti-ChE-induced seizures which also leads to the normalization of the EEG frequencies rather than to "pure" atropine rhythms.

REFERENCES

Andersen, P., & Andersson, S. A. *Physiological basis of alpha rhythm.* New York: Appleton-Century-Crofts, 1968.

Arduini, A., & Machne, X. Sul mecanismo e sul significato dell'azione convulsivante della acetilcholina. *Archivio di Fisiologia,* 1948, 48, 152-161.

Blaber, L. C., & Cuthbert, A. W. A sensitive method for the assay of acetylcholine. *Journal of Pharmacy and Pharmacology,* 1961, 13, 445-446.

Blum, B., Koppanyi, T., & Karczmar, A. G. Drug action on the central nervous system during development of urodele larvae. *Archives Internationales de Pharmacodynamie et de Therapie,* 1958, 115, 433-451.

Curtis, D. R., & Crawford, J. M. Central synaptic transmission-microelectrophoretic studies. *Annual Review of Pharmacology,* 1969, 9, 209-240.

De la Torre, J. C., Kawanaga, H. M., & Mullan, S. Seizure susceptibility after manipulation of brain serotonin. *Archives Internationales de Pharmacodynamie et de Therapie,* 1970, 188, 298-304.

DeRobertis, E., Sellinger, O. Z., Arnaiz, G., Aiberici, M., & Zieher, L. Nerve endings in methionine sulphoximine convulsant rats, a neurochemical and ultrastructural study. *Journal of Neurochemistry*, 1967, 14, 81-89.

Domino, E. F. Cholinergic mechanisms and the EEG. *Electroencephalography and Clinical Neurophysiology*, 1968, 24, 292-293.

Domino, E. F., Yamamoto, K., & Dren, A. T. Role of cholinergic mechanisms in states of wakefulness and sleep. *Brain Research*, 1968, 28, 113-133.

Eccles, J. C. Neuroanatomical basis of behavior—the ultimate units. In A. Abrams, H. H. Garner & J. E. P. Toman (Eds.), *Unfinished tasks in the behavioral sciences*. Baltimore: Williams & Wilkins, 1964.

Eccles, J. C. Postsynaptic inhibition in the central nervous system. In G. C. Quarton, T. Melnechuck & F. O. Schmitt (Eds.), *The neurosciences*. New York: Rockefeller Press, 1967.

Eccles, J. C. *The inhibitory pathways of the central nervous system*. Springfield, Ill.: Charles C Thomas, 1969.

Eccles, J. C., Fatt, P., & Koketsu, K. Cholinergic and inhibitory synapses in a pathway from motor-axon collaterals to motoneurons. *Journal of Physiology*, 1954, 216, 524-562.

Essman, W. B. Neurochemical changes in ECS and ECT. *Seminars in Psychiatry*, 1972, 4, 67-79.

Esplin, D. W., & Zablocka-Esplin, B. Mechanisms of action of convulsants. In H. J. Jasper, A. A. Ward, Jr., & A. Pope (Eds.), *Basic mechanisms of the epilepsies*. Boston: Little, Brown, 1969.

Feldberg, W. Acetylcholine. In D. Richter (Ed.), *Metabolism of the nervous system*. New York: Pergamon Press, 1957.

Finger, F. W. Convulsive behavior in the rat. *Psychological Bulletin*, 1947, 44, 201-248.

Fink, M. Cholinergic aspects of convulsive therapy. *Journal of Nervous and Mental Disease*, 1966, 24, 475-484.

Fonnum, F., & Guttormsen, D. M. Changes in acetylcholine content of rat brain by toxic doses of di-isopropyl phosphorofluoridate. *Experientia*, 1969, 25, 505-506.

Gaddum, J. H. An improved microbath. *British Journal of Pharmacology*, 1965, 23, 613-619.

Gastaut, H., & Fischer-Williams, M. The physiopathology of epileptic seizures. In J. Field (Ed.), *Handbook of physiology*. Sect. I. *Neurophysiology*. Washington, D.C.: American Physiological Society, 1959.

Giarman, N. J., & Pepeu, G. The influence of centrally acting cholinolytic drugs on brain acetylcholine levels. *British Journal of Pharmacology*, 1964, 23, 123-130.

Glisson, S. N., Jr., Karczmar, A. G., & Barnes, L. Cholinergic effects on adrenergic transmitters in rabbit brain parts. *Neuropharmacology*, 1972, 11, 465-477.

Hanigan, W. C. The effects of various pharmacological agents on the electroconvulsive seizure pattern in mice. Master of Science thesis, Loyola University, Chicago, 1972.

Hanigan, W. C., Scudder, C. L., & Karczmar, A. G. Adrenergic serotonergic and cholinergic systems and electroconvulsive seizures in mice. *Federation Proceedings*, 1970, 29, 486.

Heilbrunn, G. Prevention of hemorrhages in the brain in experimental electric shock. *Archives of Neurology and Psychiatry*, 1943, 50, 450-455.

Himwich, H. E. Reticular Activating System—current concepts of function. In J. H. Nodine & J. H. Moyer (Eds.), *Psychosomatic medicine*. Philadelphia: Lea & Febiger, 1962.

Himwich, H. E. Some specific effects of psychoactive drugs. In M. Rinkel (Ed.), *Specific and non-specific factors in psychopharmacology*. New York: Philosophical Library, 1963.

Holmstedt, B. Pharmacology of organophosphorus cholinesterase inhibitors. *Pharmacol. Rev.*, 1959, 11, 567-688.

Holmstedt, B., Härkönen, M., Lundgren, J., & Sundvall, A. Relationship between acetylcholine content and cholinesterase activity in the brain following an organophosphorus inhibitor. *Biochemical Pharmacology*, 1966, 16, 404-406.

Holmstedt, B., & Skoglund, C. R. The action on spinal reflexes of dimethyl-amido-ethoxy-phosphoryl cyanide, "tabun," a cholinesterase inhibitor. *Acta Physiologica Scandinavica*, 1953 (Suppl. 104), 410-427.

Humphrey, G. Experiments on the physiological mechanism of noise-induced seizures in the albino rat. I. The action of parasympathetic drugs. *Journal of Comparative Psychology*, 1942, 33, 315-323.

Hunt, J. R. A theory of the mechanism underlying inhibition in the central nervous system and its relation to convulsive manifestations. *Association for Research in Nervous and Mental Disease, Proceedings*, 1931, 7, 45-64.

Iwata, N., Sakai, Y., & Deguchi, T. Effects of physostigmine on the inhibition of trigeminal motoneurons by cutaneous impulses in the cat. *Experimental Brain Research*, 1971, 13, 519-522.

Karczmar, A. G. Pharmacologic, toxicologic and therapeutic properties of anticholinesterases. In W. S. Root & F. G. Hofman (Eds.), *Physiological pharmacology*. Vol. 3. New York: Academic Press, 1967.

Karczmar, A. G. Quelques aspects de la pharmacologie des synapses cholinergiques et de sa signification central. *Actualités pharmacologiques*, 1969, 22, 293-338.

Karczmar, A. G. Central cholinergic pathways and their behavioral implications. In W. G. Clark & J. del Guidice (Eds.), *Principles of psychopharmacology*. New York: Academic Press, 1970.

Karczmar, A. G. Neurophysiological behavioral and neurochemical correlates of the central cholinergic synapses. In O. Vinar, Z. Votava, & P. B. Bradley (Eds.), *Advances in neuropsychopharmacology*. Amsterdam: North-Holland, 1971.

Karczmar, A. G., & Koppanyi, T. The effect of stimulant drugs on overt behavior. *Anatomical Record*, 1947, 99, 64.

Karczmar, A. G., & Koppanyi, T. Central effects of di-isopropyl fluorophosphonate in urodele larvae. *Naunyn - Schmiedeberg's Archiv fur Experimentelle Pathologie und Pharmakologie*, 1953, 219, 261-270.

Karczmar, A. G., & Nishi, S. The types and sites of cholinergic receptors. In F. Clementi & B. Cicciarelli (Eds.) *First international symposium on cell biology and cytopharmacology*. New York: Raven Press, 1971.

Karczmar, A. G., Nishi, S., & Blaber, L. C. Investigations, particularly by means of the anticholinesterase agents, of the multiple peripheral and central cholinergic mechanisms and of their behavioral implications. *Acta Vitaminologica et Enzymologica*, 1970, 24, 131-189.

Karczmar, A. G., Nishi, S., & Blaber, L. C. Synaptic modulations. In A. G. Karczmar & J. C. Eccles (Eds.), *Brain and human behavior*. New York: Springer, 1972.

Karczmar, A. G., & Scudder, C. L. Behavioral responses to drugs and brain catecholamine levels in mice of different strains and genera. In E. J. Cafruny, G. J. Cosmides, D. P. Rall, C. R. Schroeder, & I. M. Werner (Eds.), International symposium on comparative pharmacology. *Federation Proceedings*, 1967, 26, 1186-1191.

Karczmar, A. G., & Scudder, C. L. Aggression and nuerochemical changes in different strains and genera of mice. In S. Garattini & E. B. Sigg (Eds.), *Aggresive behavior*. Amsterdam: Excerpta Medica Foundation, 1969.

Karczmar, A. G., Scudder, C. L., & Richardson, D. Interdisciplinary approach to the study of behavior in related mice types. In I. Kopin (Ed.), *Neurosciences research*. New York: Academic Press, 1973, 5, 159-244.

Karczmar, A. G., Sobotka, T. J., & Scudder, C. L. Cholinesterase of mice strains and genera. *Federation Proceedings*, 1968, 27, 471.

Kawamura, H., & Domino, E. F. Differential actions of m and n cholinergic agonists on the brainstem activating system. *International Journal of Neuropharmacy*, 1969, 8, 105-115.

Kidokoro, Y., Kubota, K., Shuto, S., & Sumino, R. Possible interneurons responsible for reflex inhibition of motoneurons of jaw-closing muscles from inferior dental nerve. *Journal of Neurophysiology*, 1968, 31, 709-716.

Koelle, G. B. Cytological distributions and physiological functions of cholinesterases. In G. B. Koelle (Ed.), *Cholinesterases and anticholinesterase agents,* Berlin: Springer-Verlag, 1963.

Koelle, G. B. Pharmacology of synaptic transmission. In H. H. Jasper, A. A. Ward, Jr., & A. Pope, (Eds.), *Basic mechanisms of the epilepsies.* 1969. (a)

Koelle, G. B. Significance of acetylcholinesterase in central synaptic transmission. In A. G. Karczmar (Ed.), Symposium on central cholinergic transmission and its behavioral aspects. *Federation Proceedings,* 1969, 28, 147-157. (b)

Koketsu, K. Cholinergic synaptic potentials and the underlying ionic mechanisms. In A. G. Karczmar (Ed.), Symposium on central cholinergic transmission and its behavioral aspects. *Federation Proceedings,* 1969, 28, 101-111.

Koketsu, K., Karczmar, A. G., & Kitamura, R. Acetylcholine depolarization of the dorsal root nerve terminals in the amphibian spinal cord. *International Journal of Neuropharmacology,* 1969, 8, 329-336.

Krnjević, K. Central cholinergic pathways. In A. G. Karczmar (Ed.), Symposium on central cholinergic transmission and its behavioral aspects. *Federation Proceedings,* 1969, 28, 113-120. (a).

Krnjević, K. Inhibition in the cerebral cortex. In R. Eigenman (Ed.), *Advances in pharmacology,* Vol. 5., Proceedings of the Fourth International Congress of Pharmacologists, Basel: Schwabe, 1969. (b)

Krnjević, K. Central excitatory transmitters in vertebrates. In P. Andersen & P. Jansen (Eds.), *Excitatory synaptic mechanisms.* Oslo: Universitetsforlaget, 1970.

Krnjević, K., Pumain, R., & Renaud, L. The mechanism of excitation by acetylcholine in the cerebral cortex. *Journal of Physiology,* 1971, 215, 247-268.

Kubota, K., Kidokoro, Y., & Suzuki, J. Postsynaptic inhibition of trigeminal and lumbar motoneurons from the superficial radial nerve in the cat. *Japanese Journal of Physiology,* 1968, 18, 198-215.

Kurokawa, M., Machiyama, Y., & Kato, M. Distribution of acetylcholine in the brain during various states of activity. *Journal of Neurochemistry,* 1963, 10, 341-348.

Lamar, C. The duration of the inhibition of glutamine synthetase by methionine sulfoximine. *Biochemical Pharmacology,* 1968, 14, 489-506.

Langlois, J. M., & Poussart, Y. Electrocortical activity following cholinergic stimulation of the caudate nucleus in the cat. *Brain Research,* 1969, 15, 581-583.

Lechner, H. On the influence of anticholinergic drugs on the EEG of recent closed craniocerebral injuries. *Electroencephalography and Clinical Neurophysiology,* 1956, 8, 714-715.

Lewis, P. R., & Shute, C. C. D. The distribution of cholinesterase in cholinergic neurons demonstrated with electrone microscope. *Journal of Cell Science,* 1966, 1, 381-390.

Longo, V. G. *Electroencephalographic atlas for pharmacological research.* Amsterdam: Elsevier, 1962.

Longo, V. G. Mechanisms of the behavioral and electroencephalographic effects of atropine and related compounds. *Pharmacological Reviews,* 1966, 18, 965-996.

Longo, V. G., & Silvestrini, B. Action of eserine and amphetamine on the electrical activity of the rabbit brain. *Journal of Pharmacology and Experimental Therapeutics,* 1957, 120, 160-170.

Lovell, R. A. Some neurochemical aspects of convulsions. In A. Lajtha (Ed.), *Handbook of Neurochemistry.* New York: Plenum Press, 1971.

Machne, X., & Unna, K. R. W. Actions at the central nervous system. In G. B. Koelle (Ed.), *Cholinesterases and anticholinesterase agents.* Berlin: Springer-Verlag, 1963.

MacLean, P. D. Chemical and electrical stimulation of hippocampus in unrestrained animals. I. Methods and electroencephalographic findings. *Archives of Neurology and Psychiatry,* 1957, 78, 113-127.

Marczynski, T. J. Topical application of drugs to subcortical brain structures and selected aspects of electrical stimulation. *Ergebnisse der Physiologie, Biologischen Chemie und Experimentellen Pharmakologie,* 1967, **59,** 86-159.

Martin, W. R., & Eades, C. G. Pharmacological studies of spinal cord adrenergic and cholinergic mechanisms and their relation to physical dependence on morphine. *Psychopharmacologia,* 1967, **11,** 195-223.

Morrell, F. Electrical signs of sensory coding. In G. C. Quarton, T. Melnechuk, & F. O. Schmitt (Eds.), *The neurosciences.* New York: Rockefeller Press, 1967.

Naruse, H., Kato, M., Kurokawa, M., Haba, R., & Yabe, T. Metabolic defects in a convulsive strain of mouse. *Journal of Neurochemistry,* 1960, **5,** 359-369.

Nishi, S. The cholinergic and adrenergic receptors at the sympathetic preganglionic nerve terminals. *Federation Proceedings,* 1970, **29,** 1457-1465.

Olivier, A., Parent, A., Simard, H., & Poirier, L. J. Cholinesterase striatopallidal and striatonigral efferents in the cat and the monkey. *Brain Research,* 1970, **18,** 273-282.

Pryor, G. T. Postnatal development of cholinesterase, acetylcholine-esterase, aromatic 1-amino acid decarboxylase and monoamine oxidase in C57B116 and DBA2 mice. *Life Sciences,* 1968, **7,** 867-874.

Reeves, C. Cholinergic synaptic transmission and its relationship to behavior. *Psychological Bulletin,* 1966, **65,** 321-335.

Richter, D., & Crossland, J. Variation in acetylcholine content of the brain with physiological state. *American Journal of Physiology,* 1949, **159,** 247-255.

Rinaldi, F., & Himwich, H. E. Cholinergic mechanisms involved in function of mesodiencephalic activating system. *Archives of Neurology and Psychiatry,* 1955, **73,** 396-402.

Schlesinger, K., Boggan, W., & Freedman, D. Genetics of audiogenic seizures. I. Relation to brain serotonin and norepinephrine in mice. *Life Sciences,* 1965, **4,** 2345.

Schlesinger, K., Boggan, W., & Freedman, D. Genetics of audiogenic seizures. II. Effects of pharmacological manipulation of brain serotonin, norepinephrine and gamma-aminobutyric acid. *Life Sciences,* 1968, **7,** 437-447.

Schlesinger, K., & Griek, B. The genetics and biochemistry of audiogenic seizures. In G. Lindzey & D. D. Thiessen (Eds.), *Contributions to behavior-genetic analysis.* New York: Appleton-Century-Crofts, 1970.

Scudder, C. L., Karczmar, A. G., Everett, G. M., Gibson, E., & Rifkin, M. Brain catechol and serotonin levels in various strains and genera of mice and a possible interpretation for the correlations of amine levels with electroshock latency and behavior. *International Journal of Neuropharmacology,* 1966, **5,** 343-351.

Scudder, C. L., Richardson, D., & Karczmar, A. G. Aggression and the orienting reflex in several genera and strains of mice. *Agressologie,* 1969, **10,** 2-10.

Sellinger, O. Z., Azcurra, J. M., Ohlsson, W. G., Kohl, H. H., & Zand, R. Neurochemical correlates of drug-induced seizures: Selective inhibition of cerebral protein synthesis by methionine sulfoximine. *Federation Proceedings,* 1972, **31,** 160-165.

Sjöstrand, T. Potential changes in the cerebral cortex arising from cellular activity and the transmission of impulses in the white matter. *Journal of Physiology,* 1937, **90,** 41.

Sobotka, T. J. Studies on acetylcholine levels in mouse brain. Doctoral thesis, Loyola University, Chicago, 1969.

Spencer, W. A., & Kandel, E. R. Synaptic inhibition in seizures. In H. J. Jasper, A. A. Ward, Jr., & A. Pope (Eds.), *Basic mechanisms of the epilepsies.* Boston: Little, Brown, 1969.

Takahashi. R., Nasu, T., Tamura, T., & Kariya, T. Relationship of ammonia and acetycholine levels to brain excitability. *Journal of Neurochemistry,* 1961, **7,** 103-112.

Tebēcis, A. K. Properties of cholinoceptive neurons in the medial geniculate nucleus. *British Journal of Pharmacology,* 1970, **38,** 117-137. (a)

Tebēcis, A. K. Studies on cholinergic transmission in the medial geniculate nucleus. *British Journal of Pharmacology,* 1970, **38,** 138-147. (b)

Toman, J. Some aspects of central nervous pharmacology. *Annual Review of Pharmacology,* 1963, 3, 153-184.

Tower, D. Nature and extent of the biochemical lesion in human epileptogenic cortex. *Neurology,* 1955, 5, 113-130.

Tower, D., & Elliott, K. Experimental production and control of an abnormality in acetylcholine metabolism present in epileptogenic cortex. *Journal of Applied Physiology,* 1953, 5, 375-391.

Tower, D., & McEachern, D. Acetylcholine and neuronal activity. I. Cholinesterase patterns and acetylcholine in the cerebrospinal fluids of patients with craniocerebral trauma. *Canadian Journal of Research, Section E,* 1949, 27, 105-119.

Usdin, E. Reactions of cholinesterases with substrates, inhibitors and reactivators. In A. G. Karczmar (Ed.), *Anticholinesterase agents.* New York: Pergamon Press, 1970.

Van Meter, W. G. Responses to anticholinesterases. Doctoral thesis, Loyola University, Chicago, 1970.

Van Meter, W. G., & Karczmar, A. G. Effects of catecholamine depletion on anticholinesterase activity in the central nervous system. *Federation Proceedings,* 1967, 26, 651.

Van Meter, W. G., & Karczmar, A. G. An effect of physostigmine on the central nervous system of rabbits, related to brain levels of norepinephrine. *Neuropharmacology,* 1971, 10, 379-390.

Vazquez, A. J., Krip, G., & Pinsky, C. Evidence for a muscarinic inhibitory mechanism in the cerebral cortex. *Experimental Neurology,* 1969, 23, 318-331.

Ward, A. A., Jr., Jasper, H. J., & Pope, A. Clinical and experimental challenges of the epilepsies. In H. J. Jasper, A. A. Ward, Jr., & A. Pope (Eds.), *Basic mechanism of the epilepsies.* Boston: Little, Brown, 1969.

Willis, W. D., Jr. The localization of functional groups of interneurons. In M. Brazier (Ed.), *The interneuron.* Berkeley: University of California Press, 1969.

Wills, J. H. Pharmacological antagonists of the anticholinesterase agents. In G. B. Koelle (Ed.), *Cholinesterases and anticholinesterase agents.* Berlin: Springer-Verlag, 1963.

Wills, J. H. Toxicity of anticholinesterases and its treatment. In A. G. Karczmar (Ed.), *Anticholinesterase agents.* New York: Pergamon Press, 1970.

Woolley, D., Timiras, P., Rosenzweig, M., Krech, D., & Bennett, E. Strain differences in seizure responses and brain cholinesterase activity in rats. *Proceedings of the Society for Experimental Biology and Medicine,* 1963, 112, 781-785.

Workman, R. L., Swinyard, E. A., Rigbly, O., & Swinyard, C. Correlation between anticonvulsant activity and plasma concentration of ethanol. *Journal American Pharmaceutical Association,* 1958, 47, 769-722.

SUMMARIES AND DISCUSSION

20
CLINICAL PROGRESS IN
CONVULSIVE THERAPY[1]

Max Fink, M.D.

Controlled convulsions were introduced as a treatment for the insane in the mid-1930s. Used first in the treatment of dementia praecox, it soon became clear that depressive states were particularly responsive. In the beginning, seizures were induced by camphor, pentelenetetrazol (Metrazol), insulin, or electrically. Electrical inductions were easy and safe, and soon replaced other inductions. The number and frequency of seizures, the duration, strength, and type of currents, and the location of the electrodes became matters of concern, not only for their impact on therapeutic efficacy, but on the prominent complications of treatment: fractures, memory loss, fear of treatment, and postseizure confusion and panic.

In the 1940s and 1950s, the treatment process improved. Muscle relaxants, as curare, gallamine (Flaxedil), and succinylcholine (Anectine) were used routinely and fractures were reduced. Short-acting barbiturate anesthesia, as thiopental and lately, methohexital reduced pretreatment anxiety, and posttreatment excitement and confusion. By the mid-1950s, the principal limitation to the widespread use of induced seizures was the effect on memory.

The introduction of psychoactive drugs, particularly the phenothiazines for schizophrenia and the thymoleptics for depressive states, led many physicians to discard induced seizures; clinical practice and research interest waned, only to be stimulated as the numbers of unresponsive depressive patients increased. Interest was also stimulated by the reports of controlled clinical studies, particularly those of the Clinical Psychiatry Committee of the British Medical Research

[1] The research in this paper was aided, in part, by Grant Nos. MH 20762 and 15561 from the National Institute of Mental Health.

Council (1965), Bruce, Crone, Fitzpatrick, Frewin, Gillis, Lascelles, Levene, and Mersky (1960), Greenblatt, Grosser, and Wechsler (1964), and McDonald, Perkins, Marjerrison, and Podilsky (1966), which clearly demonstrated the efficacy of repeated seizures in relieving depressive states.

Studies in the 1960s demonstrated that memory changes could be reduced by changing the location of electrodes; that inhalant-induced seizures using flurothyl (Indoklon) produced electrographic, behavioral, memory, and therapeutic effects very similar to electrical inductions; and that forced ventilation (hyperoxygenation) before seizures reduced the interference with memory, thus allowing therapeutic studies of multiple seizures. These clinical studies and the increased research interest in the biogenic amines and the effects of ECS on memory so improved the climate for studies of repeated convulsions, that a working conference on the psychobiology of convulsive therapy[2] was convened in April, 1972.[3]

The many studies of these four decades show that the therapeutic effect of repeated seizures lies in the seizure and its sequelae, and not in the method or the parameters of its induction. Subconvulsive currents and subconvulsive doses of flurothyl or insulin are therapeutically less effective than seizures induced by these agents (Fink, 1966). Blockade of the seizure by lidocaine (Ottosson, 1960) and reversal of postseizure EEG convulsive activity by anticholinergic drugs (Fink, 1960) reduces therapeutic results. The blockade of the peripheral (motor) components of the convulsion by succinylcholine without a reduction in therapeutic efficacy suggests that the motor convulsion is incidental to the therapeutic process. This separation of the convulsion (the motor component) from the seizure (cerebral component) emphasizes the suggestion that the significant events of the therapeutic process are cerebral (Cherkin, this volume).

Flurothyl-induced seizures elicit therapeutic results similar to electrical seizures, with almost equivalent physiologic and memory effects (Laurell, 1970; Small, I. F., this volume; Small, Small, Sharpley, & Moore, 1968) indicating

---

[2] The repeated induction of seizures in man is referred to as convulsive therapy (or, when a specific form of induction is considered, as "electroconvulsive therapy" or "unilateral ECT"). The eponyms "shock therapy," "shock," and "electroshock" are archaic, and reflect a lack of discrimination between "insulin-shock" (in which hypoglycemic coma is induced) and induced convulsions. In part, the confusion is occasioned by the frequent precipitation of convulsions in some patients receiving insulin coma therapy. Besides its inaccuracy, "shock therapy" is pejorative, eliciting anxiety and fear in patients and their families. Its continued use reflects stereotyped thinking and a lack of awareness of the sensitive influence of language on thought and behavior. The pejorative effects of "shock therapy" were clearly evident in the summer of 1972 in the U.S. presidential campaign when revelations that a candidate had received this therapy were personally and nationally tragic. It is time to reassess the therapeutic process of induced convulsions, and in this assessment, to discard the nondescriptive, frightening terms of "shock," "shock therapy," and "electroshock."

[3] This report, and the succeeding reports by Seymour Kety, and James McGaugh and Thomas A. Williams are summaries of the papers presented at that conference.

again that the therapeutic efficacy does not reside in the electric current, but in the induced seizure and its sequelae.

Modification of electrode location alters the effects on behavior, and particularly on memory tasks (Abrams, Fink, Dornbush, Feldstein, Volavka, & Roubicek, 1972; Dornbush, Abrams, & Fink, 1971; d'Elia, this volume). The conventional bitemporal electrode location elicits antidepressant effects with an impairment of various memory tasks, both verbal and nonverbal. Seizures induced through unilateral electrodes placed over the dominant hemisphere elicit greater impairment in verbal and auditory tasks than in nonverbal visual tasks. When electrodes are placed over the nondominant hemisphere, the reverse is seen, with greater impairment of visual, nonverbal tasks (d'Elia, this volume; Dornbush & Williams, this volume). By modifying electrode placement it is possible to separate antidepressant activity and memory impairment. The judicious selection of electrode locations and the rate of seizure inductions allows many patients to achieve a therapeutic result without measurable or experienced memory impairment, and provides a useful method to reduce this impediment to treatment.

The dissociation of memory impairment and therapeutic efficacy supports concepts that the therapeutic process does not depend on memory impairment, and that memory impairment is a "side-effect" and therapeutically unnecessary (Dornbush, 1972; Dornbush & Williams, this volume; McGaugh & Williams, this volume; Zornetzer, this volume). Unilateral electrode placements may elicit less antidepressant effects than conventional bilateral inductions, although some studies show the treatments to be equivalent (d'Elia, this volume).

Induced seizures also elicit many electrical cerebral changes. With the induction of a convulsion, the scalp electroencephalogram exhibits a characteristic sequence of rhythmic high-voltage spike and slow-wave patterns that accompany the tonic and clonic phases of the convulsion. This very prominent electrical activity is frequently followed by many seconds of inactivity ("flat record"), before the more usual frequencies reappear (Small, J. G., this volume). With successive seizures, the dominant frequencies of the interseizure record become progressively slower and voltages increase, so that when behavioral change ("improvement") is measurable it is accompanied by theta and even delta frequencies (3-6 Hz) with scalp voltages of 100-180 μV in the alert subject (Fink, 1966, 1972; Small, J. G., this volume). When a course of treatment is terminated, the slower frequencies gradually regress and are replaced by well regulated alpha activity, often of higher voltage and slightly slower mean frequency than that recorded before treatment (Fink, 1972).

The cerebral electrical events of the seizure and the postseizure activity vary with the mode of induction, electrode placement, amount of inducing agent (inhalant or electric current), and number and frequency of inductions (Fink & Kahn, 1957; Small, J. G., this volume, Volavka, 1972). For example, after unilateral ECT, the amount of interseizure EEG slowing is less in degree than after bilateral ECT and is accentuated on the side of the electrode placement paralleling differences in clinical response (Small, J. G., this volume; Volavka, this volume; Volavka, Feldstein, Abrams, & Fink, 1972). Bitemporal electrode placement elicits postconvulsive activity with an accentuation over the dominant (left) hemisphere even with alternating currents, suggesting that interictal slowing is responsive to cerebral factors as well as the current path (Marjerrison & Bowman, in press; Volavka et al., 1972). Interictal seizure activity persists for longer periods with successive seizures, so that after three to five inductions, interictal seizure activity extends beyond 48-72 hr, and successive seizures are induced on a modified cerebral substrate. The persistence in cerebral EEG slowing led Fink and Kahn (1957) and Fink (1966) to ascribe therapeutic relevance to the biochemical sequelae of seizures, particularly in increased persistent levels of acetylcholine among the biogenic amines. The EEG and behavioral effects of seizures are enhanced by thiopental—an observation used by Roth (1951) and Roth, Kay, Shaw, and Green (1957) as a predictor of therapeutic outcome; and reduced by anticholinergic drugs (Fink, 1958, 1960).

But direct relationships between clinical evaluations (e.g., Hamilton depression ratings) and the amount of interictal EEG slowing have not been found (Volavka, this volume). The amount of interictal EEG slowing is directly related to the number and frequency of seizures, and to a lesser extent, to the mode of induction (Fink & Kahn, 1957; Small, J. G., this volume; Volavka, this volume). Behavioral changes are also related to these factors (Fink, 1972, this volume). It has been difficult to separate the possibility that both the EEG and the clinical effects of seizures are independent processes derived from a common cause, from the possibility that the therapeutic outcome is directly related to the EEG changes. The evidence favors a common cause hypothesis (Ottosson, 1960, this volume; Small, J., G., this volume; Volavka, 1972, this volume) and it is probable that EEG slowing, like impaired memory, may more parsimoniously be viewed as "side-effect" rather than central to the therapeutic process (Fink, 1972).

The therapeutic outcome is directly related to the number and frequency of seizures, but decreasing the interseizure period to less than 48 hr usually elicits clinically unpleasant complaints of impaired memory and concentration, and clinical confusion. Early attempts to increase seizures to daily or twice daily elicited neurologic "regression" with aphasia, incontinence, and an organic mental syndrome (Abrams, this volume). In 1966, Blachly and Gowing described multiple seizures under forced oxygenation without impaired memory or an organic confusional syndrome. This observation led to trials of a therapeutic course given in 1 to 3 days. But the administration of four to six multiple seizures (MECT) did not elicit a more rapid therapeutic response than single seizures spaced more conventionally, suggesting that the therapeutic process did not lie in the seizure induction or in the seizure itself, but in the cerebral biochemical events which unfold consequent to the seizure, with a time course measured in days rather than minutes or even hours (Abrams, this volume;

d'Elia, this volume; Fink, this volume; Kety, this volume; Small, J. G., this volume). Persistent changes in monoamine oxidase after repeated seizures have been found to have a similar time course (Pryor, this volume).

Much of the confusion about the therapeutic efficacy and the mode of action of induced convulsions results from the indiscriminate nature of the populations treated (Ottosson, 1960, this volume). In the early applications of convulsive therapy, clinical "improvement" was seen in schizophrenia, mania, organic confusion, catatonia, and depressive states. This led some workers to view induced seizures as nonspecific modifiers of behavior, with the outcome dependent not only on the induced cerebral biochemical effects, but on the individual's premorbid personality. These views led to the formulation of a neurophysiologic-adaptive view of the convulsive therapy process (Fink, 1958, 1966, 1972; Fink & Kahn, 1957). Recent experience has led to the view that repeated seizures elicit "specific" antidepressant activity (Ottosson, this volume). Ottosson argues that the physiologic aspects of the depressive syndrome result from diencephalic pathophysiology,. and he sees in the therapeutic effects of the seizure and the persistent interseizure EEG slowing evidence of specific diencephalic effects. He criticizes the psychobiologic views as not necessary for understanding the therapeutic process, and asserts that such physiologic-psychologic hypotheses may have resulted from the error of studies in mixed populations, reflecting perhaps the side-effects of therapy.

One evidence for diencephalic involvement in depressive states is in the disturbances in sleep. With repeated seizures, the pattern of sleep stages is altered, approximating control patterns (Mendels, Van de Castle, & Hawkins, this volume).

The clinical studies of the past decade, particularly of the mode of induction of seizures, their rate, and different electrode placements; the quantitative neurophysiologic measures; and the biochemical and psychologic studies of ECS and memory mechanisms contribute to our understanding of the convulsive therapy process. The therapeutic process is seen to reside in the cerebral seizure and its long term consequences, and not in the motor convulsion. It is less dependent on the mode of induction than on the rate and frequency of seizures. Changing electrode placement alters the degree and type of memory impairment and interseizure EEG patterns with little effect on clinical outcome, suggesting that memory impairment is secondary to the therapeutic process. Similarly, failure to define a direct relationship between clinical outcome and the degree of interseizure EEG slowing suggests that this postseizure manifestation is more a consequence of the seizure than a significant factor in the therapeutic process. Failure to achieve rapidly effective therapeutic results by multiple ECT suggests that the therapeutic process lies in cerebral biochemical events with a time course measured in days, rather than hours, and may reside in changes in cerebral protein synthesis or biogenic amine levels (Kety, this volume). Repeated convulsions, however induced, have prominent persistent effects on the diencephalon, as reflected in changes in sleep patterns and in persistent synchronous EEG slow-wave activity. These effects, like the effects of psychoactive drugs, are seen as specifically antidepressant or antimanic, and not as "nonspecific."

From a clinical point of view, the efficacy of convulsive therapy in depressive states has been demonstrated, particularly when complications are reduced by using succinylcholine, methohexital, and unilateral nondominant electrode placements. For selected cases, flurothyl, bitemporal electrode placement, and multiple ECT provide additional therapeutic maneuvers. A more general awareness that memory impairment is not necessary for a therapeutic response, and a sensitivity to the impact of the archaic terms "shock" and "shock therapy" on our behavior should encourage a reassessment of convulsive therapy as a complex maneuver designed to change central neurohumoral states—a process closely related to the goals and methods of clinical psychopharmacology. Indeed, the interaction of psychopharmacologic agents and convulsive therapy deserve more clinical attention, particularly the impact of neurohumoral precursor loading tests, hormones, and cholinergic drugs on the antidepressant and hypothalamic effects of repeated seizures.

From these discourses, induced convulsions are best viewed as central biochemical and neurohumoral processes, rather than as purely psychologic or even psychobiologic. Further study, particularly of the neurohumoral and enzymatic effects of seizures combined with sensitive, quantitative neurophysiologic measures, and detailed behavioral assessments should increase our understanding not only of the specific therapeutic process in convulsive therapy, but depressive states as well.

REFERENCES

Abrams, R., Fink, M., Dornbush, R. L., Feldstein, S., Volavka, J., & Roubicek, J. Unilateral and bilateral ECT: Effects on depression, memory and the electroencephalogram. *Archives of General Psychiatry*, 1972, 27, 88-94.

Blachly, P. H., & Gowing, D. Multiple monitored electroconvulsive treatment. *Comprehensive Psychiatry*, 1966, 7, 100-109.

Bruce, E. M., Crone, N., Fitzpatrick, G., Frewin, S. J., Gillis, A., Lascelles, C. F., Levene, L. J., & Mersky, H. A comparative trial of ECT and Tofranil. *American Journal of Psychiatry*, 1960, 117, 76.

Clinical Psychiatry Committee of the British Medical Research Council. Clinical trial of the treatment of depressive illness. *British Medical Journal*, 1965, 1, 881-886.

Dornbush, R. S. Memory and induced ECT. *Seminars in Psychiatry*, 1972, 4, 47-54.

Dornbush, R. L., Abrams, R., & Fink, M. Memory changes after unilateral and bilateral convulsive therapy. *British Journal of Psychiatry*, 1971, 119, 75-78.

Fink, M. Effect of anticholinergic agent, Diethazine, on EEG and behavior: Significance for theory of convulsive therapy. *Archives of Neurology and Psychiatry*, 1958, 80, 380-387.

Fink, M. Effect of anticholinergic compounds on post-convulsive electroencephalogram and behavior of psychiatric patients. *Electroencephalography and Clinical Neurophysiology*, 1960, 12, 359-369.

Fink, M. Cholinergic aspects of convulsive therapy. *Journal of Nervous and Mental Disease*, 1966, 142, 475-484.

Fink, M. CNS effects of convulsive therapy: Significance for a theory of depressive psychosis. In J. Zubin & F. Freyhan (Eds.), *Disorders of mood.* Baltimore: Johns Hopkins, 1972.

Fink, M., & Kahn, R. L. Relation of EEG delta activity to behavioral response in electroshock: Quantitative serial studies. *Archives of Neurology and Psychiatry,* 1957, 78, 516-525.

Greenblatt, M., Grosser, G. H., & Wechsler, H. Differential response of hospitalized depressed patients to somatic therapy. *American Journal of Psychiatry,* 1964, 120, 935-943.

Laurell, B. Flurothyl convulsive therapy. *Acta Psychiatrica Scandinavica,* Supplement 213, 79 pp., 1970.

Marjerrison, G. & Bowman, L. Electroconvulsive therapy: EEG and clinical effects. *Canadian Medical Association Journal,* in press.

McDonald, I. M., Perkins, M., Marjerrison, G., & Podilsky, M. A controlled comparison of amitriptyline and electroconvulsive therapy in the treatment of depression. *American Journal of Psychiatry,* 1966, 122, 1427-1431.

Ottosson, J. -O. Experimental studies of the mode of action of electroconvulsive therapy. *Acta Psychiatrica et Neurologica Scandinavica,* 1960, 35 (Supplement 145), 1-141.

Roth, M. Changes in the EEG under barbiturate anesthesia produced by electro-convulsive treatment and their significance for the theory of ECT action. *Electroencephalography and Clinical Neurophysiology,* 1951, 3, 261-280.

Roth, M., Kay, D. W. K., Shaw, J., & Green, J. Prognosis and pentothal induced electroencephalographic changes in electroconvulsive treatment. *Electroencephalography and Clinical Neurophysiology,* 1957, 9, 225-237.

Small, J. G., Small, I. F., Sharpley, P., & Moore, D. F. A double-blind comparative evaluation of fluorothyl and ECT. *Archives of General Psychiatry,* 1968, 19, 79-86.

Volavka, J. Neurophysiology of ECT. *Seminars in Psychiatry,* 1972, 4, 55-66.

Volavka, J., Feldstein, S., Abrams, R., & Fink, M. EEG and clinical change after bilateral and unilateral electroconvulsive therapy. *Electroencephalography and Clinical Neurophysiology,* 1972, 32, 631-639.

21

NEUROPHYSIOLOGICAL AND BEHAVIORAL EFFECTS OF CONVULSIVE PHENOMENA

James L. McGaugh, Ph.D. and Thomas A. Williams, M.D.

An important consideration in convulsive therapy is the effect on learning and memory, which often represents a principal complaint of patients. Much of the relevant data arises from experiments that investigate the effects of electroconvulsive shock (ECS) on the performance of laboratory animals on learning tasks (McGaugh, this volume). Laboratory studies of ECS were first conducted in the early 1940s. The findings of this early research (cf. Finger, 1947; Munn, 1950) indicated that, in rats, the performance of learned responses is impaired by a series of ECS treatments. In general, the more complex the behavioral task, the greater the disruption of behavior. Subsequently, in an extensive series of investigations, Hunt and his colleagues (Hunt, 1965) found that a series of ECS treatments selectively attenuated the performance of a conditioned emotional response (CER) in rats. The degree of attenuation decreased as the delay between the CER training and the ECS treatments was increased. Apparently the behavioral convulsions were important for producing the CER attenuation, since no attenuation was found if the convulsions were prevented by anesthetizing the rats with ether prior to each ECS treatment. While it is clear from these early studies that learned performance can be disrupted by a series of ECS treatments, the bases of the effects remains obscure.

Shortly after ECT was introduced as a psychiatric treatment, it was observed that ECT impaired memory. While some of the memory effects were seen only after a series of treatments there was also evidence that an ECT treatment produces retrograde amnesia (RA) (Mayer-Gross, 1943). In the late 1940s several investigators (cf. Duncan, 1949; Gerard, 1949, 1955) initiated studies of the amnesic effects of ECS in animals. These experiments, as well as numerous others published during the past two decades, provide extensive evidence that an

ECS causes a loss of memory for experiences that had occurred shortly before the treatment (Glickman, 1961; McGaugh, 1966). While there have been numerous controversies concerning the basis of the memory loss (cf. McGaugh & Herz, 1972), the bulk of the evidence is consistent with the view that ECS treatments disrupt the processes underlying memory consolidation.

Recent research using ECS has attempted to discover the neurobiological bases of the RA (McGaugh, Zornetzer, Gold, & Landfield, 1972). It is clear that convulsions play no role in producing the amnesia. RA can be produced in animals that have been anesthetized with ether prior to the ECS treatment so that no seizure occurs. It also seems that brain seizures are not necessary for producing RA. While seizures are generally produced by current that produces RA in rats and mice, RA can be obtained by subseizure stimulation. Further, RA is not always produced by ECS current (or convulsant drugs) that produces brain seizures (McGaugh et al., 1972). Thus, the recent evidence indicates that brain seizures are neither a necessary nor a sufficient condition for producing RA. Present research is focusing on the amnesic effects of low intensity (subseizure) stimulation of specific brain regions in an attempt to find out whether some structures are particularly effective stimulation sites.

Flurothyl (Indoklon) is used extensively as a treatment in convulsive therapy. There is considerable evidence that flurothyl has effects on memory which are comparable to those produced by ECS. Cherkin (this volume) summarized his extensive investigations of the amnesic effects of flurothyl in neonatal chicks. In these experiments, chicks are trained by allowing them to peck at a small object that has been dipped in a bitter fluid. Subsequently, chicks avoid the object. However, if the chick is convulsed by flurothyl after the training session, it will subsequently peck at the object again: i.e., it will display amnesia. In this type of experiment gradients of amnesia can be obtained: the longer the delay between the training and the flurothyl seizure, the greater the tendency of the chicks to avoid the bitter object when they are tested at a later time. The degree of amnesia produced by flurothyl varies systematically with many conditions, including the concentration used as well as the duration of the treatment. Under some conditions RA can be produced by flurothyl administered even a day or so after the training. Cherkin (this volume) suggested that the effects are not due to hypoxia, since comparable effects are not produced by seizure-inducing hypoxia.

Retrograde amnesia is usually produced by conditions that elicit brain seizure activity. But, until recently, little was known about the role, if any, of brain seizures in producing RA. Zornetzer (this volume) summarized his studies of the relationship between RA and brain seizure activity in rats. In these experiments, the frontal cortex was directly stimulated with electrical current and the brain seizure activity was recorded. The stimulation elicits a short (3-10 sec) primary afterdischarge (PAD) followed by a depression of activity. A secondary afterdischarge (SAD) typically occurs 30 to 90 sec later if the current is of sufficiently high intensity. The frequency of spikes in the PAD varies with current intensity but the frequency (spikes per second) of the SAD is independent of the current intensity. Zornetzer's findings indicate that, in rats, retrograde amnesia is produced by direct cortical stimulation only if the current produces a PAD. The degree of RA produced varies directly with the intensity of the current used to stimulate the cortex. The intensity of the brain stimulation needed to produce RA varies with the intensity of the motivational stimulus (punishing shock) used in the training tasks used to study memory. Zornetzer also indicates that a brain seizure is not a sufficient condition for producing RA. RA was produced by electrical stimulation of the midbrain only if the current elicited both a PAD and a SAD recorded from the cortex. A PAD was not sufficient to produce RA. These findings indicate that the degree of RA produced by brain stimulation depends upon many factors, including the training conditions used to study memory, the region of the brain stimulated, the intensity of the current delivered to the brain, and the pattern of brain seizure activity elicitied by the stimulation (Zornetzer, this volume).

Most recent studies of the effect of convulsive stimulation on memory have focussed on the problem of retrograde amnesia. Geller (1972) reported findings of her recent research which suggest that ECS may also impair memories for well established responses. In these experiments mice were trained on an inhibitory (passive) avoidance task and were then given ECS once per day for several days. The ECS treated animals were inferior to controls on a subsequent retention test. In other experiments Geller found that retention is impaired by a single ECS treatment given even several days after training. The deficit appears to be permanent, suggesting that ECS may accelerate the forgetting of well established memories. This persistent behavioral deficit produced by a single ECS is noteworthy in view of the apparent absence of persistent memory deficits in human patients who have received as many as five electroconvulsive treatments. In discussing these data, Small (this volume) noted that, following a clinical course of ECT, patients are often unable to remember a variety of important details concerning well-established memories. Such individually specific memory losses are unlikely to be detected by standard testing procedures.

Williams (see Dornbush & Williams, this volume) discussed the significance of the findings of studies of ECT effects on memory in patients. It may be that ECS merely accentuates the normal processes which make remembering difficult. In this regard it is important to note that emotionally significant memories are much easier to remember. Further, the influence of defense mechanisms may confound attempts to measure memory in man. So too does the experimenter's inability to pin down specific memory either in time or place. The way in which we test memory is critical to the interpretation of our results. For example, "recall" is much more difficult to test than is "recognition." This is unfortunate indeed, since difficulty with recall is undoubtedly of greatest significance to the patient.

Williams pointed out that in any discussion of the effect of ECT on memory in man, it is important to distinguish between "short term" and "long term" memory. We generally think of short term memory as a mental function of limited capacity, characterized by a fast rate of decay and subject to interference with retention by auditory and visual stimuli; in contrast, we generally think of long term memory as a function of infinite capacity, with a slow decay rate and subject to interference of retention by semantic stimuli. ECT has little effect upon short term memory; tests of immediate recall are within the normal range. In contrast, ECT *does* affect long term memory function; "retrieval strategies," crucial to the operation of this function, *are* severely disrupted. The disruption of this important aspect of memory by electroconvulsive therapy will escape detection, however, unless one tests *specifically* for deficits in long-term memory.

Dornbush (this volume) discussed some problems in evaluating memory effects of seizures. In her presentation she pointed out that the clinician must accept the burden of attempting to minimize the impact of memory loss "side-effects" in the use of electroconvulsive therapy in human patients. It is thus important that the clinician be cognizant of the cerebral hemispheric localization of various important mental functions. For the "normal" right-handed patient, auditory and verbal functions are mediated mainly by the left (dominant) cerebral hemisphere; visual and non-verbal functions are mediated by the right (non-dominant) hemisphere. Thus, for example, it may be shown that ECT administered by the standard bitemporal electrode placement more severely affects auditory memory than does ECT administered by electrodes applied unilaterally to the *non*dominant hemisphere.

There is evidence that there are local effects of ECT, i.e., effects on structures immediately under the electrodes, as well as general effects of ECT. This suggests that electrodes should be placed over cortical areas not directly involved in crucial mental functions; it may be necessary to individualize electrode placement, depending upon the patient's occupation. For example, for a carpenter who must earn his living by skeletomuscular activities, i.e., nonverbal activities, unilateral electrode placement over the *dominant* hemisphere may be optimal, even though that particular placement carries a greater risk of loss in verbal memory function.

It is difficult to compare the results of studies of the effects of ECT on memory in humans with studies of the effects of ECS on memory in animals, since the human studies generally utilize measures of anterograde memory, whereas the animal studies generally utilize measures of retrograde memory. Thus, one must heed Williams' admonition that the methods for measurement of memory deficit are crucial in interpreting research on seizure-induced amnesia. Furthermore, if one assumes that ECT affects the "consolidation," i.e., the transfer of information from short term to long term memory, rather than that it affects "retrieval" (from long term storage), one would choose very different tests (Dornbush & Williams, this volume).

Thus, it is clear from the evidence summarized in this session that memory losses can be produced by convulsive therapy. The focus of research with infrahuman subjects is quite different from that with human patients. The findings that ECT produces memory losses in humans has led to the development of procedures that will minimize memory impairment. The research with animals has led increasingly to the search for conditions that will maximize memory losses produced by ECS. In these efforts, ECS and more refined techniques for administering current to the brain are used as techniques in the investigation of brain function in memory. Obviously, current administered to the brain can produce many different effects on behavior. Which effect is a side-effect depends upon the problem in question. It appears that memory losses are not a necessary consequence of convulsive therapy and are not essential for the therapeutic effects of ECT. Careful selection of electrode placement may lead to the therapeutic effects with no concomitant effects on memory. On the other hand, the fact that memory losses can be produced by stimulation of some specific brain regions suggests that such procedures will continue to be important in the investigation of the neural bases of memory.

REFERENCES

Duncan, C. P. The retroactive effect of electroshock on learning, *Journal of Comparative and Physiological Psychology*, 1949, 42, 32-44.

Finger, F. W. Convulsive behavior in the rat. *Psychological Bulletin*, 1947, 44, 201-248.

Geller, A. Unpublished communication. San Juan, P. R., April 24, 1972.

Gerard, R. W. Physiology and psychiatry. *American Journal of Psychiatry*, 1949, 106, 161-173.

Gerard, R. W. Biological roots of psychiatry. *Science*, 1955, 122, 225-230.

Glickman, S. E. Perseverative neural processes and consolidation of the memory trace. *Psychological Bulletin*, 1961, 58, 218-233.

Hunt, H. F. Electroconvulsive shock and learning. *Transactions of the New York Academy of Sciences*, 1965, 27, 923-945.

Mayer-Gross, W. Retrograde amnesia. *Lancet*, 1943, 2, 603-605.

McGaugh, J. L. Time-dependent processes in memory storage. *Science*, 1966, 153, 1351-1358.

McGaugh, J. L., & Herz, M. J. Memory consolidation. San Francisco: Albion, 1972.

McGaugh, J. L., Zornetzer, S. F., Gold, P. E., & Landfield, P. W. Modification of memory systems: Some neurobiological aspects. *Quarterly Review of Biophysics*, 1972, 5, 163-186.

Munn, N. L. Handbook of psychological research on the rat. Cambridge, Mass.: Houghton Mifflin, 1950.

22
BIOCHEMICAL AND NEUROCHEMICAL EFFECTS OF ELECTROCONVULSIVE SHOCK[1]

Seymour S. Kety, M.D.

Efforts to elucidate the biochemical and other biological mechanisms which are involved in the antidepressive and amnestic effects of electroconvulsive shock are of considerable importance. Such knowledge would be expected to contribute to an understanding of the biological processes involved in depression and in memory. In addition, were it possible to account for the beneficial therapeutic effects of electroconvulsive shock on the basis of a few well-defined mechanisms, more specific and rational types of therapy to achieve the same end could be developed.

Until that time arrives, however, electroshock therapy will probably continue to be used as an empirical but effective treatment for severe depression. It involves massive discharge over wide areas of the brain, activation of the peripheral autonomic nervous system, release of the secretions of many endocrine glands, and, unless there is neuromuscular blockade, tonic and clonic convulsions of much of the muscle mass of the body. All of these activities cause so many changes in the chemical homeostasis of the body, that there is no dearth of demonstrable biochemical changes which are found to be associated with electroconvulsive shock. Indeed, the difficulty lies not in demonstrating such changes, but in differentiating between those which are more fundamental and those which are clearly secondary, and also in attempting to discern which of the changes may be related to the important antidepressive or amnestic effects and which are quite irrelevant to these. One should point out that an effect which is obviously secondary may still play an important contributory

[1] Supported in part by United States Public Health Service Grant No. MH 16674, National Institute of Mental Health.

role. Thus, the marked rise in corticosteroids in the blood is clearly secondary to the hypothalamic and autonomic stimulation that occur during electroshock. Ottosson (this volume) points out that ACTH does not constitute an effective treatment for depression and, therefore, one can hardly account for the beneficial effects of ECT on the basis of the adrenocortical stimulation. One cannot be sure, however, that the corticosteroids do not play an important contributory role in the effects of chronic ECT. The corticosteroids are known to have important trophic effects upon a number of enzyme systems and, since they pass freely across the blood-brain barrier, one cannot discount the possibility that they may contribute to certain of the enzyme changes in the brain which may be induced by repeated shock treatments.

It is important to set up some guidelines which may help in determining the relevance of a particular biochemical effect to the important clinical or behavioral effects of ECS. I should like to suggest the following criteria:

1. A change is more likely to be relevant if it shows a similar time course to the clinical or behavioral effects. A single ECS is not sufficient to produce a detectable clinical effect, which suggests that the acute biochemical effects of a single shock are not likely to account for the antidepressant effects, although they may be helpful in giving insights into what may occur chronically. Changes of a biochemical nature which are induced by repeated ECS and which are found after recovery from the acute effects of the last shock are more apt to relate to the clinical effects.

2. There should be some evidence that the biochemical change in question is fairly specific and not one of a large number of changes which can be attributed to overactivity, anoxia, or their sequelae.

3. The relevance of a biochemical change is greatly enhanced if the change is compatible with other evidence independently arrived at from a different point of view, especially if a plausible hypothesis can parsimoniously incorporate both findings.

In 1963, Holmberg reviewed the biochemical concomitants of electroconvulsive therapy up to that time, and more recently, Ottosson (this volume) has examined the systemic biochemical effects. I tend to agree with Ottosson's general conclusion that the systemic effects are largely secondary to the central neuronal activations, although I would not want to disregard the possibility that some of the systemic effects may contribute to a persistent change within the brain which accounts for the antidepressant effects of repeated shocks. Ottosson also points out that variables such as body weight, appetite, sleep, digestion, circulation, libido, and menstruation often change early in the course of therapy and are especially apt to be disturbed in affective disorders. He suggests that these variables are controlled by diencephalic centers and that it is there that ECT has its beneficial effect. For these reasons, he is of the opinion that neurochemical events in the brain stem, perhaps on monamine neurons, may be of greater relevance to the antidepressant action of ECT than any of the systemic effects.

BIOCHEMICAL CHANGES

I should like now to turn to the effects of ECS on biochemical changes within the brain, with special reference to those which appear to be primary to the clinical or behavioral effects of ECT. Again, this massive discharge of neurons involving extensive portions of the brain would be expected to be associated with a multitude of biochemical concomitants. It may be of use to apply the criteria we mentioned earlier in order to offer some rational guess as to which of these changes may be more important or more relevant to the antidepressant or amnestic actions of ECS.

During convulsions produced by picrotoxin, it was found (Schmidt, Kety, & Pennes, 1945) that the overall oxygen consumption of the brain was doubled and, since the increase in cerebral blood flow did not keep pace with the increased metabolic demand, there was a concomitant tissue anoxia. During the postictal stupor in patients, a diminished cerebral oxygen consumption was found (Kety, Woodford, Harmel, Freyhan, Appel, & Schmidt, 1948). It is not at all surprising that the exaggerated neuronal activity induced by ECS should be associated with a marked increase in energy metabolism, but whether it or the accompanying anoxia can account for the therapeutic or behavioral effects of the shock is another question. If a diminution in the energy production within certain parts of the brain were the basis of depressive illness, it is conceivable that a series of intense stimulations of these processes could result in the induction of certain crucial enzymes or other adaptive changes which might restore the situation toward normal. However, there is no serious reason for entertaining such an hypothesis and I know of no evidence to support it. Pryor (this volume) found no increase in succinic acid dehydrogenase in the brain after a series of ECS.

Changes in permeability of the blood-brain barrier induced by the anoxia or other concomitants of ECS are known to occur and have been mentioned by Ottosson. Aside from the findings of Rosenblatt, Chanley, Sobotka, and Kaufman (1960) that permeability to norepinephrine was enhanced, I am not aware of an hypothesis which involves the increased blood-brain barrier permeability for a particular substance to account for the therapeutic effects of ECT.

Karczmar (this volume) has reviewed the relationships of acetylcholine and the cholinergic system to convulsive thresholds and raised the question regarding the possible involvement of this system in the therapeutic or behavioral effects of ECS. Although he indicated that the reported results were somewhat controversial, he felt that it was likely that there was a release of acetylcholine in many areas of the brain during ECS, followed by depletion and accompanied by an increased synthesis and turnover. He did not suggest evidence for a persistent effect on this system as a result of repetitive ECS, and Pryor (this volume) was unable to find reproducible changes in cholinesterase or acetylcholinesterase activity, even after prolonged treatment schedules. On the other hand, the antidepressant activity of certain anticholinergic drugs and the anticholinergic effects of the important antidepressant drugs suggest that the cholinergic system may be playing some role in clinical depression and in the beneficial effects of antidepressant drugs. There is no clear biochemical evidence relating to the effects of chronic ECS on acetylcholine or its enzymes, and a plausible hypothesis has not been formulated relating the therapeutic effects of ECT to changes in that transmitter.

The same cannot be said, however, regarding the biogenic amines. A substantial body of information has been accumulated over the past two decades which relates these putative neurotransmitters to mood and disorders of mood (Schildkraut & Kety, 1967; Kety, 1971a, 1971b). Although the evidence at the present time is incomplete, inconclusive, and does not permit a consistent and definitive neurobiological explanation of these states or their production or alleviation by particular drugs, it is substantial enough to support the relevance of these systems to depression and antidepressant therapy. Electroconvulsive shock has been found by a large number of investigators to have effects on one or another of the biogenic amines which are compatible with their involvement in depression and with the therapeutic effects of ECS, although they are far from proving any particular hypothesis.

Serotonin was apparently the first of the biogenic amines found to be significantly affected by ECS (Valzelli & Garattini, this volume) and with considerable consistency investigators have found an increase in this amine in the brain following a single shock (Garattini & Valzelli, 1957; Bertaccini, 1959; Garattini, Kato, Lamesta, & Valzelli, 1960; Kato, Gozsy, Roy, Groh, 1967; Essman, 1972), but some failed to find an increase (Bonnycastle, Giarman, & Paasonen, 1957; Breitner, Picchioni & Chin, 1964; Cooper, Moir, & Goldberg, 1968). An increase in serotonin in whole brain (Kato et al., 1967) or in brain regions (Kety, Javoy, Thierry, Julou, & Glowinski, 1967) has been reported after a series of electroconvulsive shocks as well as evidence for an increase in turnover of this amine (Engel, Hanson, & Roos, 1971). Cooper and associates (1968) reported a progressive increase in 5-hydroxyindoleacetic acid in the dog lateral ventricular fluid during a series of ECS.

In the case of norepinephrine, a decrease has been fairly consistently reported immediately following an acute ECS (Shatalova & Antonov, 1961; Breitner et al., 1964; Schildkraut, Schanberg, Breese, & Kopin, 1967). An increase in the metabolites of norepinephrine in the brain (Schildkraut et al., 1967) suggests that the decrease in norepinephrine levels is the result of the release of that amine induced by ECS. Following a series of electroconvulsive shocks, some investigators have reported an increase in norepinephrine levels in the brain (Kety et al., 1967; Hinesley, Norton, & Aprison, 1968). One study found no change after repeated ECS, but a doubling shortly after a single shock (Kato et al., 1967). Evidence suggesting a persistent increase in norepinephrine turnover after a series of ECS has been obtained by three groups (Kety et al., 1967; Ladisich, Steinhauff, & Matussek, 1969; Schildkraut & Draskoczy, this volume).[2]

Increased levels of dopamine have been found in the brain (Engel, Hanson, Roos, & Strombergsson, 1968) or in the caudate nucleus (Billiet, Bernard, Delaunois, & DeSchaepdryver, 1970) following ECS, and one group has reported a progressive increase in homovanillic acid in ventricular fluid in the course of a series of shocks (Cooper et al., 1968). One group (Hinesley et al., 1968) found a slight and nonsignificant increase in dopamine concentration in the cerebral hemisphere after a total of seven ECS given at 2-day intervals, as well as a slight but significant increase in norepinephrine in the hemisphere and a slight and significant increase in serotonin in the midbrain, pons, and medulla under similar conditions. Since similar changes in these amines were observed in rats which had been subjected to only one ECS preceded by six sham shocks, they interpreted their results as related in part to the attendant stress of the shock situation. The question of associative stress which has also been found by other investigators to produce an increase in one or another of these amines may be an appropriate question where pain or stress precedes the application of the current, and where the effects of the latter are attenuated by less effective electrode placement or the administration of fewer shocks at longer intervals between them, but it does not apply to studies (i.e., Kety et al., 1967) where statistically significant effects were observed between shocked animals and controls treated in exactly the same way, including the placement of the electrode, in which the only difference was the application of the current.

There is some suggestion that changes in norepinephrine or in serotonin metabolism may be occurring in the brain of patients in association with clinical improvement during the course of ECT. Schildkraut and Draskoczy (this volume) reported the urinary excretion of methoxy-hydroxy-phenylglycol, a metabolite of norepinephrine which originates predominantly in the brain, during the course of ECT in a single depressed patient. There was a significant rise during the course of clinical improvement and an even greater rise after the termination of ECT when the patient became hypomanic. Abrams (this meeting) reported observations on cerebrospinal fluid before and during the course of ECT. These showed a rise in serotonin and in 5-hydroxyindoleacetic acid, concomitant with clinical improvement. On the other hand, Nordin, Ottosson, and Roos, (1971) found no significant change in 5-hydroxyindoleacetic acid or homovanillic acid in the cerebrospinal fluid of a series of patients with endogenous depression treated with ECT despite considerable clinical improvement. It is clear that conclusive evidence implicating these biogenic

---

[2] Note added in proof: A most recent report (Ebert, Baldessarini, Lipinski, & Berv, 1973) presents similar findings, although the authors do not feel that they bear an important relationship to the action of ECT as used in the treatment of clinical depression.

amines with the clinical effects of ECT, like the clinical disorders of mood, is yet to be obtained.

The laboratory studies which suggest an association between the biogenic amines and the therapeutic effects of ECT show some persistence of the alterations in biogenic amine metabolism well beyond the immediate period following the last shock, although in no case has an effect been produced which is comparable in time to the duration of the clinical remission which is often achieved. It may, of course, never be possible to demonstrate in a normal brain the same magnitude of change which may correct a deficiency where it is present, so that until we can acquire more extensive information on the metabolism of these amines in the human brain, animal studies may be useful in suggesting the kinds of changes that may be possible and relevant. Increases in levels of these amines or their turnover which require repeated administration of shock for their induction and which persist well beyond the acute effects of the last shock, suggest an adaptive responsiveness of these systems. This responsiveness is confirmed by specific enzyme studies, as in the activitv of tyrosine hydroxylase which increases in various regions of the brain after a series of ECS (Musacchio, Julou, Kety, & Glowinski, 1969) or after immobilization stress (Kopin, 1972). It is especially interesting that in the latter study a marked increase in the activity of this enzyme was found that persisted for as long as 4 weeks.

The studies of Pryor (this volume) on the effects of repeated ECS on brain weight and brain enzymes are very cogent. Using transocular stimulation in rats, they found, after a series of daily shocks, a slight increase in brain size but no change in total protein concentration. Thus, changes in particular components, when they are found, cannot be attributed to a nonspecific increase of components generally. They also found no change in a number of enzymes including cholinesterase, acetylcholinesterase, succinic dehydrogenase and COMT, thus adding considerably to the significance of the change that was found in the enzyme monoamine oxidase. Some characteristics of this finding are interesting and instructive. Transocular electrodes were used, and it was found that the intensity of the current was important, since minimal threshold convulsions had little effect. A minimum of seven daily shocks were necessary in order to demonstrate reproducible effects and twice daily administration of the shock tended to accelerate the appearance of the effect. The increase in monoamine oxidase activity persisted for a very long time; according to Pryor, even after 6 weeks there were slight but significant increases. Evidence was adduced for *de novo* synthesis of the enzyme by the ability of ECS to restore enzymatic activity more rapidly after blockade of the enzyme by pargyline.

The effect of repeated ECS on brain monoamine oxidase is quite compatible with the observations of an increase in serotonin or norepinephrine concentrations or the more rapid turnover of these amines. If repeated ECS induces an increased activity of the synthetic enzymes for these amines, an induction of the common enzyme in their presynaptic degradation would not be unexpected. Two reports of an increase in deaminated metabolites of norepinephrine in the brain after repeated ECS (Schildkraut & Draskoczy, this volume; Ladisich et al., 1969) can be explained on the basis of an increase in monoamine oxidase activity. Thus, repeated ECS could, by virtue of repeated stimulation of serotonin and norepinephrine release, induce an increase in the synthesis of these amines which would be associated with an increase in their levels at nerve endings and an increase in the activity of their common degrading enzyme. This would be reflected in a more rapid turnover under resting circumstances and an increase in the availability of these amines at their synapses. Although this might account for an antidepressant effect of repeated ECS, it need not be the whole or even the most important neurochemical effect. Other associated effects, such as an increase in receptor or adenylcyclase activity at the postsynaptic membrane, or an increase in the number of synaptic endings, could follow upon increased transmitter activity and account for more sustained effects.

The finding that both serotonin and the catecholamines are affected by chronic ECS, presumably with enhanced synaptic activity, is quite consistent with observations which are accumulating that both are involved in affective disorders. Coppen (1971) has presented and summarized evidence for a deficiency of serotonin in the brain in both mania and depression and in either type of patient during remission. He and others have reported beneficial effects from the administration of tryptophane to patients in depression. Schildkraut, on the other hand, has adduced considerable evidence suggesting that catecholamines are increased in central synaptic activity in mania and hypomania and are deficient during depression (Schildkraut, 1970). I do not find these two hypotheses in conflict, and interpret the data as suggesting a combined involvement in clinical affective disorder (Kety, 1971b), with serotonin serving as a damper at synapses involved in mood and a deficiency in serotonin permitting physiological increases or decreases in catecholamine activity at these synapses. The changes in catecholamine activity may produce excessive changes—mania instead of elation or profound depression instead of sadness. It is interesting that electroconvulsive shock is reported to be clinically effective not only in alleviating depression but also in producing a rapid remission in mania. The effect of ECS on both serotonin and the catecholamines provides a possible explanation for the therapeutic efficacy of ECT in these divergent states.

In the case of the amnestic effects of ECS, as in its antidepressant effects, a neurochemical change which is compatible with independently arrived at neurochemical observations or hypotheses regarding memory achieves enhanced viability and relevance. Since much of the neurochemical studies with memory appears to converge on protein synthesis in the brain as a process crucially related to the consolidation of experience, the effects of ECS on protein synthesis are of special interest. Dunn, Giuditta, Wilson, and Glassman (this volume) have confirmed and extended previous findings (Cotman, Banker, Zornetzer, & McGaugh, 1971), and they have found a marked and highly significant depression in leucine incorporation into brain protein immediately after ECS and persisting for only 15 min. Dunn et al. also confirmed the observations of MacInnes, McConkey, and Schlesinger (1970) of a significant reduction in polyribosomes during the same brief interval following ECS, which is independent evidence for a depression in protein synthesis. Dunn has pointed out that the retrograde amnesia of ECS is associated with considerably less depression in protein synthesis than that which must be achieved by antibiotics to produce the same degree of amnesia and suggests that the effects on protein synthesis in the case of ECS may be concentrated at the synapse where the crucial role of protein synthesis in memory may be exerted. Essman (this volume) has reported a differential effect of ECS on the synthesis of particular proteins separated from the brain by electrophoresis. Because of the increase in serotonin produced by a single electroshock, Essman also tested and demonstrated an ability of serotonin injection into the brain to produce amnesia. This raises the possibility that the crucial effect of ECS on amnesia may be exerted through its action on one or another biogenic amine rather than directly upon protein.

The neurochemical basis for either the therapeutic or the amnestic effects of electroconvulsive shock is far from having been established. On the other hand, perceptible progress has been made in the past 5 years in the accumulation of data in a number of different laboratories indicating important effects of ECS on biogenic amines and on protein synthesis in the brain. These effects in concert with a substantial amount of independently acquired information regarding the neurochemical correlates of affective states and memory permit the formulation of plausible, heuristic, and parsimonious hypotheses to account for the antidepressant and amnestic effects of ECS.

REFERENCES

Abrams, R. A. Personal communication. San Juan, P. R. April 23, 1972.

Bertaccini, G. Effect of convulsant treatment on the 5-hydroxytryptamine content of brain and other tissues of the rat. *Journal of Neurochemistry,* 1959, 4, 217-22.

Billiet, M., Bernard, P., Delaunois, A., & DeSchaepdryver, A. Electroshock and nucleus dopamine. *Archives Internationale de Pharmacodynamie et de Therapie,* 1970, **186,** 179-181.

Bonnycastle, D. D., Giarman, N. J., & Paasonen, M. K. Anticonvulsant compounds and 5-HT in rat brain. *British Journal of Pharmacology and Chemotherapy,* 1957, **12,** 228-231.

Breitner, C., Picchioni, A., & Chin, L. Neurohormone levels in brain after CNS stimulation including electrotherapy. *Journal of Neuropsychiatry,* 1964, 5, 153-158.

Cooper, A. J., Moir, A. J. B., & Goldberg, H. C. Effect of electroconvulsive shock on the cerebral metabolism of dopamine and 5-hydroxytryptamine. *Journal of Pharmacy and Pharmacology,* 1968, 20, 729-730.

Coppen, A. Biogenic amines and affective disorders. In B. T. Ho & W. M. McIsaac (Eds.), *Brain chemistry and mental disease.* New York: Plenum Press, 1971.

Cotman, C. W., Banker, G., Zornetzer, S. F., & McGaugh, J. L. Electroshock effects on brain protein synthesis: Relation to brain seizures and retrograde amnesia. *Science,* 1971, **173,** 454-456.

Ebert, M. H., Baldessarini, R. J., Lipinski, J. F., & Berv, K. Effects of electroconvulsive seizures on amine metabolism in the rat brain. *Archives of General Psychiatry*, 1973, **29**, 397-401.

Engel, J., Hanson, L. C. F., & Roos, B. E. Effect of electroshock on 5-HT metabolism in rat brain. *Psychopharmacologia*, 1971, **20**, 197-200.

Engel, J., Hanson, L. C. F., Roos, B. E., & Strombergsson, L. E. Effect of electroshock on dopamine metabolism in rat brain. *Psychopharmacologia*, 1968, **13**, 140-144.

Essman, W. B. Neurochemical changes in ECS and ECT. *Seminars in Psychiatry*, 1972, **4**, 67-79.

Garattini, S., Kato, R., Lamesta, L., & Valzelli, L. Electroshock, brain serotonin and barbiturate narcosis. *Experientia*, 1960, **16**, 156-157.

Garattini, S., & Valzelli, L. In S. Garattini & B. Ghetti (Eds.), *Psychotropic drugs*. Amsterdam: Elsevier, 1957.

Hinesley, R. K., Norton, J. A., & Aprison, M. H. Serotonin, norepinephrine and 3,4-dihydroxyphenylethylamine in rat brain parts following electroconvulsive shock. *Journal of Psychiatric Research*, 1968, **6**, 143-152.

Holmberg, G. Biological aspects of electroconvulsive therapy. *International Review of Neurobiology*, 1963, **5**, 389-412.

Kato, L., Gozsy, B., Roy, P. B., & Groh, V. Histamine, serotonin, epinephrine and norepinephrine in the rat brain, following convulsions. *International Journal of Neuropsychiatry*, 1967, **3**, 46-51.

Kety, S. S. The biogenic amines in the central nervous system: Their possible roles in arousal, emotion and learning. In F. O. Schmitt (Ed.), *The neurosciences: Second Study Program*. New York: Rockefeller University Press, 1971. (a)

Kety, S. S. Brain amines and affective disorders: An overview. In B. T. Ho & W. M. McIsaac (Eds.), *Brain chemistry and mental disease*. New York: Plenum Press, 1971. (b)

Kety, S. S., Javoy, F., Thierry, A. M., Julou, L., & Glowinski, J. A sustained effect of electroconvulsive shock on the turnover of norepinephrine in the central nervous system of the rat. *Proceedings of the National Academy of Sciences of the United States of America*, 1967, **58**, 1249-1254.

Kety, S. S., Woodford, R. B., Harmel, M. H., Freyhan, F. A., Appel, K. E., & Schmidt, C. F. Cerebral blood flow and metabolism in schizophrenia. The effects of barbiturate semi-narcosis, insulin coma and electroshock. *American Journal of Psychiatry*, 1948, **104**, 765-770.

Kopin, I. J. Communication. San Juan, P. R., April 24, 1972.

Ladisich, W., Steinhauff, N., & Matussek, N. Chronic administration of electroconvulsive shock and norepinephrine metabolism in the rat brain. *Psychopharmacologia*, 1969, **15**, 296-304.

MacInnes, J. W., McConkey, E. H., & Schlesinger, K. Changes in brain polyribosomes following an electroconvulsive seizure. *Journal of Neurochemistry*, 1970, **17**, 457-460.

Musacchio, J. M., Julou, L., Kety, S. S., & Glowinski, J. Increase in rat brain tyrosine hydroxylase activity produced by electroconvulsive shock. *Proceedings of the National Academy of Sciences of the United States of America*, 1969, **63**, 1117-1119.

Nordin, G., Ottosson, J. -O., & Roos, B. E. Influence of convulsive therapy on 5-hydroxyindoleacetic acid and homovanillic acid in cerebrospinal fluid in endogenous depression. *Psychopharmcologia*, 1971, **20**, 315-320.

Pryor, G. T. Effect of repeated ECS on brain weight and brain enzymes. This volume.

Rosenblatt, S., Chanley, J. D., Sobotka, H., & Kaufman, M. R. Interrelationships between electroshock, the blood-brain barrier, and catecholamines. *Journal of Neurochemistry*, 1960, **5**, 172-176.

Schildkraut, J. J. *Neuropsychopharmacology and the affective disorders*. Boston: Little, Brown, 1970.

Schildkraut, J. J., & Kety, S. S. Biogenic amines and emotion. *Science*, 1967, **156**, 21-30.

Schildkraut, J. J., Schanberg, S. M., Bresse, G. R., & Kopin, I. J. Norepinephrine metabolism and drugs used in the affective disorders: A possible mechanism of action. *American Journal of Psychiatry*, 1967, **124**, 600-608.

Schmidt, C. F., Kety, S. S., & Pennes, H. S. The gaseous metabolism of the brain of the monkey. *American Journal of Physiology*, 1945, **143**, 33-52.

Shatalova, A. A., & Antonov, E. K. Content of adrenaline and noradrenaline in adrenal and brain tissues and in blood of rabbits in convulsive states. *Psychopharmacology Abstracts*, 1961, **1**, 341.

AUTHOR INDEX

Numbers in italics refer to the pages on which the complete references are listed.

A

Abra, J. C., 24, *32,* 204, *205*
Abrams, R., 3, 4, 5, 6, 11, *14, 17,* 22, 23, 24, *32,* 35, 37, *38, 39, 40,* 61, *62, 63,* 80, 81, *83,* 201, 204, *205, 206,* 273, 274, *276, 277*
Agle, D. P., 23, 24, *34*
Agranoff, B. W., 87, *94,* 192, *195,* 238, *249*
Ailion, J., 149, *168*
Aird, R. B., 211, *218*
Alan, B., 4, 5, *15,* 21, *32,* 37, *40,* 129, *140*
Alberici, M., 262, *266*
Alexandrovskaia, M. M., *195*
Allan, B., 74, *76*
Alpern, H. P., 88, 89, 91, *94, 95, 96,* 107, 114, *126,* 129, 130, 134, *140,* 192, *197*
Altschule, M. D., 213, *218*
Anchel, D., 79, *83*
Andersen, P., 258, *265*
Andersson, S. A., 258, *265*
Angel, C., 212, *218*
Anton, A. H., 144, 166, *168, 169,* 210, *218*
Antonov, E. K., 143, *170,* 233, *235,* 288, *293*
Appel, K. E., 287, *293*

Appel, S. H., 193, 194, *195, 196*
Aprison, M. H., 148, *169, 234,* 288, 289, *293*
Arduini, A., 254, *265*
Arnaiz, G., 262, *266*
Aron, C., 88, *96*
Astrachan, M., 85, *95*
Austin, L., 193, *195, 197*
Autilio, L., 193, *195*
Ax, A. F., *227*
Axelrod, J., 144, 145, 152, *168, 169, 170,* 231, 232, *234*
Azcurra, J. M., 75, *77,* 262, *269*
Azmitia, E. C., Jr., 90, *96*

B

Banker, G., 92, *94,* 186, 187, 190, 192, 194, *195, 196,* 238, *249,* 291, *292*
Banks, P., 192, *196*
Barbizet, J., 213, *218*
Barker, L. A., 222, *228*
Barnes, L., 253, *260,* 263, *266*
Barondes, S. H., 87, *94,* 192, *195,* 238, *249*
Barrera, S. E., 201, *207*
Barrett, R. J., 114, *127,* 133, *141,* 192, *197*
Bartlett, F. C., *205*
Bazán, N. G., 194, *195*

295

Bell, F. K., 65, *76*
Belton, G. P., 24, *32,* 204, *205*
Bennett, E., 260, *270*
Bennett, G. S., 191, 192, *195*
Bennett, P. J., 74, *76*
Berg, S., 61, *62*
Bergman, P. S., 61, *62*
Berkey, B., 23, 26, *33*
Berlyne, N., 212, *218*
Bernard, L. E., 79, *83*
Bernard, P., 289, *292*
Bernasconi, S., 222, 227, *229*
Bertaccini, G., 221, *227,* 288, *292*
Bidder, T. G., 23, 24, *32, 34,* 75, *76,* 80, *83, 84*
Billiet, M., 289, *292*
Birtchnell, J., 22, 23, 24, 26, *34,* 201, 203, *207*
Bisiani, M., 221, *227*
Bittman, R., 237, 238, 241, *249*
Bivens, L. W., 114, *127*
Bjerner, B., 211, *218*
Blaber, L. C., 252, 253, 256, 258, 259, 260, 261, 262, 264, *265, 267*
Blachly, P. H., 5, *14,* 61, *62,* 79, *83,* 274, *276*
Black, H., 192, *196*
Blackburn, J. M., 75, *77*
Blacker, K. H., 82, *83,* 201, 202, *206*
Blaurock, M. F., 36, *39,* 61, *62*
Bliss, E. L., 149, *168,* 211, *218*
Bloch, V., 138, *140*
Blomquist, C., 201, *205*
Blomstrand, C., 192, *196*
Blum, B., 256, *265*
Board, F., 211, *218*
Bodley, P., 23, 24, 26, 31, *32*
Boggan, W., 259, 261, *269*
Bohdanecky, Z., 88, *95,* 129, 130, *140*
Bolin, B. J., 24, *33*
Boling, L., 166, *169,* 210, *219*
Bonavita, V., 194, *197,* 237, *249*
Bone, A. D., 210, *219*
Bonnycastle, D. D., 288, *292*
Bowman, L., 274, *277*
Bowman, R., 61, *62*
Bowman, R. E., 89, *94*
Branch, C. H. H., 211, *218*
Braun, H. W., 172, *183*
Bray, J. J., 193, *195*
Breese, G. R., 143, 144, 145, 147, 161, 164, 165, *168, 170,* 231, 233, *235*

Breitner, C., 143, *168,* 221, 224, *227, 228,* 233, *234,* 288, *292*
Bresnahan, E., 93, *94*
Bresse, G. R., 288, *293*
Bridenbaugh, R. H., 80, *83*
Brinegar, W. C., 35, *40*
Brodie, B. B., 222, *229*
Brody, M. B., 75, *76*
Broman, T., 211, *218*
Brown, D. M., 191, *197*
Brown, W. C., 232, *235*
Browne, M. W., 23, 24, 26, 31, *33*
Bruce, E. M., 272, *276*
Brune, G. G., 227, *228*
Brunschwig, L., 23, 24, *32, 34,* 75, *76*
Buckholtz, N. S., 89, *94*
Bueno, O. F., 92, *94*
Bunk, J. J., 193, 194, *197*
Bureš, J., 192, *196*
Burešová, O., 192, *196*
Burton, L. E., 221, 224, *228*
Bush, D. F., 107, 109, *127*

C

Cadilhac, J. G., 213, *219*
Cajal, S. R., 116, *126*
Camarda, R., 194, *197*
Cameron, D. E., 79, *83*
Cannicott, S. M., 22, 23, 24, *32,* 204, *205*
Carr, C. J., 65, *76*
Carr, H. E., 144, *170*
Cascorbi, H. F., 138, *140*
Chanley, J. D., 166, *169,* 212, *219,* 287, *293*
Chase, T. N., 165, *168*
Chatrian, G. E., 61, *62,* 75, *76,* 130, *140*
Cherkin, A., 88, 89, 90, *94,* 107, *126,* 129, 230, 131, 132, 133, 135, 137, *140, 141*
Chernik, D. A., 42, *46*
Chevalier, J. A., 90, *94*
Chin, L., 143, *168,* 221, 224, *227, 228,* 233, *234,* 288, *292*
Chorover, S. L., 88, *94,* 130, 138, *140, 141,* 202, *205*
Chronister, R. B., 93, *96*
Clarke, D. D. A., 144, *170*
Clemedson, C. -J., 212, *218*
Cohen, B. D., 24, *32*
Cohen, H. B., 41, 42, *46*
Cohen, H. D., 192, *195*

Cohen, J., 37, *39*
Cohn, R., 199, 200, *205*
Coleman, R., 91, *95*
Collins, R. C., 191, *196*
Colwell, J. J., 171, 172, 174, *184*
Conner, H. S., 101, 125, *126*
Cooper, A. J., *168*, 224, *228*, 288, 289, *292*
Coppen, A., 10, *14*, 213, 214, *218*, 291, *292*
Costello, C. G., 24, *32*, 204, *205*
Cotman, C. W., 92, *94*, 186, 187, 190, 192, 194, *195*, *196*, 238, *249*, 291, *292*
Crawford, J. M., 252, *265*
Cremerius, J., 35, *40*
Crone, N., 272, *276*
Cronholm, B., 22, 25, 27, *32*, 85, 87, *94*, 138, *140*, 201, 203, *205*, 213, *218*
Cronin, D., 23, 24, 26, 31, *32*
Crossland, J., 261, *269*
Cuddy, L., 25, *33*
Curtis, D. R., 252, *265*
Curtis, G. C., 166, *170*, 210, *219*
Curzon, G., 211, *218*
Cuthbert, A. W., 256, 258, 260, 262, *265*

D

Davis, J. M., 2, *16*
Davison, K., 23, 24. 26. 31. *33*
Dawson, R. G., 86, 87, 91, *94*, *95*
Day, R., 200, *206*
Deadwyler, S. A., 93, *94*, 101, *127*
Dean, W., 87, *96*
Deguchi, T., 253, *267*
Dekirmenjian, H., 144, *168*
De la Torre, J. C., 261, 264, *265*
Delaunois, A., 289, *292*
de L. Horne, D. J., 23, 24, 31, *33*
d'Elia, G., 22. 23. *32*, 37, *40*, 61, *62*, 85, *94*, *140*
Dello Russo, G., 24, *32*
DeLuca, A. M., 130, 138, *140*
Dement, W. C., 41, 42, 43, 44, 45, *46*
Dennis, M. S., 74, *76*
DeRobertis, E., 262, *266*
DeSchaepdryver, A., 289, *292*
de Vito, R. A., 23, *32*
DiMascio, A., 166, *169*, 210, *219*
DiPerri, R., 23, *32*
Dodge, G. A., 147, *170*
Dolenz, B. J., 129, *140*

Domino, E. F., 258, *266*, *267*
Dorfman, L. F., 88, 89, *94*, 107, 109, 114, *126*, 192, *196*
Dornbush, R. L., 4, 6, 11, *14*, 24, 25, *32*, 35, 37, *38*, *39*, *40*, 61, *62*, *63*, 85, *94*, 199, 201, *205*, *206*, 273, *276*
Doty, R. W., 93, *95*, 101, 115, *126*
Drake, F. R., 80, *83*
Draskoczy, P. R., 152, 153, 167, *170*, 234, *235*
Dren, A. T., 258, *266*
Driscoll, D. A., 130, *141*
Drujan, B. D., 166, *170*, 210, *219*
Duffy, J. P., 23, 24, *34*
Duncan, C. P., 94, 279, *283*
Duncan, R. F., II, 41, 42, *46*
Dunn, A. J., 185, 186, 187, 191, 193, *196*, 238, *249*
Dunn, B. E., 24, *32*, 204, *205*
Dunne, D., 23, 24, *34*
Durell, J., 144, *170*

E

Eades, C. G., 254, *269*
Eccles, J. C., 252, 254, *265*, *266*
Edelman, G. M., 191, 192, *195*
Elashoff, R. M., 82, *83*, 201, 202, *206*
Elithorn, A., 214, *218*
Elliott, K., 261, *270*
Emde, J. W., 57, *62*
Emley, G., 192, *197*
Engel, J., *168*, *169*, 288, 289, *292*
Escueta, A. V., 193, 194, *195*, *196*
Esecover, H., 7, 12, *15*
Esquibel, A. J., 4, 5, *16*, 65, 74, *76*, 129, *141*
Esplin, D. W., 253, 254, *266*
Essman, W. B., 82, *83*, 168, *169*, 187, 193, 194, *196*, 221, 222, 224, 226, *228*, 237, 238, 239, 241, 244, 245, *249*, 261, *266*, 288, *293*
Everett, G. M., 261, *269*
Exner, J. E., 79, *83*

F

Farrell, W., 115, *126*, 200, *206*
Fatt, P., 254, *266*
Feighner, J. P., 66, *76*
Feinstein, R., 61, *62*
Feldberg, W., 253, *266*

Feldstein, S., 4, 6, 11, *14, 17,* 35, 37, *38, 39,* 61, *62, 63,* 273, 274, *276, 277*
Festoff, B. W., 193, *195*
Finger, F. W., 253, *266,* 279, *283*
Fink, M., 4, 5, 6, 7, 9, 10, 11, 12, 13, *14, 15, 16, 17,* 21, 24, *32,* 35, 36, 37, *38, 39, 40,* 61, *62, 63,* 74, *76,* 80, 81, *83,* 86, *94,* 129, *140,* 201, *206,* 259, 261, 265, *266,* 272, 273, 274, 275, *276, 277*
Fink, R. P., 116, *126*
Fischer, A., 82, *83,* 201, 202, *206*
Fischer-Williams, M., 259, 264, *266*
Fitzpatrick, G., 272, *276*
Fleming, T. C., 8, *15*
Fleminger, J. J., 23, 24, 31, *33*
Flexner, J. B., 192, *196,* 238, *249*
Flexner, L. B., 192, *196,* 238, *249*
Fonnum, F., 256, *266*
Ford, H. D., 22, 23, 24, *33*
Franklin, M. J., 144, *170*
Freedman, D., 259, 261, *269*
Freedman, N. L., 192, *196*
Frewin, S. J., 272, *276*
Freyhan, F. A., 287, *293*
Frost, I., 24, 26, *33*
Fulcher, J. K., 90, *95*

G

Gaddum, J. H., 258, 262, *266*
Gambetti, P. L., 193, *195*
Gander, D. R., 74, *76*
Garattini, S., 168, *169,* 221, 222, *227, 228,* 288, *293*
Gardner, R. K., 23, 24, 26, 31, *32*
Garrett, E. S., 79, *83*
Gastaut, H., 259, 264, *266*
Geiger, A., 187, 192, *196*
Geller, A., 88, 90, *94, 96,* 100, *126,* 202, *206,* 281, *283*
Gerard, R. W., *94,* 192, *197,* 279, *283*
Ghezzi, D., 222, *229*
Giacalone, E., 222, *228*
Giaquinto, D., 115, *126*
Giarman, N. J., 263, *266,* 288, *292*
Gibbs, F. A., 36, *39,* 61, *62*
Giberti, F., *33*
Gibson, E., 261, *269*
Gillis, A., 272, *276*
Gitlow, S. E., 144, *170*
Giuditta, A., 185, 187, 188, *196, 197*

Gleser, G. C., 4, *17*
Glickman, S. E., 86, 87, *94,* 115, *126,* 280, *283*
Glisson, S. N., Jr., 253, 260, 263, *266*
Glowinski, J., 145, 149, 156, 167, *169, 170,* 181, *184,* 231, 232, 233, *234, 235,* 288, 289, 290, *293*
Glueck, B. C., Jr., 79, *83*
Goddard, G. V., 115, *126*
Goff, W., 200, *206*
Gold, P. E., 89, 90, 91, 92, 93, *94, 95,* 115, *126,* 138, *140,* 200, 202, *206,* 280, *283*
Goldberg, H. C., 288, 289, *292*
Goldberg, M. E., 222, *228*
Goldfien, A., 166, *169*
Gonzalez, C. R., 66, *77*
Goodman, L. S., 22, *34,* 232, *235*
Gordon, E. K., 144, 165, *168, 169, 170*
Gordon, H. L., *15*
Gordon, R., 149, *169*
Gottlieb, G., 24, *33, 34*
Gowing, D., 5, 61, *62,* 79, *83,* 274, *276*
Gozsy, B., 143, *169,* 221, 224, *228,* 233, *235,* 288, 289, *293*
Graber, H. K., 79, *83*
Gravenstein, J. S., 166, *169,* 210, *218*
Green, J., 4, 7, 10, *16,* 36, 39, *40,* 217, *219,* 274, *277*
Green, M. A., 4, 5, 6, *15,* 21, *32,* 37, *40,* 74, *76,* 129, *140*
Green, W. J., 42, *46*
Greenblatt, M., 3, *15, 272, 277*
Greenough, W. T., 90, *95*
Griek, B., 261, *269*
Grinker, R. R., 75, *77*
Griswold, R. L., 166, *169,* 210, *218*
Groh, V., 143, *169,* 221, 224, *228,* 233, *235,* 288, 289, *293*
Gross, M., 211, *219*
Grosser, G. H., 3, *15, 272, 277*
Guldberg, H. C., *168,* 224, *228*
Gulevich, G., 42, 43, 44, 45, *46*
Guterman, B., 7, *16*
Guttormsen, D. M., 256, *266*
Guze, S. B., 66, *76*
Gygax, P. A., 116, *127*
Gynther, M. D., 66, *77*

H

Haba, R., 259, *269*
Härkönen, M., 255, *266*

Halliday, A. M., 23, 24, 26, 31, *33*
Handcock, K. A., 79, *83*
Hanigan, W. C., 260, 262, 263, *266*
Hanlon, T. E., 4, 5, *16*
Hanson, L. C. F., 168, *169*, 288, 289, 292
Hargreaves, W. A., 82, *83*, 201, 202, *206*
Harmel, M. H., 287, *293*
Hartelius, H., 212, *218*
Hartwig, C. D., 42, *46*
Havens, L. L., 166, *169*, 210, *219*
Haycock, J. W., 89, 90, 91, 92, *95*, 202, *206*
Hebb, D. O., 203, *206*
Heilbrunn, G., 263, *266*
Heimer, L., 116, *126*
Heldman, E., 222, *228*, 237, 238, 241, *249*
Herz, M. J., 86, 87, 88, 90, 93, *95*, *96*, 100, 101, 114, 115, *126*, *127*, 137, *141*, 280, *283*
Hess, W. R., 215, *219*
Hickman, C., 37, *40*
Himwich, H. E., 258, *266*, *269*
Hinesley, R. K., 148, *169*, *234*, 288, 289, *293*
Hoagland, H., 4, *15*, 35, *40*
Holmberg, G., 8, *15*, 212, *218*, *219*, 221, 228, 231, *235*, 286, *293*
Holmstedt, B., 253, 255, *266*, *267*
Horvath, N., 187, 192, *196*
Humphrey, G., 264, *267*
Hunt, E. B., 107, 109, *127*
Hunt, H. F., 86, *95*, 279, *283*
Hunt, J. R., 265, *267*

I

Impastato, D. J., 22, 24, 26, *33*, 61, *62*
Inglis, J., 25, *33*, 199, 200, *206*
Isaković, K., 193, 194, *197*
Itil, T., 37, *40*
Iversen, L. L., 149, *170*
Iwata, N., 253, *267*

J

Jacoby, M. C., 79, *83*
Jaffe, J., 7, 12, *15*
Jamieson, J. L., 88, 89, *95*
Janis, I. L, 85, *95*
Janković, B. D., 193, 194, *197*

Jarvik, M. E., 88, 89, 90, 91, *94*, *95*, *96*, 100, 107, 109, 114, *126*, 129, 130, 137, *140*, *141*, 192, *196*, *197*, 202, *206*
Jasper, H. J., 264, 265, *270*
Javoy, F., 149, 156, 167, *169*, *170*, 181, *184*, 232, 233, *235*, 288, 289, *293*
Johnson, L. C., 36, *40*
Johnson, M., 36, *40*
Jonas, M. A., 80, *84*
Jones, A. L., 7, 10, 12, *16*
Jones, C. T., 192, *196*
Jonsson, L. E., 11, *15*
Julou, L., 156, 167, *169*, 181, *184*, 232, 233, 234, *235*, 288, 289, 290, *293*
Jung, R., 35, *40*, 214, *219*

K

Kaelbling, R., 22, *34*, 42, *46*
Kafi, A., 74, *76*
Kahn, R. L., 4, 5, 6, 7, 9, 10, 12, *15*, *16*, 17, 21, *32*, 35, 36, 37, 39, *40*, 74, *76*, 129, *140*, 273, 274, 275, *277*
Kalinowsky, L., 2, *16*, 35, *40*
Kallio, I. V. I., 211, *219*
Kandel, E. R., 265, *269*
Kapp, B., 88, *96*
Karczmar, A. G., 252, 253, 254, 255, 256, 257, 258, 259, 260, 261, 262, 263, 264, *265*, *266*, *267*, 268, *269*, *270*
Kariya, T., 259, 260, *269*
Karliner, W., 22, 24, 26, *33*, 65, 74, *76*
Karp, E., 4, 5, 7, *15*, *16*, 21, *32*, 37, *40*, 74, 76, 129, *140*
Katenelbogen, S., 36, *40*
Kato, L., 143, *169*, 221, 224, *228*, 233, *235*, 288, 289, *293*
Kato, M., 259, *268*, *269*
Kato, R., 221, 227, *228*, 288, *293*
Kaufman, I. C., 4, *15*, 35, *40*
Kaufman, K. P., 93, *96*
Kaufman, M. R., 212, *219*, 287, *293*
Kawakita, Y., 187, 192, *196*
Kawamura, H., 258, *267*
Kawanaga, H. M., 261, 264, *265*
Kay, D. W. K., 4, 7, 10, *16*, 36, 39, *40*, 217, *219*, 274, *277*
Keddie, K. M. G., 23, 24, *34*
Kelly, D. H. W., 74, *76*

Kennedy, C. J. C., 79, *83*
Kesner, R. P., 93, *95,* 101, 115, 125, *126, 127*
Kety, S. S., 149, 156, 167, *169, 170,* 181, *184,* 227, *229,* 232, 233, 234, *235,* 287, 288, 289, 290, 291, *293*
Kidokoro, Y., 253, 264, *267, 268*
Kimble, D. P., 129, 130, 134, *140*
Kimura, D., 25, *33,* 199, 200, *206*
King, C. D., 43, *46*
King, L. J., 190, *196*
King, P. D., 79, *83*
King, R. A., 115, *126,* 200, *206*
Kishore, B., 138, *141*
Kitamura, R., 264, *268*
Klein, D. F., 2, *16*
Knight, D. R., 23, 24, 31, *34,* 61, *63*
Knook, H. L., 116, *126*
Koelle, G. B., 252, 253, *268*
Kohl, H. H., 75, *77,* 262, *269*
Koketsu, K., 252, 254, 264, *266, 268*
Kopin, I. J., 143, 144, 145, 147, 165, *168, 169, 170,* 231, 232, 233, *234, 235,* 288, 290, *293*
Kopp, R., 88, 91, *95,* 129, 130, *140,* 192, *196*
Koppanyi, T., 254, 256, 257, *265, 267*
Korin, H., 4, *16*
Koski, E. G., 42, *46*
Kral, P., 200, *206*
Krantz, J. C., Jr., 4, 5, *16,* 65, 74, *76,* 77, 129, 138, *141*
Krech, D., 260, *270*
Kreeger, L. C., 23, 24, 26, 31, *33*
Kreinicke, C. J., 101, *126*
Krip, G., 265, *270*
Křivaněk, J., 191, 192, *196*
Krnjević, K., 252, 253, 265, *268*
Kruglikov, R. I., *195*
Kubota, K., 253, 264, *267, 268*
Kupfermann, I., 192, *196*
Kurland, A. A., 4, 5, *16,* 65, 74, *76,* 129, *141*
Kurokawa, M., 259, *268, 269*
Kwalwasser, S., 4, *16*

L

Ladisich, W., 156, *169,* 181, *184,* 234, *235,* 289, 290, *293*
Lagergren, A., 201, 203, *205*
Lamar, C., 262, *268*

Lamesta, L., 288, *293*
Lancaster, N., 24, 26, *33*
Landfield, P. W., 100, *127,* 280, *283*
Landis, D. H., 164, *169*
Langlois, J. M., 254, *268*
Lascelles, C. F., 272, *276*
Laurell, B., 21, *33,* 61, *62,* 74, 77, 129, 130, 137, *141,* 213, *219,* 272, 277
Lechner, H., 265, *268*
Lee-Teng, E., 91, *95,* 109, 114, 115, *126,* 138, *141,* 192, *196*
Lefevre, D., 139, *141*
Lefkowits, H. J., 4, 5, *15,* 21, *32,* 37, *40,* 74, *76,* 129, *140*
Lennox, M. A., 7, *16*
Levene, L. J., 272, *276*
Levine, M. S., 101, *126*
Levy, N. A., 75, *77*
Levy, R., 23, 24, *33,* 201, 204, *206*
Lewis, D. J., 87, 90, *95,* 138, *141*
Lewis, P. R., 252, *268*
Liberson, W. T., 22, *33,* 213, *219*
Lidsky, T. I., 101, *126*
Lindsay, P. H., 25, *33, 34*
Ling, A. S. C., 65, 74, *76,* 129, 138, *141*
Ling, J. S. L., 65, *77*
Lishman, W. A., 213, *219*
Lo, P. S., 152, 153, *167, 170*
Loecher, C. K., 138, *140*
Logue, M. A., 147, *170*
Lohrenz, J. G., 79, *83*
Longo, V. G., 252, 254, 255, 258, 259, 265. *268*
Lorimer, F. M., 36, *39,* 61, *62*
Lovell, R. A., 264, *268*
Lowry, O. H., 190, *196*
Lu, G., 65, *76,* 77
Lundgren, J., 255, *266*
Luttges, M. W., 90, *95*

M

Maas, J. W., 144, 164, *168, 169*
McAdam, D. W., 200, *206*
McAndrew, J., 23, 26, *33*
McBride, W. J., 192, *197*
McConkey, E. H., 188, *196,* 292, *293*
McCoy, F., 114, *127*
McDonald, E. C., 22, 23, 24, *33*
McDonald, I. M., 272, *277*
McDonough, J. H., Jr., 93, *95,* 101, *127*
McEachern, D., 261, *270*

McEwen, B. S., 90, *96,* 192, *197*
McGaugh, J. L., 86, 87, 88, 89, 90, 91, 92, 93, *94, 95, 96, 97,* 100, 102, 103, 105, 106, 107, 108, 109, 111, 113, 114, 115, *126, 127, 128,* 130, 137, 138, *140, 141,* 186, 187, 190, 192, 194, *196, 197,* 202, *206,* 238, *249,* 280, *283,* 291, *292*
Machiyama, Y., 259, *268*
Machne, X., 254, 255, *265, 268*
McHugh, R. B., 79, *83*
McIlwain, H., 222, *228*
MacInnes, J. W., 188, *196,* 292, *293*
McIntyre, D. C., 115, *127*
MacLean, P. D., 254, *268*
Macri, J., 89, 90, 91, 92, 93, *95,* 202, *206*
Maher, B. A., 87, *95*
Mahler, H. R., 192, *197*
Mahut, H., 101, 115, *127*
Malamud, W., 4, *15,* 35, *40*
Man, P. L., 24, *33*
Manacorda, A., 22, *34*
Marczynski, T. J., 254, *269*
Marjerrison, G., 61, *62,* 272, 274, *277*
Martin, G., 107, 109, *127*
Martin, W. L., 22, 23, 24, *33*
Martin, W. R., 254, *269*
Masserman, J. H., 215, *219*
Mastrosimone, F., 22, *34*
Mathas, J., 74, *77*
Mather, M. D., 23, 24, 26, 31, *32*
Matthew, C., 23, 26, *33*
Matussek, N., 156, *169,* 181, *184,* 234, *235,* 289, 290, *293*
Mayer-Gross, W., 85, 87, *95,* 201, 203, *206,* 279, *283*
Meduna, L. J., 212, *219*
Meduri, M., 23, *32*
Megna, G., 23, *32*
Mendels, J., 42, *46*
Mendlowitz, M., 144, *170*
Mersky, H., 272, *276*
Messiha, F. S., 166, *169*
Messina, C., 23, *32*
Meyer, A., 139, *141*
Meyer, V., 25, *33*
Migeon, C. J., 211, *218*
Mihailović, L., 193, 194, *197*
Millar, E., 4, 8, 10, *16,* 203, *206*
Miller, A. J., 89, 90, *96,* 109, *127*
Miller, R. R., 90, *95, 96,* 138, *141*
Milligan, W. L., 79, *83*

Millman, N., 222, *229*
Milner, B., 25, *33, 34,* 199, 200, *206*
Milstein, V., 48, *62*
Misanin, J. R., 90, *95,* 138, *141*
Mockbee, C. W., 79, *83*
Moir, A. T. B., *168,* 224, *228,* 288, 289, *292*
Molander, L., 27, *32,* 201, *205,* 213, *218*
Montagu, J. D., 210, *219*
Moore, D. F., 48, *62,* 272, *277*
Moore, W. J., 192, *197*
Morgan, I. G., 193, *195, 197*
Moriarty, J. D., 36, *40*
Morrell, F., 253, *269*
Morrell, L. K., 200, *206*
Mosovich, A., 36, *40*
Mullan, S., 261, 264, *265*
Muller, D. J., 26, *34*
Munn, N. L., 279, *283*
Munoz, R., 66, *76*
Murillo, L. G., 79, *83*
Musacchio, J. M., 156, *169,* 181, *184,* 233, 234, *235,* 290, *293*

N

Nair, N. P. V., 23, 24, 31, *33*
Naruse, H., 259, *269*
Nasu, H., 194, *197*
Nasu, T., 259, 260, *269*
Nauta, W. J. H., 116, 117, *127*
Neff, N. H., 222, *229*
Neki, J. S., 138, *141*
Nelson, D. H., 211, *218*
Nielson, H. C., 90, *96*
Nishi, S., 252, 253, 259, 260, 261, 264, *267, 269*
Noach, E. L., 193, 194, *197*
Noblin, C. D., 24, *32*
Nordin, G., 166, *169,* 289, *293*
Norton, J. A., 148, *169,* 234, 288, 289, *293*
Nott, P. N., 23, 24, 31, *33*

O

Ohlsson, W. G., 75, *77,* 262, *269*
Okumura, N., 194, *197*
Oliver, J. E., 23, 24, 31, *34,* 61, *63*
Olivier, A., 252, *269*
O'Regan, T. J., 80, *83*
Otis, L. S., 171, 172, 174, 177, 181, *184*

Otsuki, S., 194, *197*
Ottosson, J.-O., 4, 8, 10, *16*, 21, 22, *32,
*34, 36, *40*, 138, 139, *140, 141*, 166,
169, 201, 202, *206*, 209, 213, 214,
218, 219, 231, *235*, 272, 274, 275,
277, 289, *293*

P

Paasonen, M. K., 288, *292*
Padula, L., 65, 74, *76*
Pagano, R. R., 107, 109, *127*
Pagliuca, N., 185, *196*
Pancheri, P., 24, *34*
Parent, A., 252, *269*
Passonneau, J. V., 190, *196*
Patton, R. A., 172, *183*
Peache, S., 171, 177, 178, 181, 182, *184*
Pearlman, C. A., 192, *197*
Pecile, A., 224, *228*
Peeke, H. V. S., 90, 93, *95, 96*, 101, 114,
115, *126, 127*
Pennes, H. S., 287, *293*
Pepeu, G., 263, *266*
Perez, H. C., 23, *34*, 48, *62*
Perez, R. E., 138, 139, *141*
Perkins, M., 272, *277*
Perris, C., 22, *32*, 37, *40*, 61, *62*
Petersen, M. C., 61, *62*, 75, *76*, 130, *140*
Petković, M., 193, 194, *197*
Petrinovich, L. F., 87, *96*
Pettis, P., 193, *195*
Picchioni, A., 143, *168*, 221, 224, *227,
*228, 233, *234*, 288, *292*
Piccoli, F., 194, *197*, 237, *249*
Pincus, G., 4, *15*, 35, *40*
Pinel, J. P. J., 138, *141*
Pinsky, C., 265, *270*
Pittinger, C. B., 138, 139, *141*
Plum, F., 191, *196*, 212, *219*
Podilsky, M., 272, *277*
Poirier, L. J., 252, *269*
Pollack, M., 4, 5, 7, 12, *15, 16*, 21, *32*, 37,
40, 74, *76*, 129, *140*
Pope, A., 264, 265, *270*
Posner, J. B., 191, *196*, 212, *219*
Potts, L., 23, 24, 26, 31, *32*
Poussart, Y., 254, *268*
Provost, C., 191, *197*
Pryer, R. S., 192, *197*

Pryor, G. T., *83*, 171, 172, 174, 175, 177,
178, 181, 182, *184*, 259, *269, 293*
Puca, F. M., 23, *32*
Pumain, R., 252, 253, *268*

Q

Quartermain, D., 90, *96*, 192, *197*

R

Ransmeier, R. E., 192, *197*
Rapaport, D., 191, *197*
Rawie, J., 91, *95*
Ray, O. S., 114, *127*, 133, *141*, 192, *197*
Reeves, C., 259, *269*
Reiss, H., 79, *83*
Renaud, L., 252, 253, *268*
Richardson, D., 255, 256, 260, 262, 263,
267
Richter, D., 261, *269*
Rifkin, M., 261, *269*
Rigbly, O., 264, *270*
Rinaldi, F., 22, *34*, 258, *269*
Roberts, A. J., 212, *218*
Roberts, R. B., 238, *249*
Roberts, S., 191, *197*
Robins, E., 66, *76*
Robustelli, F., 88, *96*
Roos, B. E., 166, 168, *169*, 288, 289, *292,
293
Rose, J. T., 6, *16*
Rosenbaum, A. L., 23, 24, *34*
Rosenblatt, S., 166, *169*, 212, *219*, 287,
293
Rosenzweig, M., 260, *270*
Ross, B., 93, *96*
Roth, M., 4, 7, 10, 12, *16*, 20, 36, 39, *40*,
217, *219*, 274, *277*
Rothschild, D., 79, *83*
Roubicek, J., 4, 6, 11, *14*, 37, *39*, 61, *62*,
273, *276*
Routtenberg, A., 93, *94*
Roy, P. B., 143, 221, 224, *228*, 233, *235*,
288, 289, *293*
Rubin, R. D., 138, *141*
Ruby, I. J., 211, *219*
Ruch, T. C., 7, *16*
Rush, S., 130, *141*
Russel, G. F. M., 213, *219*
Russell, R. W., 86, *96*, 172, *183*

S

Sakai, Y., 253, *267*
Salama, A. I., 222, *228*
Salamy, J., 200, *206*
Samuels, L. T., 211, *218*
Sara, S. J., 139, *141*
Sayre, D. F., 144, *168*
Scalon, W. G., 74, *77*
Schanberg, S. M., 143, 144, 145, 147, 161, 164, 165, *170*, 231, 232, 233, *235*, 288, *293*
Schildkraut, J. J., 143, 144, 145, 147, 152, 153, 161, 165, 167, 168, *170*, 227, *229*, 231, 232, 233, 234, *235*, 288, *294*
Schiller, P. H., 88, *94*, 202, *205*
Schlesinger, K., 188, *196*, 259, 261, *269*, 292, *293*
Schmidt, C. F., 287, *294*
Schneider, A. M., 88, *96*
Schuberth, J., 11, *15*
Schuck, S. L., 138, *141*
Schwartz, K. E., 101, *127*
Schwartzbaum, J. S., 101, *126*
Schwartzmann, A. E., 79, *83*
Schwitzgebel, R. L., 90, *95*
Scott, M. K., 171, 172, 174, 175, 177, 178, 181, 182, *184*
Scudder, C. L., 255, 256, 260, 261, 262, 263, *266, 267, 269*
Segal, M. M., 36, *39*, 61, *62*
Sellinger, O. Z., 75, *77*, 262, *266, 269*
Serota, H. M., 75, *77*
Shagass, C., 7, 10, 12, *16*
Shapiro, G., 37, *40*
Sharpley, P., 23, *34*, 48, *62*, 272, *277*
Shatalova, A. A., 143, *170*, 233, *235*, 288, *294*
Shaw, J., 4, 7, 10, *16*, 36, 39, *40*, 217, *219*, 274, *277*
Shea, J. J., 80, *84*
Sheets, C. S., 4, 5, *16*
Shinkman, P. G., 93, *96*
Shipton, H. W., 57, *62*
Shore, P. A., 231, *235*
Shulman, A. A., 138, *141*
Shute, C. C. D., 252, *268*
Shuto, S., 253, *267*
Siemens, J. C., 6, *40*
Silverman, A. J., 24, *32*
Silvestrini, B., 258, *268*

Simard, H., 252, *269*
Simmonds, M. A., 149, *170*
Sines, J. O., 36, *40*
Sjoerdsma, A., 149, *169*
Sjöstrand, T. 254, *269*
Skoglund, C. R., 253, *267*
Sloane, R. B., 210, *219*
Small, I. F., 5, 6, *16*, 23, *34*, 37, *40*, 48, *62, 65, 66, 77*, 129, 130, *141*, 272, *277*
Small, J. G., 5, 6, *16*, 23, *34*, 37, *40*, 48, *62, 65, 66, 77*, 129, 130, *141*, 272, *277*
Smith, K., 4, *17*, 36, *40*
Sobotka, H., 212, *219*, 287, *293*
Sobotka, T. J., 259, 261, 262, *267, 269*
Sourkes, T. L., 166, *170*, 210, *219*
Spector, S., 149, *169*
Speers, L., 65, *76*
Spencer, W. A., 265, *269*
Spevack, A. A., 87, *96*
Spooner, C. E., 130, *141*
Spreche, D., 74, *77*
Springer, A. D., 90, *96*
Squire, L. D., 87, *94*
Stajduhar, P. P., 42, *46*
Stanger, R. L., 222, *229*
Steinberg, H., 138, *141*
Steinert, R., 24, 26, *33*
Steinhauff, N., 156, *169*, 181, *184*, 234, *235*, 289, 290, *293*
Stellar, E., 192, *196*
Stephens, G., 88, *96*
Stones, M., 201, *206*
Strachan, M., 212, *218*
Strain, J. J., 23, 24, *32, 34*, 75, *76*, 80, *83*, 84
Strombergsson, L. E., 168, *169*, 289, *292*
Suboski, M. D., 87, *96*, 192, *196*
Sumino, R., 253, *267*
Sundvall, A., 255, *266*
Sundwall, A., 11, *15*
Sutherland, E. M., 23, 24, 31, *34*, 61, *63*
Suzuki, J., 253, 264, *268*
Swensson, A., 211, *218*
Swinyard, E. A., 22, *34*, 232, *235*, 264, *270*

T

Takahashi, R., 259, 260, *269*
Tala, E. O. J., 211, *219*

Tamura, T., 259, 260, *269*
Taylor, R. H., 211, *219*
Tebēcis, A. K., 252, *269*
Tedeschi, D. H., 22, *34*
Termansen, P. E., 79, *83*
Tetlow, A. G., 166, *169*, 210, *218*
Teuber, H. L., *34*
Thierry, A. M., 149, 156, 167, *169, 170*, 181, *184*, 232, 233, *235*, 288, 289, *293*
Thompson, R., 87, *96*, 192, *197*
Tillotson, J., 213, *218*
Timiras, P., 260, *270*
Tobin, J. C., 23, 24, 26, 31, *32*
Todd, R. E., 74, *76*
Toman, J., 260, *270*
Tomkiewicz, M., 138, *141*
Tooth, G., 75, *77*
Tower, D., 261, *270*
Towler, M. L., 22, 23, 24, *33*
Tozer, T. N., 222, *229*
Troy, B., 212, *219*
Truitt, E. B., Jr., 65, 74, *76*, 129, 138, *141*
Tulving, E., 25, *33, 34*
Turek, I., 166, *169*
Turner, E., 213, *219*

U

Udenfriend, S., 149, *169*
Ulett, G. A.. 4, *17*. 36. *40*
Unna, K. R. W., 254, 255, *268*
Usdin, E., 253, *270*

V

Valentine, M., 23, 24, *34*
Valsecchi, A., 224, *228*
Valzelli, L., 168, *169*, 221, 222, *227, 228, 229*, 288, *293*
Van Gordon, D. J., 79, *83*
Van Houten, Z., 79, *83*
Van Meter, W. G., 255, 257, 258, *270*
Vardaris, R. M., 101, *127*
Varjabedian, A., 79, *83*
Vazquez, A. J., 265, *270*
Venson, V., 190, *196*
Vesco, C., 188, *197*

Volavka, J., 4, 6, 10, 11, *14, 17*, 35, 37, *38, 39, 40*, 61, *62, 63*, 81, *83*, 273, 274, *276*, 277

W

Wadeson, R., 211, *218*
Waggoner, R. W., 22, 24, *32*, 204, *205*
Ward, A. A., Jr., 264, 265, *270*
Webster, K. E., 114, *127*
Wechsler, H., 3, *15*, 272, *277*
Weil, A. A., 35, *40*
Weil, P. L., 79, *84*
Weil-Malherbe, H., 144, 166, *170*, 210, *219*
Weinstein, E. A., 4, 9, 10, 12, *15, 17*
Weiskrantz, L., 88, *96*, 204, *206*
Weissman, A., 91, *96*
Whitaker, H. A., 200, *206*
Whitby, G., 144, *170*
White, F. P., 192, *197*
White, R. K., 80, *84*
Whitlock, D. G., 117, *127*
Whitty, C. W. M., 213, *219*
Wiener, S. M., 166, *169*, 210, *218*
Wijling, A., 193, 194, *197*
Wilburn, M. W., 101, *127*
Wilk, S., 144, *170*
Williams, M., 85, 87, *94, 96*, 201, 203, *206*
Willis, W. D., Jr., 252, *270*
Williston, J. S., 93, *96*, 101, 115, *127*
Wills, J. H., 252, 254, 256, *270*
Wilson, I. C., 24, *33, 34*
Wimer, R. E., 138, *141*
Winokur, G., 66, *76*
Wood, C., 200, *206*
Woodford, R. B., 287, *293*
Woodruff, R. A., Jr., 66, *76*
Woolley, D., 260, *270*
Workman, R. L., 264, *270*
Wyers, E. J., 93, *94, 96*, 101, 115, *127*

Y

Yabe, T., 259, *269*
Yamamoto, K., 258, *266*
Yates, A., 25, *33*
Yen, C. Y., 222, *229*

Z

Zablocka-Esplin, B., 253, 254, *266*
Zamora, E. N., 22, *34*
Zand, R., 75, *77*, 262, *269*
Zarcone, V., 42, 43, 44, 45, *46*
Zieher, L., 262, *266*
Zileli, M. S., 166, *169*, 210, *219*
Zinkin, S., 22, 23, 24, 26, *34*, 90, *96*,
  109, *127*, 201, 203, *207*

Zomzely, C. E., 191, *197*
Zornetzer, S. F., 89, 90, 91, 92, 93, *94, 96,*
  97, 102, 103, 105, 106, 108, 109,
  111, 113, 114, 115, 117, 119, 121,
  122, 123, 124, *127, 128,* 130, 137,
  141, 186, 187, 190, 192, 194, *196,*
  197, 238, *249,* 280, *283,* 291, *292*
Zubin, J., 201, *207*
Zwanziger, J., 149, *168*

SUBJECT INDEX

ECT and convulsive therapy are not indexed separately but are presumed to be the reference for all citations in the volume. ECT refers to seizures induced in man. Seizures induced in other species are labelled "ECS" and indexed.

A

Acetylcholine, 9, 10, 174, 183, 251, 274, 287
  brain, 251–252, 260
  and catecholamines, 253
  convulsive susceptibility, 259–261
  CSF, 261
  desynchronizing effects, 253, 258
  and ECS, 260, 262, 287
  EEG, 9, 174, 255–256, 258, 274
  focal spikes, 254–257
  seizures, 257, 261–265
  and serotonin, 253
  spinal cord, 253–254
Acetylcholinesterase (AChE), 174, 183, 252, 255, 290
  CSF, 261
  DFP, 257
  seizures, 260
n-Acetyl-5-hydroxytryptamine, 241
Adenosine triphosphate (ATP), 190–191
Adrenal cortex, 211, 217
Adrenal corticotrophic hormone (ACTH), 211, 286
Adrenal medulla, 210, 217

Aggressivity
  and 5-HT, 221–227
  in mice, isolated, 222
  in rats, 222
α-methyl-p-tyrosine, 258
Amino acids, 187, 238
Amitriptyline, 211
Amnesia
  anterograde, 27, 133, 137, 200–203
  retrograde, 24, 27–29, 43, 87–93, 100–101, 107, 110, 114–115, 129–130, 133, 136–137, 200–203, 237–239, 241, 279–282, 292
  convulsant drugs, 87–89
  and convulsions, 91
  gradient, 87, 114
  and midbrain, 125
  protein inhibition, 87–88
  protein synthesis, 192
  and seizures, 92–93, 285
Amphetamine, 258
Amygdala, 93, 101
Anesthesia, 136, 138
Anterograde amnesia (see Amnesia, anterograde)

Anterograde memory, 282
Anticholinergic drugs, 7, 10, 35–36, 265,
    272, 288
    and antidepressant drugs, 288
    and EEG, 7, 262, 272, 288
Anticholinesterase, 252
    desynchronizing effects. 253
    EEG, 255
    focal spikes, 254–257
    seizures, 253–257, 261, 264
    spinal reflex, 253–254
Antihistamine, 7, 10
Appetite, 6, 214
Aspartic acid, 187
Atropine, 252, 256, 265
    seizures, 256
    spinal reflex, 254
    synchronization, 259
Audiogenic seizure, 264
Avoidance learning, 129, 139

B

Basal ganglia, protein synthesis, ECS, 242–
    244
Benactyzine (see Anticholinergic drugs)
Betz cell, 252
Blood-brain barrier, 211, 217, 287
    and memory, 212
Brain
    norepinephrine uptake, 159–160, 163
    RNA and ECS, 185, 193–194
    seizure (see Seizure)
    stem, norepinephrine, 232–233
    weight, 174, 183
Bundle of Forel, 116–117
Butyrylcholinesterase (BuChE), 252, 255
    CSF, 261

C

California F Scale, 12
Carbon dioxide, 212, 217
Catecholamines
    and acetylcholine, 253
    brain, 9, 10, 210, 217
        and ECS, 23, 261
    cold exposure, 149–152
    mood, 231, 291
    and stress, 148–152
    therapeutic effects, 289–291
Catechol-O-methyl transferase, 155, 181,
    183

Caudate nucleus, 93, 101, 116, 179–180,
    252
    acetylcholine, 252
    cholinesterase, 252
    electrical stimulation, 116
    MAO activity, 179–180
    retrograde amnesia, 93, 101
Cerebellum, 159–163, 179–180, 242–
    244, 252
    acetylcholine, 252
    cholinesterase, 252
    MAO activity, 179–180
    norepinephrine turnover, 159–163
    protein synthesis, 242–244
Cerebral asymmetry, 38–39, 57–62
Cerebral cortex, 233
    acetylcholine, 252
    cholinesterase, 252
    norepinephrine, 233
    protein synthesis, 242–244, 247
    synaptosomes, 238
Cerebral dominance, 24, 282
Cerebrospinal fluid, acetylcholine, 261
Cerebrovascular permeability (see Blood-
    brain barrier)
Chlordiazepoxide, 226
Chlorpromazine, 211
Choline acetylase, 252
Cholinesterase, 174, 183, 252, 290
    seizures, 260
^{14}C-leucine, 185, 190, 194, 238, 240–
    244, 292
    and age, 240
Clonus, limb, 121
Cocaine, 212
Cold exposure and catecholamines, 149–152
Conditioned Emotional Respone (CER),
    86, 279
Confusion, 24, 29, 43, 69, 81–82
    post-ictal. 201
Consolidation, memory, 87–88, 282
Convulsion, 101, 130, 134, 279, 287
    and CER, 279
    cerebral blood flow, 287
    oxygen consumption, 287
Corpus callosum, 116
Cortex
    anterior, 115–116
    dorsal, 177–181
    frontal, 89, 102, 106–108, 110, 114,
        116
    posterior, 89, 91
    ventral, 177–180

Cortex (*Cont'd.*)
    whole, 159–160, 174, 177
Corticosteroids, blood, 286
Curare, 271
Current, electric
    antidepressant effects, 209
    duration, 100, 114
    intensity, 100, 104, 109, 113–115
    and memory, 203
    path, 108, 274
    protein synthesis, 190
Cycloheximide, 192–193

D

Denial, 7, 12
Depression
    endogenous, 31, 36, 43–45, 49, 67–69
    post-ictal, 115, 130
Deprivation, water, 106, 112, 120
Desipramine, 226
Desmethylimipramine (DMI), 145
    and ECS, 145–149
Desynchronization, EEG, 253, 258
    acetylcholine, 258
    amphetamine, 258
Diencephalon, 214–217, 275
    norepinephrine, 232–233
    protein synthesis, 238, 242–244
    sleep, 274
Diethazine (*see* Anticholinergic drugs)
Dihydro-β-erythroidine, 252
Diisopropyl phosphofluoridate (DFP)
    acetylcholinesterase, 257
    convulsions, 263
    ECS, 262–264
    and EEG, 256
Diphenhydramine (*see* Antihistamine)
Diphenylhydantoin, 211
Ditran (*see* Anticholinergic drugs)
Dopamine
    ECS, 260, 289
    urinary, 166

E

ECS
    and age, 239
    aggressive behavior, 221–227
    antidepressant effect, 291
    catecholamines, 143
    CER, 279

ECS (*Cont'd.*)
    consolidation, 280
    and desmethylimipramine, 145–149
    electrode location: cerebral, 92–93
        "sham," 240–241
        transcorneal, 92, 237–241
        transocular, 232
    learning, 85–93, 279
    memory, 85–93, 100, 107
    norepinephrine, 144–149, 152–163
    protein synthesis, 237–249
ECT
    history, 2, 271–272
    mechanism of action, 275, 285
    theory (*see* Theory of ECT)
EEG, 215–217, 273
    acetylcholine, 255, 258–259
    alpha activity, 4
    amplitude, 58–60
    atropine, 265
    and behavior, 35–39, 274
    bilateral ECT, 37–39, 48–50, 52, 69
        compared to flurothyl, 47–62
    DFP, 256
    flurothyl, 47–62, 69
        chick, 129
        compared to ECT, 47–62
    interictal, 4, 10, 20, 35–39, 47–62, 274
        effects of anticholinergics, 7, 10, 36,
            265, 272
        effects of antihistaminics, 10
        effects of barbiturates, 7, 10
    multiple ECT, 81
    paroxysmal activity, 35–39, 55, 81
    post-seizure, 272
    seizure activity, 48–52
    slowing, 4, 10, 20, 35–39, 55, 80–81
        as "side-effect." 274
    thiopental, 274
    unilateral ECT, 35–39, 51, 57, 273
Electrical currents, 5, 91–93
Electrocorticogram, 102
Electrode placement (ECT), 200, 234,
        272–273
    anterior-frontal, 6, 200
    antidepressant effects, 273
    bilateral, 6, 35–39, 48–62, 65–76, 80–
        82, 144, 273
        and EEG, 6, 35, 37–39, 48–50, 52,
            69, 273
        and norepinephrine, 163–167
    bitemporal (*see* bilateral)
    and memory, 26–32, 200, 204, 273, 282

Electrode placement (*Cont'd.*)
  unilateral: dominant, 21–32, 273
    and EEG, 35–39, 51, 57, 273
    non-dominant, 4–6, 21–32, 35–39,
      144, 200, 273
  (*See also* ECS, electrode location)
Electroshock, as pejorative term, 272
Engram, 101
Enhancement, retrograde, 135, 138
Epilepsy, 2
Epinephrine
  blood, 210, 217
  urinary, 144, 165–166, 168, 210
Euphoria, 7, 12

F ⋅

Facial flushing, 69
Flurothyl (Indoklon), 65–78, 129–130,
    272, 280
  clinical results, 67, 72
  combined with methoxyflurane, 136
  compared to ECT, 5–6, 21, 47–62, 67–
    74, 213
  dose-dependent effects, 139
  duration of exposure, 133
  EEG, 47–62, 51–52, 69, 129
  follow-up results, 72–75
  and memory, 69–71, 73–74, 129–140
  seizures, 5, 21, 48–62, 65–76
Footshock, 200
Forebrain, mouse, 237

G

Gallamine (Flaxedil), 271
Gamma-animobutyric acid, 262
Glutamic acid, 187, 262
Grand-mal seizure (*see* Seizure)

H

Head trauma, 10
Hippocampus, 93, 101, 179–180, 200,
    212–213
  medial, 241
Homovanillic acid
  CSF, 166
  urinary, 166
5-Hydroxyindolacetic acid (5HIAA)
  aggression 223–227
  brain, 222–227

5-Hydroxyindolacetic acid (5HIAA)
    (*Cont'd.*)
  CSF, 166, 224
  ECS, 223
5-Hydroxytryptamine (5-HT), 237–239,
    241–242, 247
  aggression, 223
  brain, 221–227
  forebrain, 238–239
Hyperoxia, cerebral, 132, 136–137
Hypothalamic release, 215
Hypothalamus, 20, 159–160, 163, 179–180,
    215, 254, 286
Hypoxia
  cerebral, 132, 136–137, 139, 212–213,
    217
  and protein synthesis, 192

I

Imipramine, 10, 211, 226
Indoklon (*see* Flurothyl)
Inhalant induction (*see* Flurothyl)
Internal capsule, 116
Ion concentration, 8

K

Korsakoff syndrome, 213

L

Language measures, 7, 12
Leucine, radioactive (*see* ^{14}C-leucine)
Libido, 7, 214
Lidocaine, 214–216, 272
Limbic forebrain, 117
Limbic midbrain, 117
Lobectomy, temporal, 200
Lysine, radioactive, 187

M

Maintenance ECT, 5
Mean energy content (*see* EEG, ampli-
    tude)
Medial thalamus, 101
Memory, 4, 5, 8, 11, 19–20, 24, 32, 69–
    75, 85–86, 99, 101, 106–107
  auditory, 4, 6, 25
  consolidation, 203, 282–283
  dissociation from therapy, 279–283

Memory (*Cont'd.*)
  and electric currents, 21, 25, 70–72, 82
  electrode location, 26–32, 200, 204, 272–273, 282
  fixation, 238
  and flurothyl, 69–71, 73–74, 129–140
  and learning, 201, 204
  long-term, 75, 100, 201, 281
  non-verbal, 25
  recall, 204
  recognition, 204
  retention, 201, 281
  short-term, 100, 201, 281
  as "side effect," 273–274, 282
  storage, 87
  and stress, 138
  and therapeutic effect, 199–204, 273, 279–283
  verbal, 25
  visual, 4, 6, 25
  (*See also* Amnesia, anterograde; Amnesia, retrograde)
Menstruation, 214
Mesencephalon
  acetylcholine, 252
  cholinesterase, 252
  norepinephrine, 232–233
  reticular formation, 117
Metanephrine, 168
Methionine sulfoximine (MSI), 261
  and protein synthesis, 262
Methohexital, sodium (Brevital), 144
Methoxyflurane, 132
  combined with flurothyl, 136
5-Methoxy-1-methyltryptamine, 241
Methyl anthranilate (MeA), 131
Metrazol, and protein synthesis, 192
MHPG (3-methoxy-4-hydroxyphenylglycol)
  and clinical state, 164–166, 168
  urinary, 144, 160, 163
Midbrain
  afterdischarge, 120
  and amnesia, 122
  limbic, 117, 122
  protein synthesis, 242–244
  ventral tegmentum, 119–120
Mineral metabolism, 213–214, 217
Mitochondria, 244–245, 247–248
  ECS, 245
Monoamine oxidase, 174–183, 224, 275, 290
  inhibitor, 183

Motivation, 113
Multiple ECT (MECT), 5, 61, 79–83, 274
Muricidal rats, 222
Muscarinic response, 252
Muscle relaxants, 271
  curare, 271
  gallamine, 271
  succinylcholine, 271
Myelin, 244

N

Neurophysiologic-adaptive hypothesis, 9–13, 20, 275
Nicotine, 252
Nicotinic response, 252
Nonconvulsive Therapy (*see* Subconvulsive currents)
Noradrenaline (*see* Norepinephrine)
Norepinephrine, 163–168, 174, 183, 221, 241, 289–291
  and acetylcholine, 258
  blood, 210, 217
  cerebrospinal fluid, 212, 217
  ECS, chronic, 156–163, 236, 288, 290
  intracisternal, 144–152, 156
  and mood, 231
  and normetanephrine, 152–153
  tritiated, 143, 145–149, 162
  turnover, 143, 149–152, 155, 168, 232
  uptake, 147, 149–152, 160
  urinary, 144, 165, 210
Normetanephrine
  and ECT, 167–168
  tritiated, 143, 145–149
  urinary, 144
Nortriptyline, 211, 226
Nucleotides, 237

O

O-methylation, 152, 160
Organic mental syndrome, 209, 274
Organic "shock" syndrome, 209
Orientation, 30, 43
Oxygenation in MECT, 81–82

P

Pargyline, 183
Passive avoidance, 88, 241–242
Peck suppression, chick, 131–132

Pentylenetetrazol threshold and anticholinesterase, 253
Permeability, cerebrovascular (*see* Blood-brain barrier)
Personality, 11
Physostigmine, 262, 264
Pituitary, 211
Polyribosome, 187, 195
Pons, 116
    medulla, 159–160, 163, 179–180
Population for ECT, 275
Post-seizure effects, extended duration, 181–183, 194
Potassium, intracellular, 213
Primary afterdischarge (PAD), 102, 106, 108–109, 113–116, 120, 124, 280–281
    cortical, 120
    duration, 106
    frequency, 106
    threshold, 110
Protein synthesis, 185–195, 237–249, 291–292
    and amnesia, 192
    antimetabolite, 238
    and electric currents, 190–191
    inhibition, 190–193, 238, 241
    and MSI, 262
    synaptosomes, 242–244
Purkinje cell, 252
Puromycin, 192–193

R

Recall, delayed, 25
Recruitment, 104
Remembering, 281
Reminder effect, 90–93
Renshaw cell (interneuron), 252
Reserpine, depression, 231
    and anticholinesterase, 258
Retention, memory, 281
Retrograde amnesia (*see* Amnesia, retrograde)
Retrograde memory, 282
Ribonucleic acid (RNA), 237, 241
Ribosome, 187–195
Rorschach test, 12

S

Sarin, EEG, 255
Schizophrenia, 43, 49, 67–69, 79–81

Scopolamine, 252
    spinal reflex, 254
Secondary After-Discharge (SAD), 102, 104–105, 109, 113–115, 120, 124, 280–281
    threshold, 110
Seizure, 35–39, 47–62, 99–125, 130, 251–261
    acetylcholine, 251, 253, 260, 261–264
    and amnesia, retrograde, 101, 111, 280
    antidepressant effect, 19, 209–210
    camphor, 271
    and depression, 209–210, 272, 275
    duration of, 61, 69–70, 81
    and EEG, 3, 13, 21, 35–39, 47–62, 69–70, 81, 91–93, 273
    electrical induction, 3, 21–22, 35–39, 48–62, 67–76, 80–82, 91–93, 271
    frequency, 4, 80–82
    as "hypersynchrony," 259
    inhalant, 3, 48–62, 65–76
    insulin, 2, 271
    and lidocaine, 272
    and memory, 203
    number of, 5, 72, 80–82, 86
    pentelenetetrazol (Metrazol), 2, 27
    threshold, 102, 120
Serotonin, 10, 174, 183
    and acetylcholine, 253
    cerebrospinal fluid, 212
    and ECS, 261, 288–291
Sham rage, 215
Shock, 231
    foot, 112
    mouth, 106, 110, 120
    as pejorative term, 272
Simultaneous tactile tests, 12
Sleep, 6, 41–45, 214
    REM: deprivation, 41
        ECS, cats, 41–42
        latency, 44–45
    slow-wave sleep, 43
Sodium, intracellular, 213
Spike, paroxysmal, 104
Spinal cord
    acetylcholine, 252
    cholinesterase, 252
    norepinephrine, 232–233
    reflexes, 253–254
Spreading depression, 192
Stress, 8, 234, 290

Stress (*Cont'd.*)
  and catecholamines, 148–152
  and memory, 138
Strychnine threshold, anticholinester-
      ases, 253
Subconvulsive currents, 5, 190, 272
  as "therapy," 5
Subcortex, 174, 177–180
Succinic acid dehydrogenase, 181, 183,
      287, 290
Succinylcholine chloride (Anectine), 144,
      271
Suppression ratio, bar-press, 110, 112–
      113, 121
Synaptosomes
  and 5-HT, 238
  and protein synthesis, 242–245
Synchronization, EEG, by atropine, 259
Syphilis, CNS, 2

T

Tachistoscopy, 12
Telencephalon, and norepinephrine, 232–
      233
Temporal lobe, 200
  lobectomy, 200
Thalamus
  acetylcholine, 252
  cholinesterase, 252
Theory of ECT, 4, 7–9, 19–20, 217, 231,
      265, 272, 274, 282–283, 285–
      292
  biochemical, 8, 11, 19–20, 82, 217,
      231, 265, 285–292
  neurophysiologic, 7, 9–13, 35–39,
      60–62, 272, 274
  psychologic, 8, 9–13, 85, 282–283
Therapeutic results
  behavior change, 7, 12
  compared to antidepressants, 2
    to chlorpromazine, 3
    to flurothyl, 5, 67–75
    to MAOI, 3
    to MECT, 80–83

Therapeutic results (*Cont'd.*)
  in depression, 2, 6, 19–24, 40–75,
      209–210, 274–275
  and EEG, 4, 20, 35–39, 47–62
  and electric currents, 21
  and electrode placement, 22–24, 37–39
  with flurothyl, 67–73
  follow-up, 72–75
  and memory, 6, 19–20, 22, 71, 73–74,
      85–86, 199–204, 273–274,
      279–283
  with multiple treatments, 79–82
  and personality, 7
  in schizophrenia, 3, 79–75, 274–275
  with unilateral electrode placement,
      26–30, 37–39
Time course, ECT, 286
Tricyclic antidepressants and ECS, 227
Trypan blue, 211
Tryptophan and 5-HT, 211
Tryptophan pyrrolase, 211
d-Tubocurarine, 252
Tyrosine hydroxylase, 156, 233, 290

U

Uridine, radioactive, 193–194

V

Vapor concentration, 131–133
Vasopressin, 214
VMA (3-methoxy-4-hydroxy-mandelic
      acid), 144, 168

W

Water, intracellular, 213, 217
Wechsler Memory Scale, 69, 71–74
Weight
  body, 6, 171–173, 214
  brain, 174–176, 183